PHYSICS LABORATORY EXPERIMENTS

Sixth Edition

JERRY D. WILSON
Lander University

CECILIA A. HERNÁNDEZ HALL
American River College

Houghton Mifflin Company
Boston New York

Publisher: Charles Hartford
Executive Editor: Richard Stratton
Editorial Associate: Rosemary Mack
Associate Project Editor: Shelley Dickerson
Senior Marketing Manager: Katherine Greig
Marketing Associate: Alexandra Shaw
Senior Manufacturing Coordinator: Marie Barnes

Cover image credits: Photo of students and computer—Jon Hanks/PASCO scientific;
Photo of Pendulum © Loren Winters/Visuals Unlimited

Printed in the U.S.A.

Library of Congress Control Number: 2003115599

ISBN-13: 978-0-618-20740-4
ISBN-10: 0-618-20740-6

"What is the meaning of it all, Mr. Holmes?"
"Ah. I have no data. I cannot tell," he said.

Arthur Conan Doyle, *The Adventures of the Copper Beeches,* 1892

Contents

Note:

In this Table of Contents, the experiments that incorporate both traditional and computer instruction are denoted with a "TI/CI" abbreviation in front of the title of the experiment. In some instances, the TI and CI components are not the same, so the title for each component is listed separately. The experiments that only involve traditional instruction do not have any abbreviations next to them.

Preface

Physics Laboratory Experiments was written for students of introductory physics—in fact, it was written at the request of my students. The main purpose of laboratory experiments is to augment and supplement the learning and understanding of basic physical principles, while introducing laboratory procedures, techniques, and equipment. This sixth edition of *Physics Laboratory Experiments* has 33 experiments, with 16 more available for customization, providing an ample number of experiments to choose from for a 2-semester or 3-quarter laboratory physics course. Those features that proved effective in previous editions have been retained, and new and exciting features have been added. Here are some of the new features of this edition that we feel are especially important.

Computerized Instruction Integrated into Selected Experiments

In the previous edition, we included a supplement on Integrating Computerized Instruction and made note of available computer equipment for particular experiments. In the last few years, the use of computerized instruction and equipment has become increasingly popular in introductory physics laboratories. Therefore, for this sixth edition, we have integrated this component into the book, providing both computerized instruction (CI) and traditional instruction (TI) for 10 of the 33 experiments.

We suggest that students first do the hands-on TI experiment to gain a basic knowledge of what is being measured and of graphical analysis. It is here that the physical parameters of an experiment are clearly associated with principles and with the desired results. Once the students have this type of acquaintance with the concept at hand, they can perform the CI experiment or can view it as a demonstration. Now the student will better understand the computer procedure and analysis of electronically recorded data, with resulting graphs immediately plotted on the screen. The computerized and traditional components treat the same principle, but from different perspectives, together giving the student a more comprehensive understanding of the underlying physical concepts.

With this sixth edition, we carefully selected ten experiments to have both TI and CI components, thereby giving the instructor the option of doing the TI experiment, the CI experiment (using PASCO equipment), or *both,* as suggested above. Four more TI and CI experiments are available for customization.

New Co-Author

To make all this possible, Professor Cecilia A. Hernández Hall at American River College in Sacramento, California, has joined the project as co-author. Having used computerized instruction with hundreds of her students, she is highly qualified to present the CI experiments. Professor Hernández received her MS in physics from the University of Puerto Rico, Mayagüez Campus, in 1993. After teaching for two years at the Mayagüez and Cayey campuses, she joined the Physics Education Research Group at the University of Nebraska, Lincoln, where research in physics education was conducted with an emphasis on computerized instruction. Professor Hernández joined the faculty of American River College in 1998 and has worked for PASCO Scientific in Roseville, California, helping develop computer-assisted lab activities for college physics, as well as writing manuals for new equipment.

Additional Experiments Available for Customized Publishing

Also new to this edition of *Physics Laboratory Experiments* is a handy customizable option—a way for instructors to build their own lab manual that fits the need of their specific course. We've pared down this sixth edition of the manual to 33 experiments from the 49 experiments that appeared in the fifth edition. To produce a shorter, more manageable text, we chose the 33 experiments most used by professors. However, the extra 16 experiments, including 4 integrated TI and CI experiments, are still available through Houghton Mifflin's Custom Courseware website, accessible via **catalog.college.hmco.com.**

Using this online book-building system, instructors can select from the complete set of 49 experiments to create text materials customized to their course objectives and can arrange the experiments in whatever sequence they prefer. Thus students pay only for the content they need. Instructors may also want to add their own materials, experiments, lab reports, or handouts to make the book even more relevant to the students.

To learn more about customizable options for *Physics Laboratory Experiments,* visit the online catalog page for this manual at **catalog.college.hmco.com** and search by author. You can also request a sample copy of the experiments by calling Houghton Mifflin's Faculty Services at 1-800-733-1717 or by requesting a copy via our online catalog at **catalog.college.hmco.com.** Because instructors can either choose this sixth-edition bound volume, with its selection of the most popular experiments, or assemble a custom package, there is an option appropriate for every introductory physics laboratory course. Here is a list of the additional experiments found on the Houghton Mifflin Custom Courseware website:

34. The Scientific Method: The Simple Pendulum
35. **(TI/CI)** Rotational Motion and Moment of Inertia
36. Conservation of Angular Momentum: The Ballistic Pendulum
37. Elasticity: Young's Modulus
38. Air Column Resonance: The Speed of Sound in Air
39. **(TI)** Latent Heats: Heats of Fusion and Vaporization of Water
    (CI) Latent Heat of Fusion for Water
40. Newton's Law of Cooling: The Time Constant of a Thermometer
41. The Potentiometer: emf and Terminal Voltage
42. The Voltmeter and Ammeter
43. Resistivity
44. Multiloop Circuits: Kirchhoff's Rules
45. Earth's Magnetic Field
46. Introduction to the Oscilloscope
47. **(TI/CI)** Phase Measurements and Resonance in ac Circuits
48. **(TI/CI)** Electromagnetic Induction
49. The Mass of an Electron: *e/m* Measurement

Organization of the Sixth Edition

Both the TI and the CI experiments are generally organized into the following sections:

- **Advance Study Assignment**
- **Introduction and Objectives**
- **Equipment Needed**
- **Theory**
- **Experimental Procedure**
- **Laboratory Report**
- **Post-lab Questions**

Features include:

Laboratory safety. Safety is continually stressed and highlighted in the manual. This critical issue is expanded upon in the Introduction to the manual.

Advance Study Assignments. Students often come to the laboratory unprepared, even though they should have read the experiment before the lab period to familiarize themselves with it. To address this problem, an Advance Study Assignment precedes each experiment. The assignment consists of a set of questions drawn from the Theory and Experimental Procedures sections of the experiment. To answer the questions, students must read the experiment before the lab period; consequently, they will be better prepared. We recommend that the Advance Study Assignment be collected at the beginning of the laboratory period.

Example Calculations. In the Theory section of some experiments, sample calculations that involve the equations and mathematics used in the experiment have been included where appropriate. These demonstrate to the student how experimental data are applied.

Illustrations. Over 200 photographs and diagrams illustrate experimental procedures, equipment, and computer programs. To allow for variation in laboratory equipment, different types of equipment that can be used are often illustrated.

Laboratory Reports. Because a standardized format for laboratory reports greatly facilitates grading by the instructor, a Laboratory Report is provided for both TI and CI experiments. These reports provide a place for recording data, calculations, experimental results, and analyses. Only the Laboratory Report and post-lab Questions that follow it need to be submitted for grading. The Laboratory Report tables are organized for easy data recording and analysis. Students are reminded to include the units of measurement.

Maximum Application of Available Equipment. Laboratory equipment at many institutions is limited, and often only standard equipment, purchased from scientific suppliers, is available. The TI experimental procedures in this manual are described for different types of common laboratory apparatus, thus maximizing the application of the manual.

Instructor's Resource Manual

The Instructor's Resource Manual is a special feature and resource for the instructor. It is available online on the instructor website prepared to accompany the sixth edition of *Physics Laboratory Experiments.* To view a sampling of instructor materials, go to **http://college.hmco.com,** click on the instructor tab, and select *Physics* and then this textbook.

Professor Fred B. Otto, previously of the Maine Maritime Academy, who has over 20 years of teaching and laboratory experience, has revised this manual. He retained the general format of the previous edition. For each experiment, there are (1) Comments and Hints, (2) Answers to post-Experiment Questions, and (3) Post-lab Quiz Questions [completion and multiple-choice (with answers), and essay]. The Instructor's Resource Manual also includes laboratory safety references, lists of scientific equipment suppliers and physics software suppliers, and graph paper copy masters.

Of course, the publication of this manual would not have been possible without a great deal of help. Professor Hernández and I would like to thank the people at PASCO—in particular, Paul A. Stokstad, Dave Griffith, and Jon and Ann Hanks—for their support and help. We thank Fred B. Otto for his in-depth review of the experiments. We are grateful to Richard Stratton, executive editor, to Rosemary Mack, editorial associate, to Shelley Dickerson, associate project editor, to Katherine Greig, senior marketing manager, and to Alexandra Shaw, marketing associate—all at Houghton Mifflin—and to Merrill Peterson at Matrix Productions Inc. We both hope that you will find the sixth edition of *Physics Laboratory Experiments* helpful and educational. And we urge anyone—student or instructor—to pass on to us any suggestions that you might have for improvement.

Jerry D. Wilson
Emeritus Professor of Physics
Lander University
Greenwood, South Carolina
jwilson@greenwood.net

Cecilia A. Hernández Hall
Professor of Physics
American River College
Sacramento, California
hernanc@arc.losrios.edu

Introduction

Why We Make Experimental Measurements

When you can measure what you are speaking about and express it in numbers, you know something about it; but when you cannot measure it, when you cannot express it in numbers, your knowledge is of a meager and unsatisfactory kind.

LORD KELVIN

As Lord Kelvin so aptly expressed, we measure things to know something about them—so that we can describe objects and understand phenomena. Experimental measurement is the cornerstone of the *scientific method,* which holds that no theory or model of nature is tenable unless the results it predicts are in accord with experiment.

The main purpose of an introductory physics laboratory is to provide "hands-on" experiences of various physical principles. In so doing, one becomes familiar with laboratory equipment and procedures and with the scientific method.

In general, the theory of a physical principle will be presented in an experiment, and the predicted results will be tested by experimental measurements. Of course, these well-known principles have been tested many times before, and there are accepted values for certain physical quantities. Basically you will be comparing your experimentally measured values to accepted theoretical or measured values. Even so, you will experience the excitement of the scientific method. Imagine that you are the first person to perform an experiment to test a scientific theory.

General Laboratory Procedures

Safety

The most important thing in the laboratory is your safety and that of others. Experiments are designed to be done safely, but proper caution should always be exercised.

A potential danger comes from a lack of knowledge of the equipment and procedures. Upon entering the physics lab at the beginning of the lab period, you will probably find the equipment for an experiment on the laboratory table. Restrain your curiosity and do not play with the equipment. You may hurt yourself and/or the equipment. A good general rule is:

> *Do not touch or turn on laboratory equipment until it has been explained and permission has been given by the instructor.*

Also, certain items used in various experiments can be particularly dangerous, for example, hot objects, electricity, mercury lamps, and radioactive sources. In some instances, such as with hot objects and electricity, basic common sense and knowledge are required.

However, in other instances, such as with mercury lamps and radioactive sources, you may not be aware of the possible dangers. Mercury lamps may emit ultraviolet radiation that can be harmful to your eyes. Consequently, some sources need to be properly shielded. Some radioactive sources are solids and are encapsulated to prevent contact. Others are in liquid form and are transferred during an experiment, so there is a danger of spillage. Proper handling is therefore important.

In general, necessary precautions will be given in the experiment descriptions. *Note them well.* When you see the arrow symbol in the margin as illustrated here, you should take extra care to follow the procedure carefully and adhere to the precautions described in the text. As pointed out earlier, experiments are designed to be done safely. Yet a common kitchen match can be dangerous if used improperly. Another good rule for the laboratory is:

> *If you have any questions about the safety of a procedure, ask your instructor before doing it.*

The physics lab is a place to learn and practice safety.

Equipment Care

The equipment provided for the laboratory experiment is often expensive and in some instances quite delicate. If used improperly, certain pieces of apparatus can be damaged. The general rules given above concerning personal safety also apply to equipment care.

Even after familiarizing oneself with the equipment, it is often advisable or required to have an experimental setup checked and approved by the instructor before putting it into operation. This is particularly true for electrical experiments. Applying power to improperly wired circuits can cause serious damage to meters and other pieces of apparatus.

If a piece of equipment is broken or does not function properly, it should be reported to the laboratory instructor. Also, after you complete an experiment, the experimental setup should be disassembled and left neatly as found, unless you are otherwise instructed,

If you accidentally break some equipment or the equipment stops working properly during an experiment, *report it to your instructor.* Otherwise, the next time the equipment is used, a great deal of time may be wasted trying to get good results.

Laboratory Reports

A Laboratory Report is provided for each experiment in which experimental data are recorded. This should be done *neatly.* Calculations of experimental results should be included. Remember, the neatness, organization, and explanations of your measurements and calculations in the Laboratory Report represent the quality of your work.

Do
pg 1-2
problems 1-6
pg. 15-18 all +i-2i
or 1-2i?
pg. 19-20 1-5
graphs! (3)
☆ sig figures ☆

* turn in graphs etc attached to labs out of book!

Jaelle Head

EXPERIMENT 1

Experimental Uncertainty (Error) and Data Analysis

Introduction and Objectives

Laboratory investigations involve taking measurements of physical quantities, and the process of taking any measurement always involves some experimental uncertainty or error.* Suppose you and another person independently took several measurements of the length of an object. It is highly unlikely that you both would come up with exactly the same results. Or you may be verifying the value of a known quantity and want to express uncertainty, perhaps on a graph. Therefore, questions such as the following arise:

- Whose data are better, or how does one express the degree of uncertainty or error in experimental measurements?
- How do you compare your experimental result with an accepted value (if known)?
- How does one graphically analyze and report experimental data?

In this introductory study experiment, we examine the types of experimental uncertainties and some methods of error and data analysis that may be used in subsequent experiments.

After performing the experiment and analyzing the data, you should be able to do the following:

1. Categorize the types of experimental uncertainty (error), and explain how they may be reduced.
2. Distinguish between measurement accuracy and precision, and understand how they may be improved experimentally.
3. Define the term *least count* and explain the meaning and importance of significant figures (or digits) in reporting measurement values.
4. Express experimental results and uncertainty in appropriate numerical values so that someone reading your report will have an estimate of the reliability of your data.
5. Represent measurement data in graphical form so as to illustrate experimental data and uncertainty visually.

* Although *experimental uncertainty* is more descriptive, the term *error* is commonly used synonymously.

Equipment Needed

- Pencil and ruler
- Hand calculator
- 3 sheets of Cartesian graph paper
- French curve (optional)

Theory

A. Types of Experimental Uncertainty

Experimental uncertainty (error) generally can be classified as being of two types: (1) random or statistical error and (2) systematic error: These are also referred to as (1) indeterminate error and (2) determinate error, respectively. Let's take a closer look at each type of experimental uncertainty.

Random (Indeterminate) or Statistical Error

Random errors result from unknown and unpredictable variations that arise in all experimental measurement situations. The term *indeterminate* refers to the fact that there is no way to determine the magnitude or sign (+, too large; −, too small) of the error in any individual measurement. Conditions in which random errors can result include

1. Unpredictable fluctuations in temperature or line voltage
2. Mechanical vibrations of an experimental setup
3. Unbiased estimates of measurement readings by the observer

Repeated measurements with random errors give slightly different values each time. The effect of random errors may be reduced and minimized by improving and refining experimental techniques.

Systematic (Determinate) Errors

Systematic errors are associated with particular measurement instruments or techniques, such as an improperly calibrated instrument or bias on the part of the observer. The term *systematic* implies that the same magnitude and sign of experimental uncertainty are obtained when the

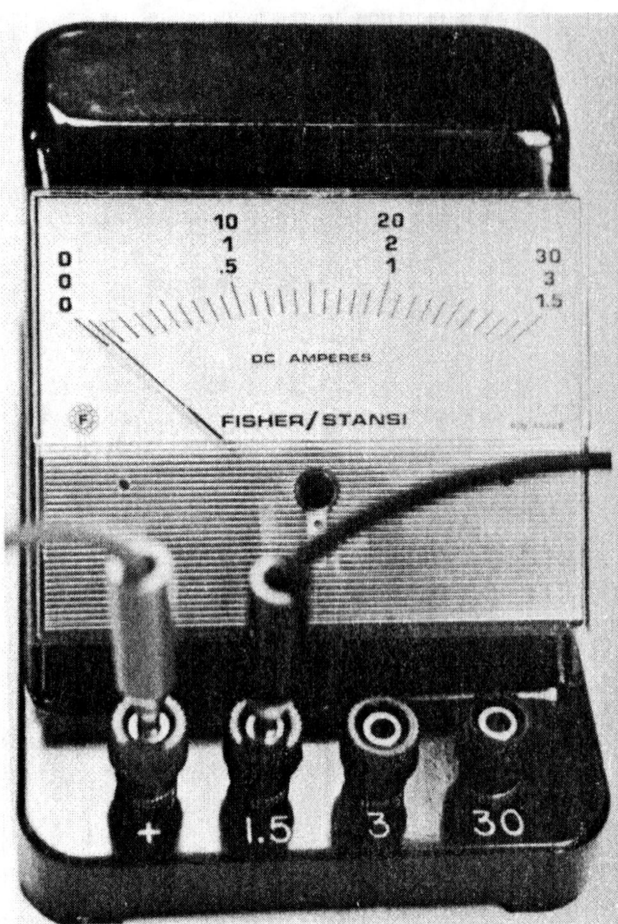

Figure 1 Systematic error. An improperly zeroed instrument gives rise to systematic error. In this case the ammeter, which has no current through it, would systematically give an incorrect reading larger that the true value. (After correcting the error by zeroing the meter, which scale would you read when using the ammeter?)

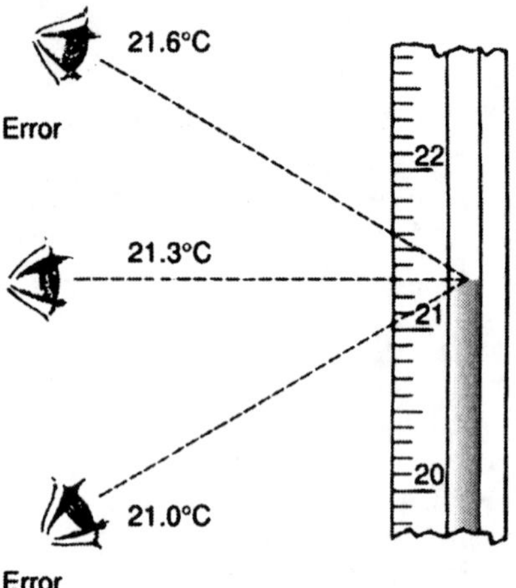

(a) Temperature measurement

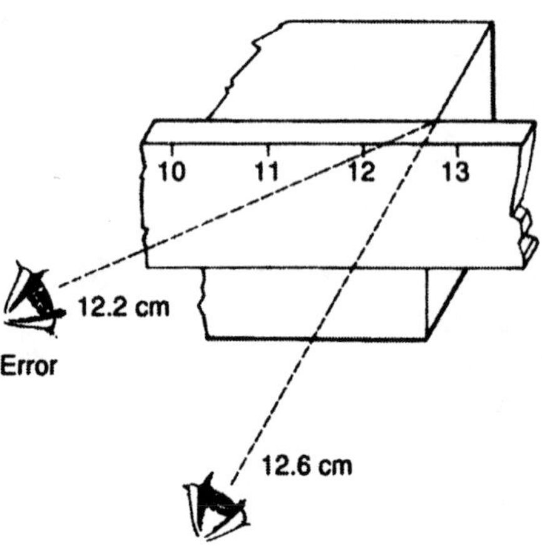

(b) Length measurement

Figure 2 Personal error. Examples of personal error due to parallax in reading (a) a thermometer and (b) a meterstick. Readings may systematically be made either too high or two low.

measurement is repeated several times. *Determinate* means that the magnitude and sign of the uncertainty can be determined if the error is identified. Conditions from which systematic errors can result include

1. An improperly "zeroed" instrument, for example, an ammeter as shown in ● Fig. 1.
2. A faulty instrument, such as a thermometer that reads 101°C when immersed in boiling water at standard atmospheric pressure. This thermometer is faulty because the reading should be 100°C.
3. Personal error, such as using a wrong constant in calculation or always taking a high or low reading of a scale division. Other examples of personal systematic error are shown in ● Fig. 2. Reading a value from a scale generally involves lining up something, such as a mark on the scale. The alignment—and hence the value of the reading—can depend of the position of the eye (parallax).

Avoiding systematic errors depends on the skill of the observer to recognize the sources of such errors and to prevent or correct them.

B. *Accuracy and Precision*

Accuracy and *precision* are commonly used synonymously, but in experimental measurements there is an important distinction. The **accuracy** of a measurement signifies how close it comes to the true (or accepted) value—that is, how nearly correct it is.

Example 1 Two independent measurement results using the diameter d and circumference c of a circle in the determination of the value of π are 3.140

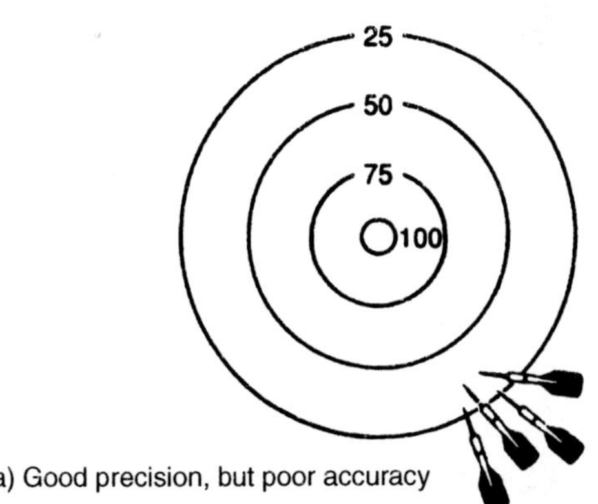

(a) Good precision, but poor accuracy

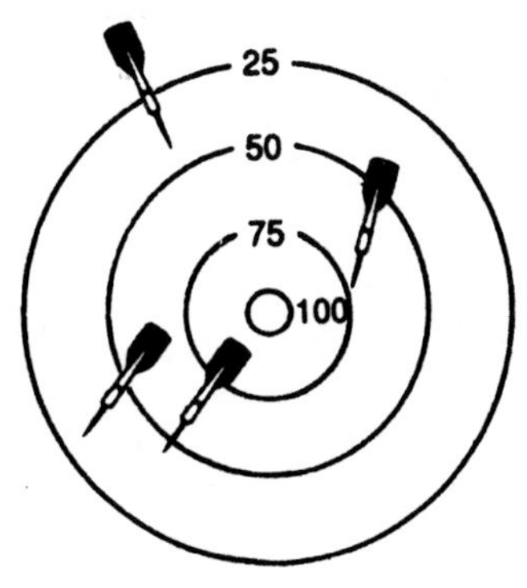

(b) Poor precision and poor accuracy

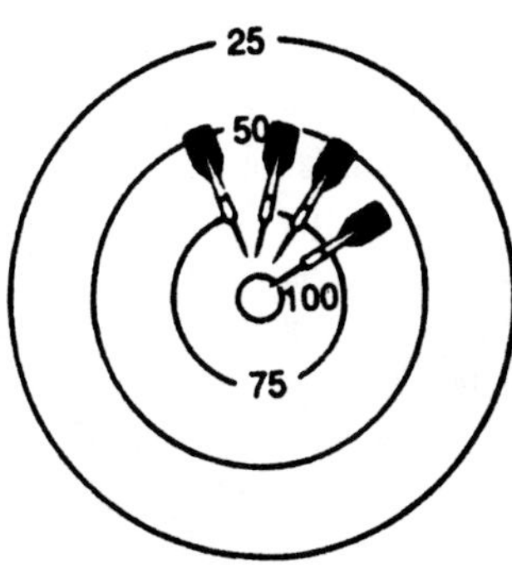

(c) Good precision and good accuracy

Figure 3 Accuracy and precision. The true value in this analogy is the bull's eye. The degree of scattering is an indication of precision—the closer together a dart grouping, the greater the precision. A group (or symmetric grouping with an average) close to the true value represents accuracy.

and 3.143. (Recall that $\pi = c/d$.) The second result is more accurate than the first because the true value of π, to four figures, is 3.142.

Precision refers to the agreement among repeated measurements—that is, the "spread" of the measurements or how close they are together. The more precise a group of measurements, the closer together they are. However, a large degree of precision does not necessarily imply accuracy, as illustrated in ● Fig. 3.

Example 2 Two independent experiments give two sets of data with the expressed results and uncertainties of 2.5 ± 0.1 cm and 2.5 ± 0.2 cm, respectively.

The first result is more precise than the second because the spread in the first measurements is between 2.4 and 2.6 cm, whereas the spread in the second measurements is between 2.3 and 2.7 cm. That is, the measurements of the first experiment are less uncertain than those of the second.

Obtaining *greater accuracy* for an experimental value depends in general on *minimizing systematic errors.* Obtaining *greater precision* for an experimental value depends on *minimizing random errors.*

C. Least Count and Significant Figures

In general, there are *exact* numbers and *measured* numbers (or quantities). Factors such as the 100 used in calculating percentage and the 2 in $2\pi r$ are exact numbers. Measured numbers, as the name implies, are those obtained from measurement instruments and generally involve some error or uncertainty.

In reporting experimentally measured values, it is important to read one's instruments correctly. The degree of uncertainty of a number read from a measurement instrument depends on the quality of instrument and the fineness of its measuring scale. When one is reading the value from a calibrated scale, only a certain number of figures or digits can properly be obtained or read. That is, only a certain number of figures are *significant.* This depends on the **least count** of the instrument scale, which is the smallest subdivision on the measurement scale. This is the unit of the smallest reading that can be made without estimating. For example, the least count of a meterstick is usually the millimeter (mm). We commonly say "the instrument is calibrated in centimeters (numbered major divisions) with a millimeter least count." (See ● Fig. 4.)

The **significant figures** (sometimes called **significant digits**) of a measured value include all the numbers that can be read directly from the instrument scale, *plus* one doubtful or estimated number—the fractional part of the least

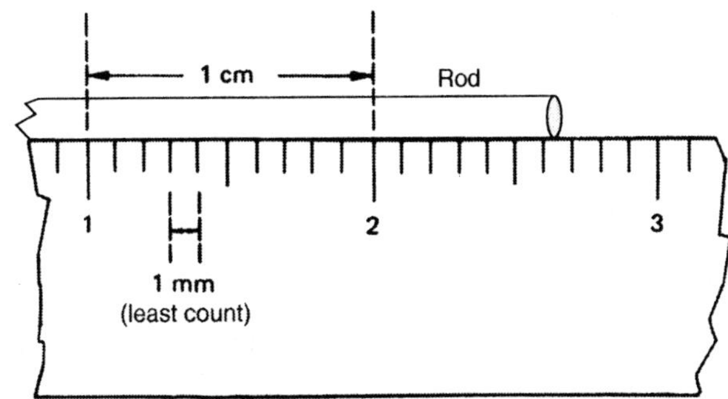

Figure 4 Least count. Metersticks are commonly calibrated in centimeters (cm), the numbered major divisions, with a least count, or smallest subdivision, of millimeters (mm).

count smallest division. For example, the length of the rod in Fig. 4 (as measured from the zero end) is 2.64 cm. The rod's length is known to be between 2.6 cm and 2.7 cm. The estimated fraction is taken to be 4/10 of the least count (1 mm), so the doubtful figure is 4, giving 2.64 cm with three significant figures.

Thus, measured values contain inherent uncertainty or doubtfulness because of the estimated figure. However, the greater the number of significant figures, the greater the reliability of the measurement the number represents. For example, the length of an object may be read as 2.54 cm (three significant figures) on one instrument scale and as 2.5405 cm (five significant figures) on another. The latter reading from an instrument with a finer scale (why?) gives more information and reliability.

Zeros and the decimal point must be properly dealt with in determining the number of significant figures in a result. For example, how many significant figures does 0.0543 m have? What about 209.4 m? 2705.0 m? In such cases, we will use the following rules:

1. Zeros at the beginning of a number are not significant. They merely locate the decimal point. For example,

   0.0543 m has three significant figures (5, 4, and 3).

2. Zeros within a number are significant. For example,

   209.4 m has four significant figures (2, 0, 9, and 4).

3. Zeros at the end of a number after the decimal point are significant. For example,

   2705.0 has five significant figures (2, 7, 0, 5, and 0).

Some confusion may arise with whole numbers that have one or more zeros at the end without a decimal point. Consider, for example, 300 kg, where the zeros (called trailing zeros) may or may not be significant. In such cases, it is not clear which zeros serve only to locate the decimal point and which are actually part of the measurement (and hence are significant). That is, if the first zero from the left ($3\underline{0}0$ kg) is the estimated digit in the measurement, then only two digits are reliably known, and there are only two significant figures.

Similarly, if the last zero is the estimated digit ($30\underline{0}$ kg), then there are three significant figures. This ambiguity may be removed by using *scientific* (powers-of-10) *notation:*

3.0×10^2 kg has two significant figures.

3.00×10^2 kg has three significant figures.

This procedure is also helpful in expressing the significant figures in large numbers. For example, suppose that the average distance from Earth to the Sun, 93,000,000 miles, is known to only four significant figures. This is easily expressed in powers-of-10 notation: 9.300×10^7 mi.

D. Computations with Measured Values

Calculations are often performed with measured values, and error and uncertainty are "propagated" by the mathematical operations—for example, multiplication or division. (That is, error is carried through to the results by the mathematical operations.)

The error can be better expressed by statistical methods; however, a widely used procedure for *estimating* the uncertainty of a mathematical result involves the use of significant figures.

The number of significant figures in a measured value gives an indication of the uncertainty or reliability of a measurement. Hence, you might expect that the result of a mathematical operation can be no more reliable than the quantity with the least reliability, or smallest number of significant figures, used in the calculation. (That is, you can't *gain* reliability through a mathematical operation.)

It is important to report the results of mathematical operations with the proper number of significant figures. This is accomplished by using rules for (1) multiplication and division, and (2) addition and subtraction. To obtain the proper number of significant figures, one rounds the results off. Here are some general rules that will be used for mathematical operations and rounding.

Significant Figures in Calculations

1. When multiplying and dividing quantities, leave as many significant figures in the answer as there are in the quantity with the least number of significant figures.
2. When adding or subtracting quantities, leave the same number of decimal places (rounded) in the answer as there are in the quantity with the least number of decimal places.

Rules for Rounding*

1. If the first digit to be dropped is less than 5, leave the preceding digit as is.
2. If the first digit to be dropped is 5 or greater, increase the preceding digit by one.

Notice that in this method, five digits (0, 1, 2, 3, and 4) are rounded down and five digits (5, 6, 7, 8, and 9) are rounded up.

What the rules for significant figures mean is that the result of a calculation can be no more accurate than the least accurate quantity used. That is, **you cannot gain accuracy in performing mathematical operations.**

These rules come into play frequently when one is doing mathematical operations with a hand calculator that may give a string of digits. ● Fig. 5 shows the result of the division of 374 by 29. The result must be rounded off to two significant figures—that is, to 13. (Why?)

* It should be noted that these rounding rules give an approximation of accuracy, as opposed to the results provided by more advanced statistical methods.

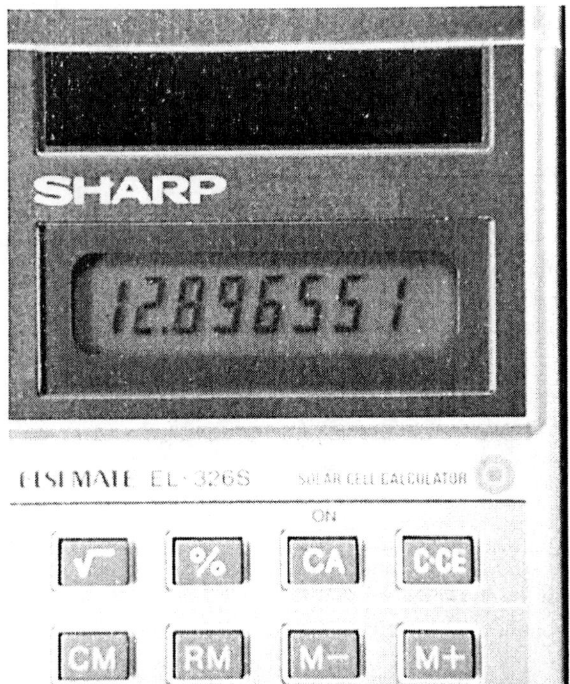

Figure 5 Insignificant figures. The calculator shows the result of the division operation 374/29. Because there are only two significant figures in the 29, a reported result should have no more than two significant figures, and the calculator display value should be rounded off to 13.

Example 3 Applying the rules.

Multiplication:

$$\underset{(2\ sf)}{2.5\text{ m}} \times \underset{(4\ sf)}{1.308\text{ m}} = \underset{(2\ sf)}{3.3\text{ m}}$$

Division:

$$\frac{\overset{(4\ sf)}{882.0\text{ s}}}{\underset{(3\ sf)}{0.245\text{ s}}} = 3600\text{ s} = 3.60 \times 10^3\text{ s}$$

(represented to three significant figures; why?)

Addition:

$$\begin{array}{r} 46.4 \\ 1.37 \\ 0.505 \\ \hline 48.275 \end{array} \longrightarrow 48.3$$

(rounding off)

(46.4 has the least number of decimal places)

Subtraction:

$$\begin{array}{r} 163 \\ -4.5 \\ \hline 158.5 \end{array} \longrightarrow 159$$

(rounding off)

(163 has the least number of decimal places, none)

E. Expressing Experimental Error and Uncertainty

Percent Error

The object of some experiments is to determine the value of a well-known physical quantity—for example, the value of π.

The **accepted or "true" value** of such a quantity found in textbooks and physics handbooks is the most accurate value (usually rounded off to a certain number of significant figures) obtained through sophisticated experiments or mathematical methods.

The **absolute difference** between the experimental value E and the accepted value A, written $|E - A|$, is the positive difference in the values, e.g., $|2 - 4| = |-2| = 2$ and $|4 - 2| = 2$. Simply subtract the smaller value from the larger, even though the symbols may be written in reverse order. For a set of measurements, E is taken as the average value of the experimental measurements.

The **fractional error** is the ratio of the absolute difference to the accepted value:

$$\text{Fractional error} = \frac{\text{absolute difference}}{\text{accepted value}}$$

or

$$\text{Fractional error} = \frac{|E - A|}{A} \tag{1}$$

The fractional error is commonly expressed as a percentage to give the **percent error** of an experimental value.*

$$\text{Percent error} = \frac{\text{absolute difference}}{\text{accepted value}} \times 100\%$$

or

$$\text{Percent error} = \frac{|E - A|}{A} \times 100\% \tag{2}$$

Example 4 A cylindrical object is measured to have a diameter d of 5.25 cm and a circumference c of 16.38 cm. What are the experimental value of π and the percent error of the experimental value if the accepted value of π is 3.14?

Solution with $d = 5.25$ cm and $c = 16.38$ cm,

$$c = \pi d \quad \text{or} \quad \pi = \frac{c}{d} = \frac{16.38}{5.25} = 3.12$$

* It should be noted that percent error only gives a measure of experimental error or uncertainty when the accepted or standard value is highly accurate. If an accepted value itself has a large degree of uncertainty, then the percent error does not give a measure of experimental uncertainty.

Then $E = 3.12$ and $A = 3.14$, so

$$\text{Percent error} = \frac{|E - A|}{A} \times 100\%$$

$$= \frac{|3.12 - 3.14|}{3.14} \times 100\%$$

$$= \frac{0.02}{3.14} \times 100\% = 0.6\%$$

Note: To avoid rounding errors, the preferred order of operations is addition and subtraction before multiplication and division.*

If the uncertainty in experimentally measured values as expressed by the percent error is large, you should suspect and check for possible sources of error. Additional measurements should then be made to reduce the uncertainty. Your instructor may wish to set a maximum percent error for experimental results.

PERCENT DIFFERENCE

It is sometimes instructive to compare the results of two measurements when there is no known or accepted value. The comparison is expressed as a **percent difference,** which is the ratio of the absolute difference between the experimental values E_2 and E_1 to the average or mean value of the two results, expressed as a percent.

$$\text{Percent difference} = \frac{\text{absolute difference}}{\text{average}} \times 100\%$$

or

$$\text{Percent difference} = \frac{|E_2 - E_1|}{(E_2 + E_1)/2} \times 100\% \qquad (3)$$

Dividing by the average or mean value of the experimental values is logical, because there is no way of deciding which of the two results is better.

Example 5 What is the percent difference between two measured values of 4.6 cm and 5.0 cm?

Solution With $E_1 = 4.6$ cm and $E_2 = 5.0$ cm,

$$\text{Percent difference} = \frac{|E_2 - E_1|}{(E_2 + E_1)/2} \times 100\%$$

$$= \frac{|5.0 - 4.6|}{(5.0 + 4.6)/2} \times 100\%$$

$$= \frac{0.4}{4.8} \times 100\% = 8\%$$

As in the case of percent error, when the percent difference is large, it is advisable to check the experiment and make more measurements.

In many instances there will be more than two measurement values.

When there are three or more measurements, the percent difference is found by dividing the absolute value of the difference of the extreme values (i.e., the values with greatest difference) by the average or mean value of all the measurements.

AVERAGE (MEAN) VALUE

Most experimental measurements are repeated several times, and it is very unlikely that identical results will be obtained for all trials. For a set of measurements with predominantly random errors (i.e., the measurements are all equally trustworthy or probable), it can be shown mathematically that the true value is most probably given by the average or mean value.

The **average** or **mean value** $\bar{x}$ of a set of N measurements is

$$\bar{x} = \frac{x_1 + x_2 + x_3 + \cdots + x_N}{N} = \frac{1}{N}\sum_{i=1}^{N} x_i \qquad (4)$$

where the summation sign Σ is a shorthand notation indicating the sum of N measurements from x_1 to x_N. ($\bar{x}$ is commonly referred to simply as the *mean.*)

Example 6 What is the average or mean value of the set of numbers 5.42, 6.18, 5.70, 6.01, and 6.32?

$$\bar{x} = \frac{1}{N}\sum_{i=1}^{N} x_i$$

$$= \frac{5.42 + 6.18 + 5.70 + 6.01 + 6.32}{5}$$

$$= 5.93$$

DEVIATION FROM THE MEAN (OPTIONAL)†

Having obtained a set of measurements and determined the mean value, it is helpful to report how widely the individual measurements are scattered from the mean. A quantitative description of this scatter, or dispersion, of measurements will give an idea of the precision of the experiment.

* Although percent error is generally defined using the absolute difference $|E - A|$, some instructors prefer to use $(E - A)$, which results in positive (+) or negative (−) percent errors, e.g., −0.6% in Example 4. In the case of a series of measurements and computed percent errors, this gives an indication of systematic error.

† A discussion of standard deviation and the method of least squares may be found in Appendix C.

The **deviation** d_i from the mean of any measurement with a mean value $\bar{x}$ is

$$d_i = x_i - \bar{x} \quad \textbf{(5)}$$

(d_i is sometimes referred to as the **residual** rather than the deviation.)

As defined, the deviation may be positive or negative, since some measurements are larger than the mean and some are smaller. The average of the deviations of a set of measurements is always zero, so the mean of the deviations is not a useful way of characterizing the dispersion.

Mean Deviation (Optional)

To obtain what is called the **mean** or **average deviation** of a set of N measurements, the absolute deviations $|d_i|$ are determined; that is,

$$|d_i| = |x_i - \bar{x}| \quad \textbf{(6)}$$

The *mean deviation* $\bar{d}$ is then

$$\bar{d} = \frac{|d_1| + |d_2| + |d_3| + \cdots + |d_N|}{N} = \frac{1}{N}\sum_{i=1}^{N} |d_i| \quad \textbf{(7)}$$

(Although $\bar{d}$ is commonly called the mean deviation, a more appropriate term would be the **mean absolute deviation.**)

Example 7 What is the mean deviation of the set of numbers given in Example 6?

Solution First find the absolute deviation of each of the numbers, using the determined mean of 5.93.

$$|d_1| = |5.42 - 5.93| = 0.51$$

$$|d_2| = |6.18 - 5.93| = 0.25$$

$$|d_3| = |5.70 - 5.93| = 0.23$$

$$|d_4| = |6.01 - 5.93| = 0.08$$

$$|d_5| = |6.32 - 5.93| = 0.39$$

Then

$$\bar{d} = \frac{1}{N}\sum_{i=1}^{N} |d_i|$$

$$= \frac{0.51 + 0.25 + 0.23 + 0.08 + 0.39}{5} = 0.29$$

The mean deviation is a measure of the dispersion of experimental measurements about the mean (i.e., a measure of precision). It is common practice to report the experimental value E of a quantity in the form

$$E = \bar{x} \pm \bar{d}$$

In Example 7, this would be $E = 5.93 \pm 0.29$. The $\pm$ term gives a measure of the *precision* of the experimental value. The *accuracy* of the mean value of a set of experimental measurements (5.93 in the above example) may be expressed in terms of percent error or percent difference.

The dispersion of an experimental measurement may be expressed by other means (such as standard deviation; see Appendix C), so the method should be specified when reporting.

F. Graphical Representation of Data

It is often convenient to represent experimental data in graphical form, not only for reporting, but also to obtain information.

Graphing Procedures

Quantities are commonly plotted using rectangular Cartesian axes (X and Y). The horizontal axis (X) is called the *abscissa,* and the vertical axis (Y), the *ordinate*. The location of a point on the graph is defined by its coordinates x and y, written (x, y), referenced to the origin O, the intersection of the X and Y axes.

When plotting data, choose axis scales that are easy to plot and read. The graph in ● Fig. 6A shows an example of scales that are too small. This "bunches up" the data, making the graph too small, and the major horizontal scale values make it difficult to read intermediate values. Choose scales so that most of the graph paper is used. The graph in ● Fig. 6B shows data plotted with more appropriate scales.*

Also note in Fig. 6.A that scale units on the axes are not given. For example, you don't know whether the units of displacement are feet, meters, kilometers, or whatever. *Scale units should always be included,* as in Fig. 6B. It is also acceptable, and saves time, to use standard unit abbreviations, such as N for newton and m for meter. This will be done on subsequent graphs.

When the data points are plotted, draw a smooth line described by the points. *Smooth* means that the line does not have to pass exactly through each point but connects the general areas of significance of the data points (*not* connecting the data points as in Fig. 6A). The graph in Fig. 6B with an approximately equal number of points on each side of the line gives a "curve of best fit."

* As a general rule, it is convenient to choose the unit of the first major scale division to the right or above the origin or zero point as 1, 2, or 5 (or multiples or submultiples thereof, e. g., 10 or 0.1) so that the minor (intermediate) scale divisions can be easily interpolated and read.

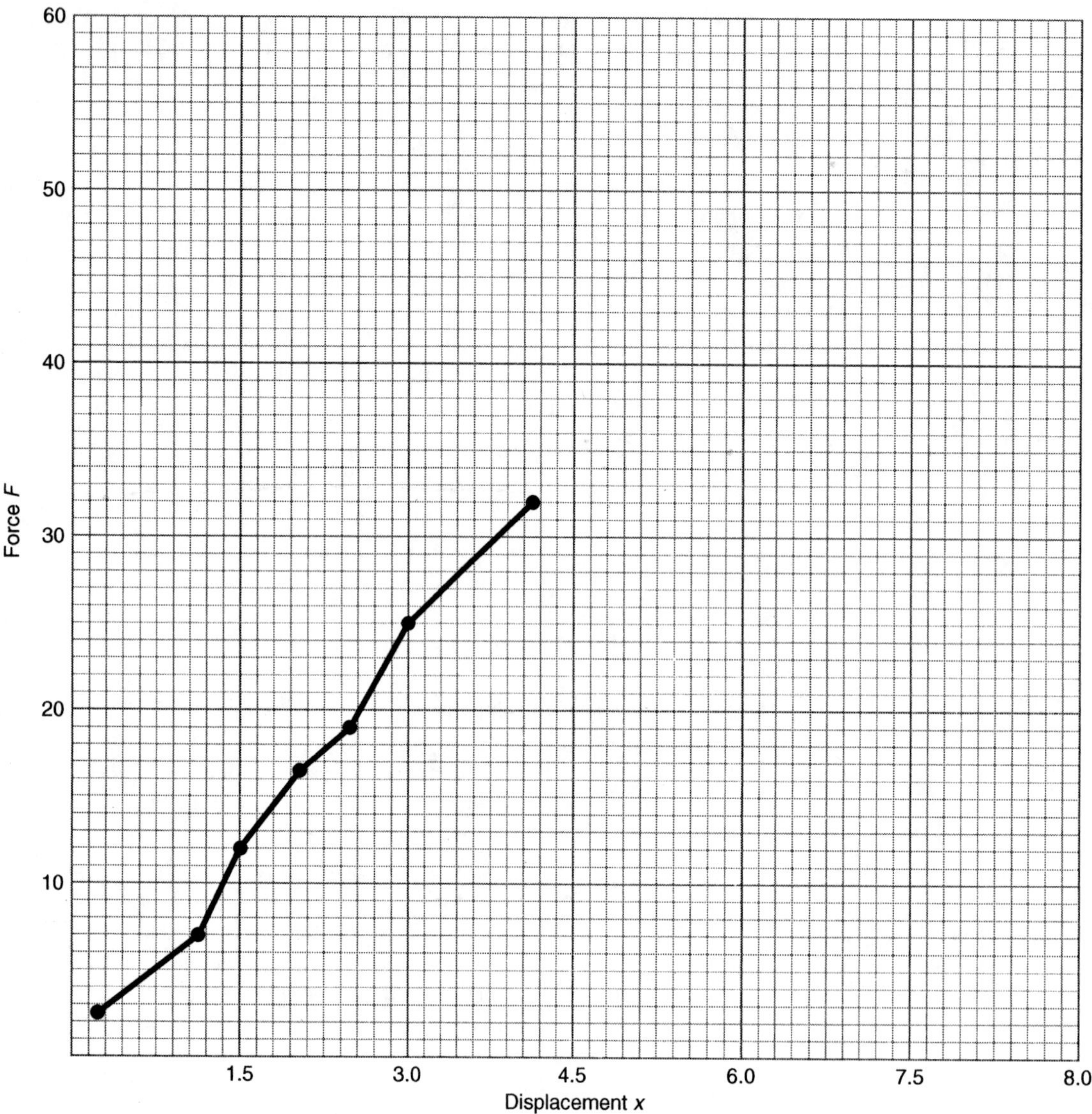

Figure 6A Poor graphing. An example of an improperly labeled and plotted graph. See text for description.

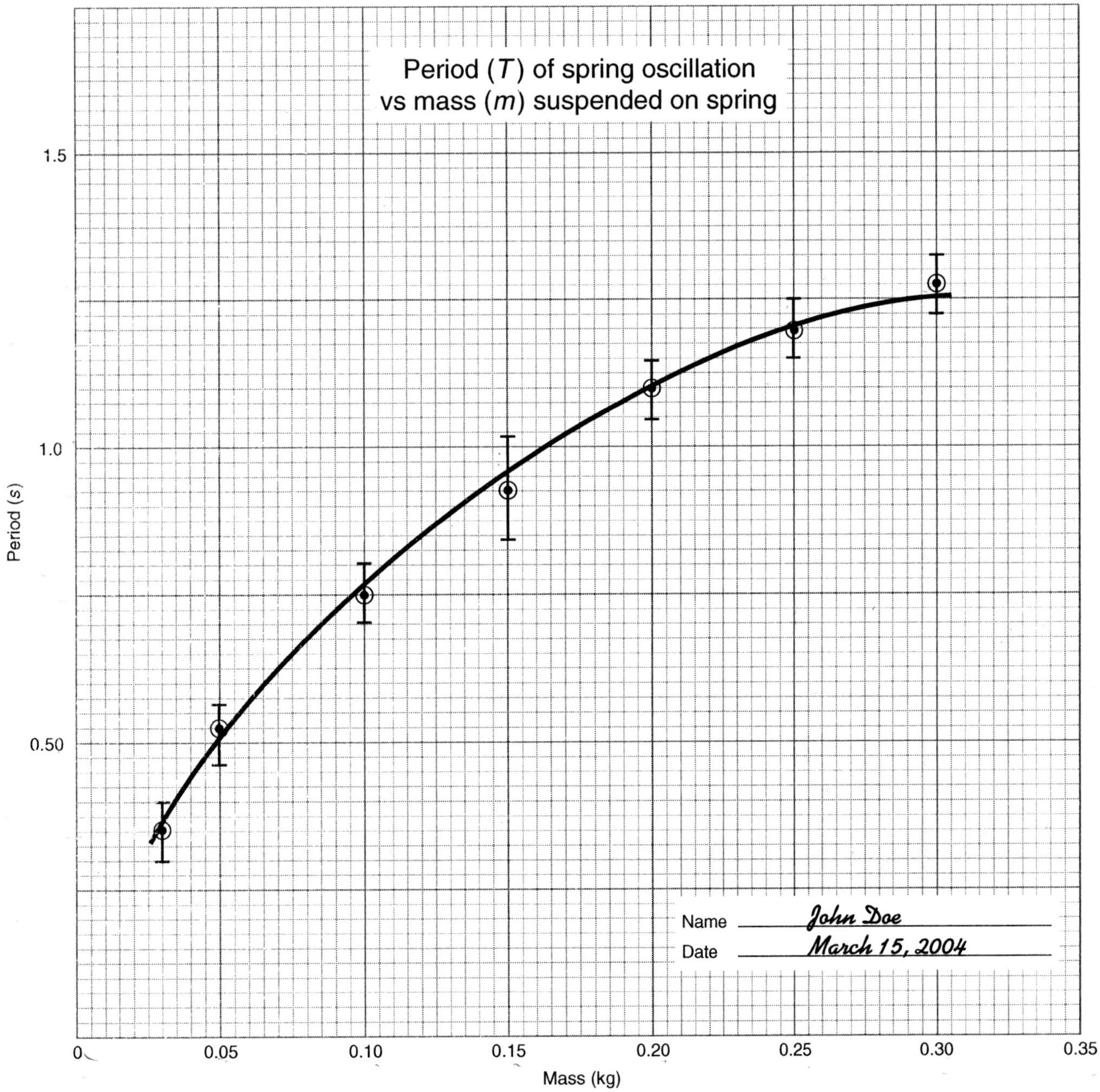

Period (*T*) of spring oscillation
vs mass (*m*) suspended on spring
1.5
1.0
0.50
Period (*s*)
0
0.05
0.10
0.15
0.20
0.25
0.30
0.35
Mass (kg)
Name John Doe
Date March 15, 2004

Figure 7 Error bars. An example of graphically presented data with error bars. An error bar indicates the precision of a measurement. In this case, the error bars represent mean deviations.

Mass (Kg)	Period	(s)^2
.025	~~1.44~~	~~1.88~~
.050	~~.2809~~	.14
.10	~~.5625~~	.28
.15	~~.8164~~	.56
.20	~~1.21~~	.85
.25	~~1.44~~	1.2
.30	~~1.69~~	1.4
		1.7

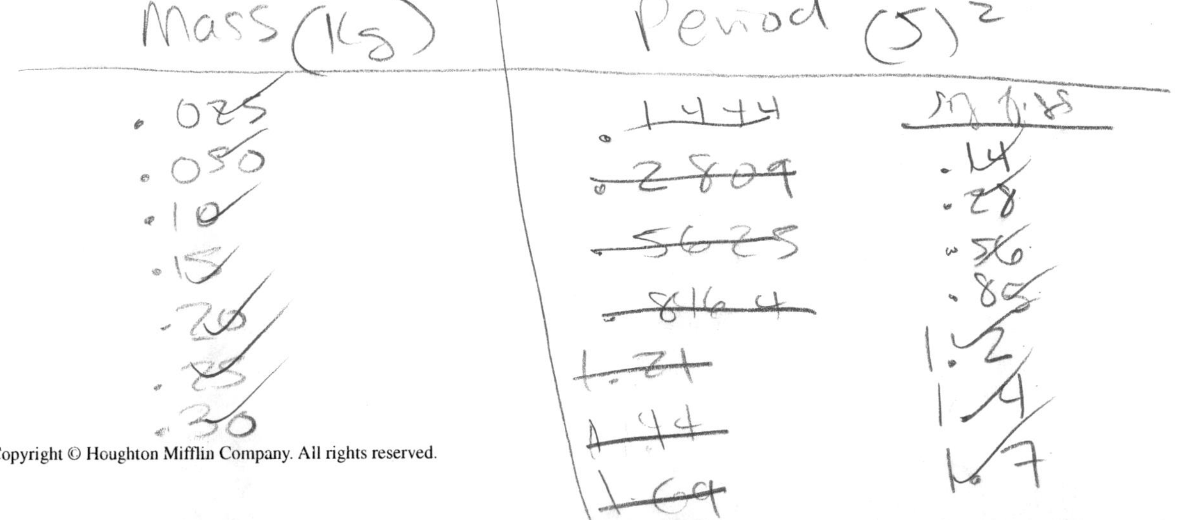

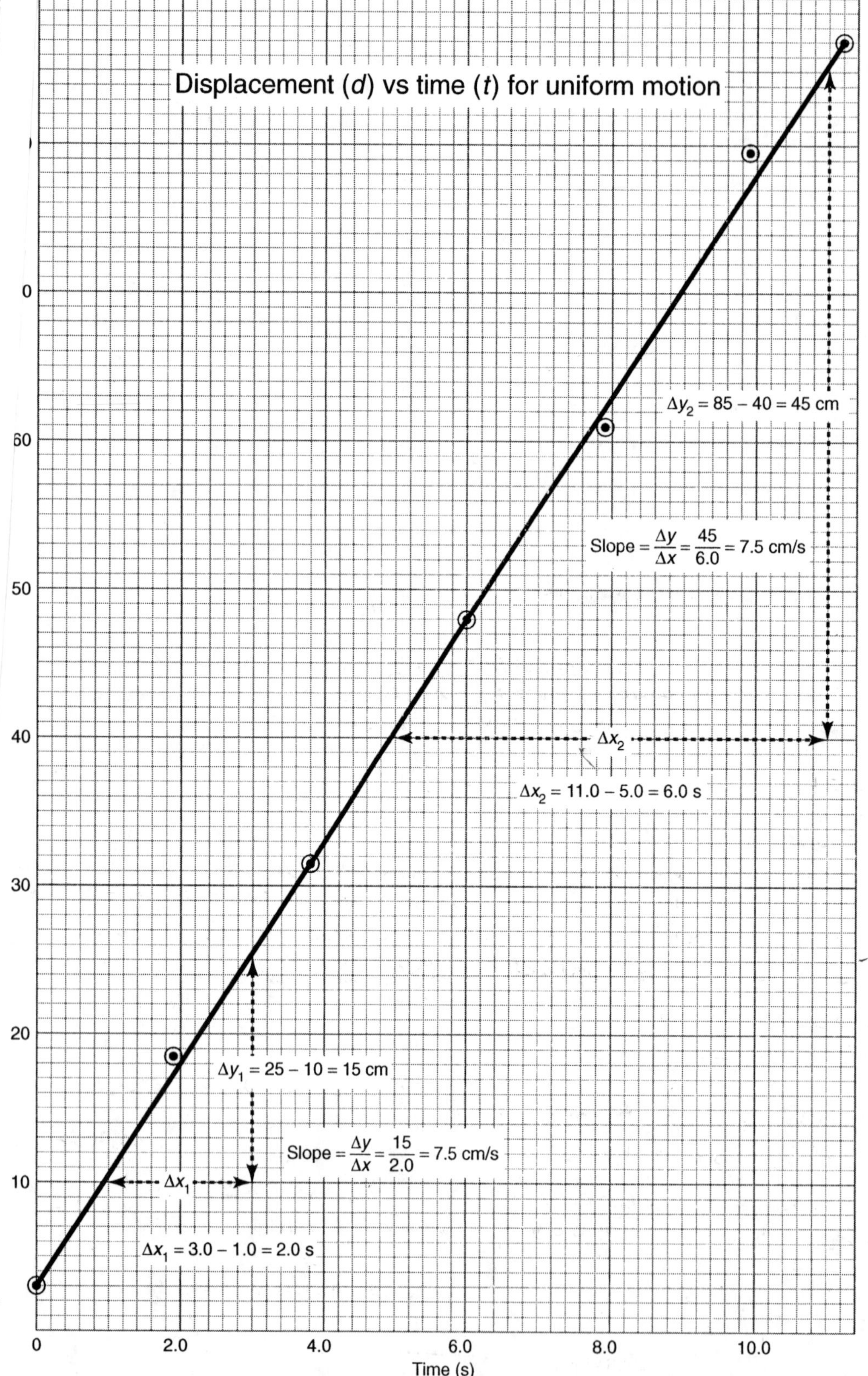

Figure 8 Straight-line slope. Examples of intervals for determining the slope of a straight line. The slope is the ratio of $\Delta y/\Delta x$ (or $\Delta d/\Delta t$). Any set of intervals may be used, but the endpoints of an interval should be relatively far apart, as for $\Delta y_2/\Delta x_2$.

Measurement Instruments (Mass, Volume, and Density)

Introduction and Objectives

Common laboratory measurements involve the determination of the fundamental properties of mass and length. Most people are familiar with the use of scales and rulers or metersticks. However, for more accurate and precise measurements, laboratory balances and vernier calipers or micrometer calipers are often used, particularly in measurements involving small objects.

In this initial experiment on measurement, you will learn how to use these instruments and what advantages they offer. Density, the ratio of mass to volume, will also be considered, and the densities of several materials will be determined experimentally.

After performing this experiment and analyzing data, you should be able to do the following:

1. Use the vernier caliper and read the vernier scale.
2. Use the micrometer caliper and read its scale.
3. Distinguish between mass and density, and know how to determine experimentally the density of an object substance.

Equipment Needed

- Laboratory balance
- Vernier caliper
- Micrometer caliper (metric)
- Meterstick
- Graduated cylinder
- Cylindrical metal rod (e.g., aluminum, brass, or copper)
- Sphere (metal or glass, e.g., a ball bearing or marble)
- Short piece of solid copper wire
- Rectangular piece of metal sheet (e.g., aluminum)
- Irregularly shaped metal object

Theory

A. Laboratory Balances

Some common types of laboratory balances are shown in ● Fig. 1. Mechanical balances or "scales" are used to balance the weight of an unknown mass m against that of a known mass m_1 (i.e., $mg = m_1g$ or $m = m_1$), and the mass of the unknown is read directly in mass units, usually grams. The weight w of an object is its mass m times a constant g, the acceleration due to gravity; $g = 9.80\ \text{m/s}^2 = 980\ \text{cm/s}^2$ (i.e., $w = mg$ or $m = w/g$). Some scales, such as bathroom scales, are calibrated in weight (force) units (such as pounds) rather than in mass units.

A set of known masses is used to balance an unknown mass on a pan balance (Fig. 1a). On a beam balance, the riders on the beams are used to balance the unknown mass on the platform (Fig. 1b). The common laboratory beam balance is calibrated in grams. In this case, the least count is 0.1 g and a reading can be estimated to 0.01 g.* (See Experiment 1 for a review of least count.)

* The official abbreviation of the gram unit is g (in roman type). The standard symbol for acceleration due to gravity is *g* (in italic type), where weight is given by *mg*, which is not to be confused with mg for miligram. Look closely so as to avoid confusion with these symbols.

Before making a mass determination, check whether the balance is zeroed. Adjustments can be made by various means on different scales.

Electronic balances with digital readouts are becoming increasingly common (Fig. 1c). They have the advantages of accuracy and ease of operation. However, electronic balances are much more delicate. The mass value is displayed automatically, and the accuracy or number of significant figures depends on the particular balance. Some electronic balances have autocalibration, and other have a keypad for calibration by the user.† Most electronic balances are zeroed by pressing a "tare" button. This has the advantage that one can place an empty dish on the balance before pressing the "tare" button, and then, when the material is added to the dish, the balance displays the mass of the contents alone.

† In general, an electronic balance has a suspended beam, and the balancing force on the end of the beam opposite the weighing pan is electromagnetic. The force is supplied by a current-carrying coil of wire in the field of a permanent magnet. The force is directly proportional to the current, which is controlled automatically by a photosensitive diode whose resistance is a function of the light incident on it.

Any tilting of the beam increases the light from a source on the diode, and a feedback circuit calls for more current in the coil. The increase in current (and hence in force) is adjusted so as to keep the beam in horizontal equilibrium. The current that balances the beam is read out on a digital ammeter calibrated in grams or milligrams.

(a) (b) (c) (d)

Figure 1 Laboratory balances. (a) A double-beam, double platform Harvard trip balance, which is also called an *equal-arm balance.* (b) A single-platform, triple-beam balance. (c) High-form beam balances. The balance on the left has a dial mechanism that replaces the lower-mass beams. (d) A digital electronic balance. (Courtesy of Sargent-Welch.)

Because of the wide variety of electronic balances available, if you are using one in this experiment you should first familiarize yourself with its operation. Your instructor may brief you, or an operation manual should be available. (When first using an electronic instrument, it is always advisable to read the operation manual supplied by the manufacturer.)

B. The Vernier Caliper

In 1631, a Frenchman, Pierre Vernier, devised a way to improve the precision of length measurements. The **vernier caliper** (● Fig. 2), commonly called a **vernier,** consists of a rule with a main engraved scale and a movable jaw with an engraved vernier scale. The span of the lower jaw is used to measure length and is particularly convenient for measuring the diameter of a cylindrical object. The span of the upper jaw is used to measure distances between two surfaces (such as, the inside diameter of a hollow cylindrical object).

The main scale is calibrated in centimeters with a millimeter least count, and the movable vernier scale has 10 divisions that cover 9 divisions on the main scale. When making a measurement with a meterstick, it is necessary to estimate, or "eyeball," the fractional part of the smallest scale division (the tenth of a millimeter). The function of the vernier scale is to assist in the accurate reading of the fractional part of the scale division, thus increasing the precision.

The leftmost mark on the vernier scale is the zero mark (lower scale for metric reading and upper scale for inches). The zero mark is often unlabeled. A measurement is made by closing the jaws on the object to be measured and read-

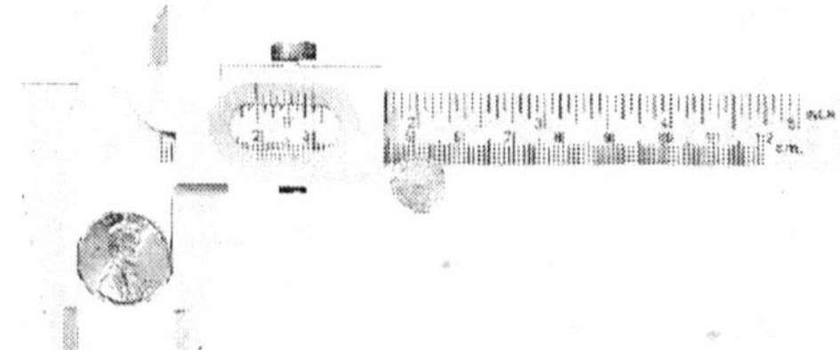

Figure 2 A vernier caliper. A good instrument for measuring rectangular dimensions and circular diameters. This caliper has scales for both metric and English measurements. See text for description. (Courtesy of Sargent-Welch.)

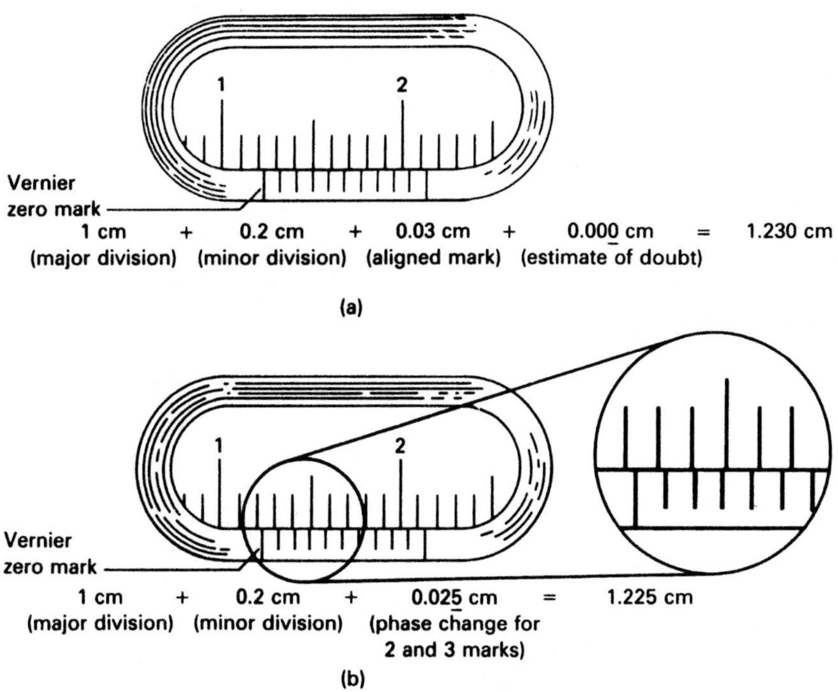

Figure 3 The vernier scale. An example of reading the vernier scale on a caliper. See text for description.

ing where the zero mark on the vernier scale falls on the main scale (See ● Fig. 3). Some calipers, as the one here, have vernier scales for both metric and British units.

The first two significant figures are read directly from the main scale in Fig. 3. The vernier zero mark is past the 2-mm line after the 1-cm major division mark, so we have a reading of 1.2 cm for both (a) and (b). The next significant figure is the fractional part of the smallest subdivision on the main scale. This is obtained by referring to the vernier scale markings below the main scale.

If a vernier mark coincides with a mark on the main scale, then the vernier mark number is the fractional part of the main-scale division (see Fig. 3a). In the figure, this is the third mark to the right of the vernier zero, so the third significant figure is 3 (0.03 cm). Finally, since the 0.03-cm reading is known exactly, a zero is added as the doubtful figure, for a reading of 1.230 cm or 12.30 mm. Note how the vernier scale gives more significant figures or extends the precision.

However, a mark on the vernier scale may not always line up exactly with one on the main scale (Fig. 3b). In this case, there is more uncertainty in the 0.001-cm or 0.01-mm figure, and we say there is a change of "phase" between two successive vernier markings.

Notice how in Fig. 3b the second vernier mark after the zero is to the right of the closest main-scale mark, and the third vernier mark is to the left of the next main-scale mark. Hence, the marks change "phase" between the 2 and 3 marks, which means the reading is between 1.22 cm and 1.23 cm. Most vernier scales are not fine enough for us to make an estimate of the doubtful figure, so a suggested method is to take the middle of the range. Thus we would put a 5 in the thousandth-of-a-centimeter digit, for a reading of 1.225 cm.*

ZEROING

Before making a measurement, one should check the zero of the vernier caliper with the jaws completely closed. It is possible that through misuse the caliper is no longer zeroed and thus gives erroneous readings (systematic error). If this is the case, a zero correction must be made for each reading.

In zeroing, if the vernier zero lies to the right of the main-scale zero, measurements will be too large and the error is said to be *positive*. In this case, the zero correction is made by subtracting the zero reading from the measurement reading. For example, the "zero" reading in ● Fig. 4 is +0.05 cm, and this amount must be subtracted from each measurement reading for more accurate results.

Similarly, if the error is *negative*, or the vernier zero lies to the left of the main-scale zero, measurements will be too small, and the zero correction must be added to the measurement readings.

Summarizing these corrections in equation form,

$$\text{Corrected reading} = \text{actual reading} - \text{zero reading}$$

For example, for a *positive* error of +0.05 cm as in Fig. 4,

$$\text{Corrected reading} = \text{actual reading} - 0.05\text{ cm}$$

If there is a *negative* correction of −0.05 cm, then

$$\begin{aligned}\text{Corrected reading} &= \text{actual reading} - (-0.05)\text{ cm}\\ &= \text{actual reading} + 0.05\text{ cm}\end{aligned}$$

* E. S. Oberhofer, "The Vernier Caliper and Significant Figures," *The Physics Teacher,* Vol. 23 (November 1985), 493.

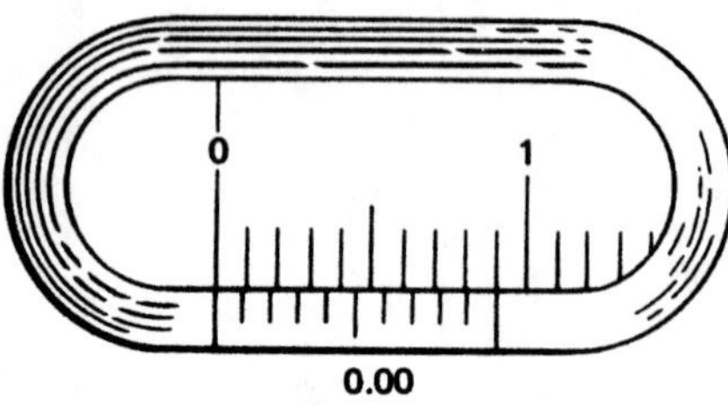

(a) Properly zeroed

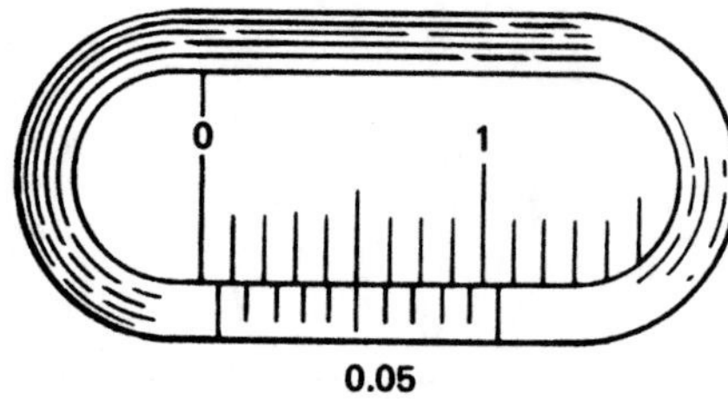

(b) Positive error, + 0.05 cm
(subtracted from measurement reading)

Figure 4 Zeroing and error. The zero of the vernier caliper is checked with the jaws closed. (a) Zero error. (b) Positive error, +0.05 cm.

C. The Micrometer Caliper

The **micrometer caliper** (● Fig. 5), commonly called a **mike,** provides for accurate measurements of small lengths and is particularly convenient in measuring the diameters of thin wires and the thicknesses of thin sheets. It consists of a movable spindle (jaw) that is advanced toward another, parallel-faced jaw (called an anvil) by rotating the thimble. The thimble rotates over an engraved sleeve (or "barrel") mounted on a solid frame.

Most micrometers are equipped with a ratchet (ratchet handle is to the far right in the figure) that allows slippage of the screw mechanism when a small and constant force is exerted on the jaw. This permits the jaw to be tightened on an object with the same amount of force each time. Care should be taken not to force the screw (particularly if the micrometer does not have a ratchet mechanism), so as not to damage the measured object and/or the micrometer.

The axial main scale on the sleeve is calibrated in millimeters, and the thimble scale is calibrated in 0.01 mm (hundredths of a millimeter). The movement mechanism of the micrometer is a carefully machined screw with a pitch of 0.5 mm. The pitch of a screw, or the distance between screw threads, is the lateral linear distance the screw moves when turned through one rotation.

The axial line on the sleeve main scale serves as a reading line. Since the pitch of the screw is 0.5 mm and there are 50 divisions on the thimble, when the thimble is turned through one of its divisions, the thimble moves (and the jaws open or close) $\frac{1}{50}$ of 0.5 mm, or 0.01 mm ($\frac{1}{50} \times 0.5$ mm = 0.01 mm).

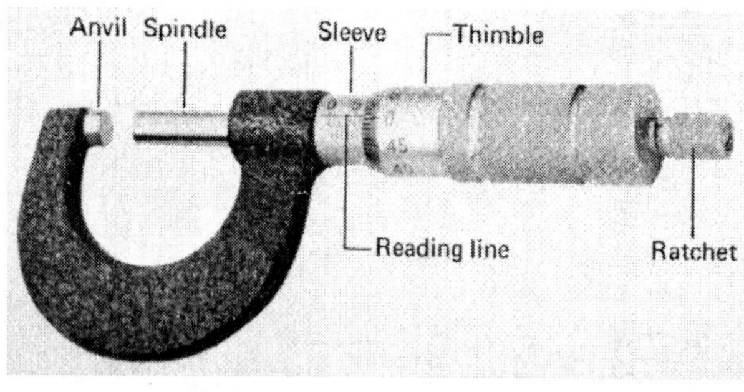

(a)

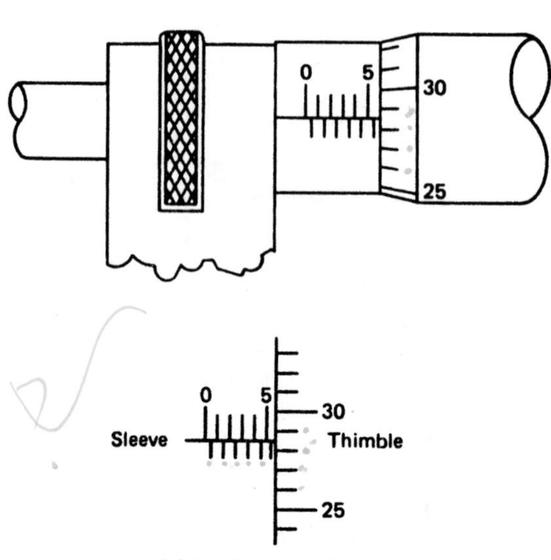

(b) Reading of 5.785 mm

Figure 5 A micrometer caliper and an example of a micrometer reading. (a) This particular mike has the 1.0-mm and 0.5-mm scale divisions below the reading line. (b) In this diagram, as on some mikes, the 1.0-mm divisions are above the reading line and the 0.5-mm divisions are below it. The thimble in the diagram is in the second rotation of millimeter movement, as indicated by its being past the 0.5-mm mark. The reading is 5.500 + 0.285 mm, or 5.785 mm, where the last 5 is the estimated figure. (Photo courtesy of Sargent-Welch.)

One complete rotation of the thimble (50 divisions) moves it through 0.5 mm, and a second rotation moves it through another 0.5 mm, for a total of 1.0 mm, or one scale division along the main scale. That is, the first rotation moves the thimble from 0.00 through 0.50 mm, and the second rotation moves the thimble from 0.50 through 1.00 mm.

It is sometimes instructive to think of the 1-mm main-scale divisions as analogous to dollar ($) divisions and of the thimble scale divisions as cents ($0.01). The first rotation of the thimble corresponds to going from $0.00 to $0.50 (50 cents), and the second rotation corresponds to going from $0.50 to $1.00, so that two complete rotations go through 100 cents, or $1.00, of the main scale.

Some micrometers have a scale that indicates the 0.5-mm marks of the main-scale divisions and hence tells which rotation the thimble is in (see Fig. 5). Cheaper mikes do not have this extra graduation, and the main scale must be closely examined to determine which rotation the thimble is in.

If a mike does not have the 0.5-mm scale, you must determine whether the thimble is in its first rotation, in which case the thimble reading is between 0.00 and 0.50 mm (corresponding to the actual engraved numbers on the thimble), or in the second rotation, in which case the reading is between 0.50 and 1.00 mm (the actual thimble scale reading plus 0.50).

This can be determined by judging whether the edge of the thimble is in the first or the second half of the main-scale division. Notice that the zero mark on the thimble is used to indicate both 0.00 mm (beginning of the first rotation) and 0.50 mm (beginning of the second rotation).

Measurements are taken by noting the position of the edge of the thimble on the main scale and the position of the reading line on the thimble scale. For example, for the drawing in Fig. 5, the mike has a reading of 5.785 mm. On the main scale is a reading of 5.000 mm plus one 0.500-mm division (scale below reading line), giving 5.500 mm. That is, in the figure, the thimble is in the second rotation of a main-scale division.

The reading on the thimble scale is 0.285 mm, where the 5 is the estimated or doubtful figure; that is, the reading line is estimated to be midway between the 28 and the 29 marks. (Some mikes have vernier scales on the sleeves to help the user read this last significant figure and further extend the precision.)

As with all instruments, a zero check should be made and a zero correction applied to each reading if necessary, as described in Section B. A zero reading is made by rotating the screw until the jaw is closed or the spindle comes into contact with the anvil. The contacting surfaces of the spindle and anvil should be clean and free of dust. (Micrometers can be adjusted to zero readings by means of a spanner wrench. *Do not attempt to do this* without your instructor's permission or supervision.)

D. Density

The **density** ρ of a substance is defined as the mass m per unit volume V (i.e., $\rho = m/V$). Thus the densities of substances or materials provide comparative measures of the amounts of matter in a particular (unit) space. Note that there are two variables in density—mass and volume. Hence, densities can be affected by the masses of atoms and/or by their compactness.

As can be seen from the defining equation ($\rho = m/V$), the SI units of density are kilogram per cubic meter (kg/m^3). However, measurements are commonly made in the smaller metric units of grams per cubic centimeter (g/cm^3), which can easily be converted to standard units.*

Figure 6 Density, mass, and volume. The marble and the Styrofoam ball have equal masses but different densities ($\rho = m/V$). Because the volume of the ball is greater than that of the marble, its density is less.

Density may be determined experimentally by measuring the mass and volume of a sample of a substance and calculating the ratio m/V. The volume of regularly shaped objects may be calculated from length measurements. For example;

Rectangle
$V = l \times w \times h$ (length × width × height)

Cylinder
$V = Al = (\pi r^2)l$ (circular cross-sectional area $A = \pi r^2$, where r is the radius, times the length l of the cylinder)

Sphere
$V = \frac{4}{3}\pi r^3$ (where r is the radius of the sphere)

To illustrate how density provides a measure of compactness of matter, consider the marble and Styrofoam ball in ● Fig. 6. Both have the same mass (5.0 g), but the marble has greater density. (Why?) With measured radii of $r_m = 0.75$ cm and $r_b = 6.0$ cm for the marble and ball, respectively, the calculated densities are

$$\rho_m = \frac{m_m}{V_m} = \frac{m_m}{\frac{4}{3}\pi r_m^3} = \frac{5.0 \text{ g}}{\frac{4}{3}\pi(0.75 \text{ cm})^3} = 2.8 \text{ g/cm}^3$$

$$\rho_b = \frac{m_b}{V_b} = \frac{m_b}{\frac{4}{3}\pi r_b^3} = \frac{5.0 \text{ g}}{\frac{4}{3}\pi(6.0 \text{ cm})^3} = 0.0055 \text{ g/cm}^3$$

* In the British fps (foot–pound–second) system, density is expressed in terms of weight rather than mass. For example, the weight density of water is 62.4 lb/ft^3.

(Notice that the calculated results have only two significant figures. Why?) In standard SI units, these results are 2.8×10^3 kg/m^3 and 5.5 kg/m^3, respectively.

But how does one find the volume of an irregularly shaped object? This may be done by immersing it in water (or some other liquid) in a graduated container. Since the object will displace a volume of water equal to its own volume, the difference in the container readings before and after immersion is the volume of the object. Cylinders commonly have scale divisions of milliliters (mL) and 1 mL = 1 cm^3.* [cm^3 (cubic centimeter) is sometimes written on glassware as cc.]

The physical property of density can be used to identify substances in some cases. If a substance is not pure or is not homogeneous (that is, its mass is not evenly distributed), an average density is obtained, which is generally different from that of a pure or homogeneous substance.

EXPERIMENTAL PROCEDURE

A. *Least Count of an Instrument Scale*

1. List the least count and the estimated fraction of the least count for each of the measuring instruments in Data Table 1 of the laboratory report. For example, for a meterstick, these would be 1 mm and 0.1 mm, respectively. (Review Experiment 1 if necessary.)

B. *Thickness Measurements*

2. Using the micrometer caliper, take a zero reading and record it in Data Table 3. Then take several measurements of a single page of this manual, incorporating the zero correction if necessary, to determine the average thickness per page. Record the data and result in Data Table 2.

3. With the micrometer, take thickness measurements of a group of several pages together [e.g., 10 pages (sheets of paper)], and record the data in Data Table 2. Calculate the average thickness per page.

4. With the vernier caliper, take several measurements of the total thickness of the manual (*excluding* covers).† Record the data in Data Table 2, and compute the average overall thickness of the manual. (Did you remember to take a zero reading and record in Data Table 3?)

5. Using the values of the average thickness per page determined in procedures 2 and 3 and the overall average thickness of the manual from procedure 4, compute the number of pages (sheets of paper) in your manual. For example, if the average thickness per page is 0.150 mm and the average overall thickness is 35.5 mm (3.55 cm), the calculated number of papers is

$$\frac{35.5 \text{ mm}}{0.150 \text{ mm/page}} = 236.6666 = 237 \text{ pages}$$

6. Determine the actual number of pages (sheets of paper) in the manual. (Remember to subtract any pages handed in from Experiment 1, the Advance Study Assignment for this experiment, and any others that might be missing.) Compute the percent error for each of the two experimentally determined values.

C. *Density Determinations*

7. The densities of the materials of the various objects are to be determined from mass and volume (length) measurements. Taking the mass and length measurements will give you experience in using the laboratory balance and the vernier and micrometer calipers.

8. Using the appropriate measuring instrument(s), take several measurements to determine the average dimensions of the regularly shaped objects so that their volumes can be calculated. Record the data in Data Table 3. Remember to make a zero correction for each reading if necessary.

9. Calculate the volume of each of the objects, and record in Data Table 4.

10. Determine the volume of the irregularly shaped metal object by the method described in Theory section D. Record the volume in Data Table 4.

11. Using a laboratory balance, determine the mass of each object, and record the results in Data Table 4.

12. Calculate the density of the material of each object, and find the percent error of each experimental result. (Accepted density values are given in Appendix A, Table A1.)

* *Milliliter* is abbreviated both ml and mL. The mL abbreviation is generally preferred in order to avoid confusion of a lowercase l ("ell") with the number 1.

† Be sure the pages are compacted as much as possible before you take the measurements.

EXPERIMENT 3

The Addition and Resolution of Vectors: The Force Table

INTRODUCTION AND OBJECTIVES

Physical quantities are generally classified as either scalar or vector quantities. The distinction is simple. A **scalar** quantity (or *scalar*) is one with magnitude only (including units)—for example, speed (15 m/s) and temperature (20°C). A **vector** quantity (or *vector*), on the other hand, has both magnitude *and* direction. Such quantities include displacement, velocity, acceleration, and force—for example, a velocity of 15 m/s north or a force of 10 N along the $+x$ axis.

Because vectors have the property of direction, the common method of addition, scalar addition, is not applicable to vector quantities. To find the **resultant** or **vector sum** of two or more vectors, we use special methods of vector addition, which may be graphical and/or analytical. Several of these methods will be described, and we shall investigate the addition of force vectors. The results of graphical and analytical methods will be compared with the experimental results obtained from a force table. The experimental arrangements of forces (vectors) will physically illustrate the principles of the methods of vector addition.

After performing this experiment and analyzing the data, you should be able to do the following:

1. Add a set of vectors graphically to find the resultant.
2. Add a set of vectors analytically to find the resultant.
3. Appreciate the difference in convenience between using graphical and using analytical methods of vector addition.

EQUIPMENT NEEDED

- Force table with four pulleys
- Four weight hangers
- Set of slotted weights (masses), including three of 50 g and three of 100 g
- String
- Protractor
- Ruler
- Level
- 3 sheets of Cartesian graph paper

THEORY

A. Methods of Vector Addition: Graphical

PARALLELOGRAM METHOD

Vectors are represented graphically by arrows (● Fig. 1). The length of a vector arrow (drawn to scale on graph paper) is proportional to the magnitude of the vector, and the arrow points in the direction of the vector.

The length scale is arbitrary and is usually selected for convenience and so that the vector graph fits nicely on the graph paper. A typical scale for a force vector might be 1 cm:10 N. That is, each centimeter of vector length represents 10 newtons. The *scaling factor* in this case in terms of force per unit length is 10 N/cm. (Note the similarity with the common food cost factor of price/lb—for example, 10 ¢/lb.)

When two vectors **A** + **B** (Fig. 1a) are added, the parallelogram of which **A** and **B** are adjacent sides is formed. The arrow diagonal of the parallelogram **R** is the resultant or vector sum of **A** + **B**; in other words, by vector addition, **R** = **A** + **B**. The magnitude R of the resultant vector is proportional to the length of the diagonal arrow, and the direction of the resultant vector is that of the diagonal arrow **R**. The direction of **R** may be specified as being at an angle θ relative to **A**.

TRIANGLE METHOD

An equivalent method of finding **R** is to place the vectors to be added "head to tail" (head of **A** to tail of **B**, Fig. 1b). Vector arrows may be moved as long as they remain pointed in the same direction. The head-to-tail method gives the same resultant as the parallelogram method.

POLYGON METHOD

If more than two vectors are added, the head-to-tail method forms a polygon (Fig. 1c). For three vectors, the resultant **R** = **A** + **B** + **C** is the vector arrow from the tail of the **A** arrow to the head of the **C** vector. The length (magnitude) and the angle of orientation of **R** can be measured from the vector diagram. Note that this is equivalent to applying the head-to-tail method (two vectors) twice (**A** and **B** are added to give $\mathbf{R}_1$, and then **C** is added to $\mathbf{R}_1$ to give **R**).

The magnitude (length) R and the orientation angle θ of the resultant vector **R** in a graphical method can be measured directly from the vector diagram using a ruler and a protractor.

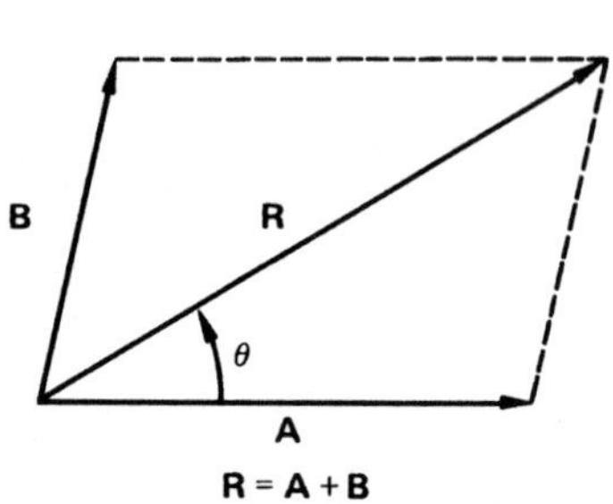

(a) Parallelogram Method

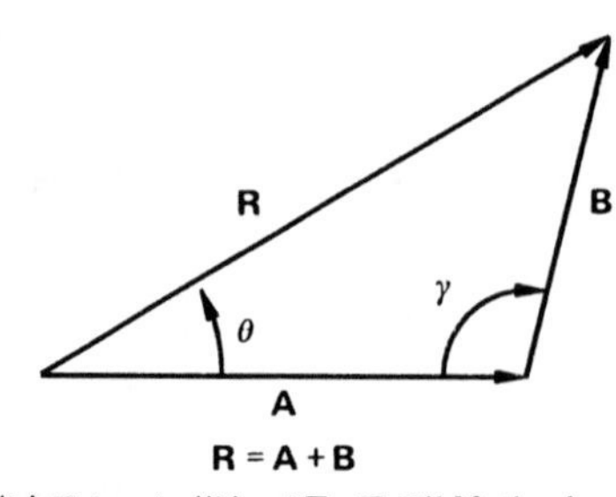

(b) Triangle "Head-To-Tail" Method

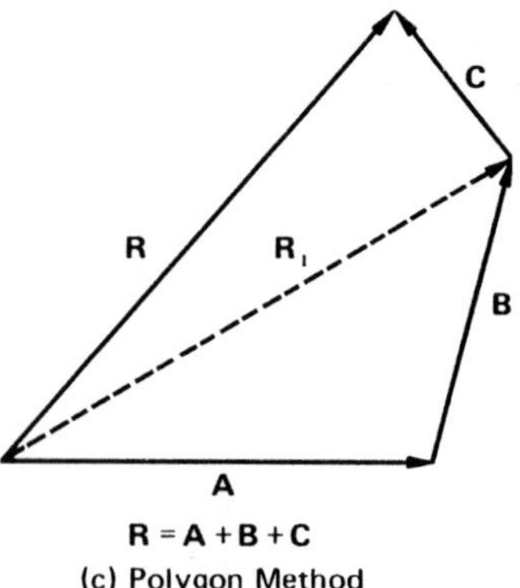

(c) Polygon Method

Figure 1 Vector addition. Different methods of vector addition. Vectors are represented graphically by arrows. See text for description.

Example 1 To illustrate scaling and the graphical triangle method, let **A** and **B** represent forces at angles of 0° and 60°, respectively, with magnitudes of $A = 2.45$ N and $B = 1.47$ N.

Then, choosing a scaling factor (say, 0.50 N/cm), we find a vector length by dividing its magnitude by the scaling factor (magnitude/scaling factor). Note the unit cancellation:

A: 2.45 N/(0.50 N/cm) = 4.9 cm

B: 1.47 N/(0.50 N/cm) = 2.9 cm

Here, the 0.50-N/cm scaling factor was chosen so as to keep ● Fig. 2 an appropriate size. In drawing your vector diagrams, you should choose a scaling factor that will use most of the allotted space on the graph paper—much as in plotting a graph in Experiment 1. Also, a factor with two significant figures was chosen because graph paper grids are usually not fine enough to plot more digits accurately.

The triangle has been drawn in Fig. 2, where **R** = **A** + **B**. The **R** vector is measured (with ruler and protractor) to have a length of 6.8 cm and a direction angle of $\theta = 22°$ relative to the **A** vector. The magnitude of **R** in newtons is found using the scaling factor:

$$R = (\text{scaling factor})(\text{measured length}) = (0.50 \text{ N/cm})(6.8 \text{ cm}) = 3.4 \text{ N}$$

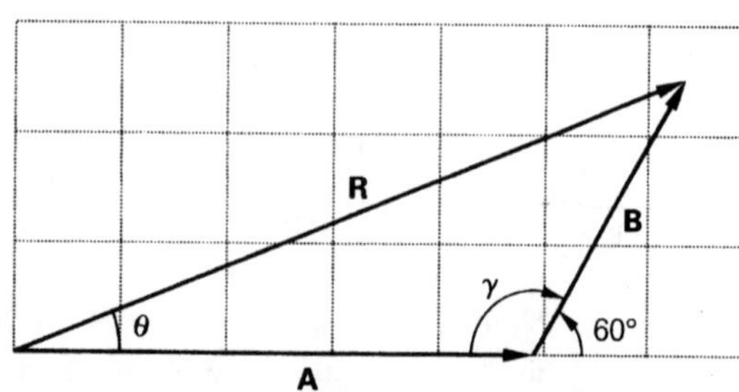

gure 2 **Drawing to scale.** Figures are often scaled ɪwn so as to maintain a convenient size. Here the vector angle is shown to scale, with a scaling factor of 0.50 cm. See text for description.

B. Methods of Vector Addition: Analytical

TRIANGLE METHOD

The magnitude of **R** in Fig. 2 can be computed from the law of cosines if the angle γ (angle opposite **R**) is known. We know γ, and with the given magnitudes of **A** and **B**,

$$R^2 = A^2 + B^2 - 2AB\cos\gamma \tag{1}$$

The angle θ (between **R** and **A**) can then be computed using the law of sines because the magnitudes of sides **B** and **R** are known, and

$$\frac{B}{\sin\theta} = \frac{R}{\sin\gamma} \tag{2}$$

From Example 1, the magnitudes of **A** and **B** are 2.45 N and 1.47 N, respectively, and, as can be seen directly from Fig. 2, $\gamma = 120°$. (Why?) Then, using the law of cosines (Eq. 1):

$$\begin{aligned} R^2 &= A^2 + B^2 - 2\ AB\cos\gamma \\ &= (2.45)^2 + (1.47)^2 - 2(2.45)(1.47)\cos 120° \\ &= 6.00 + 2.16 - 2(3.60)(-0.500)^* \\ &= 11.76 \end{aligned}$$

and

$$R = 3.43 \text{ N}$$

(Units were neglected in the initial calculation for convenience.)

* Value obtained by calculator or from trig table with cos 120° = cos (180° − 120°) = −cos 60° using the trigonometric identity cos $(A - B) = \cos A \cos B + \sin A \sin B$.

The directional angle θ may be found using the law of sines (Eq. 2):

$$\theta = \sin^{-1}\left(\frac{B \sin \gamma}{R}\right)$$
$$= \sin^{-1}\left(\frac{1.47g \sin 120°}{3.43g}\right) = 21.8°$$

Remember that this is the angle between vectors **R** and **A**.

Component Method

If two vectors **A** and **B** are at right (90°) angles (● Fig. 3a), then the magnitude of their resultant is given by the **Pythagorean theorem,** $R = \sqrt{A^2 + B^2}$ (the hypotenuse of a right triangle is equal to the square root of the sum of the squares of the legs of the triangle). Notice that the law of cosines reduces to this formula with $\gamma = 90°$ (because $\cos 90° = 0$). The angle of orientation is given by $\tan \theta = B/A$, or $\theta = \tan^{-1}(B/A)$.

By the inverse process, we may resolve a vector into x and y components (Fig. 3b). That is, the vector **R** is the resultant of $\mathbf{R}_x$ and $\mathbf{R}_y$, and $\mathbf{R} = \mathbf{R}_x + \mathbf{R}_y$, where $R_x = R \cos \theta$ and $R_y = R \sin \theta$. The magnitude of R is given by

$$R = \sqrt{R_x^2 + R_y^2} \quad (3)$$

and

$$\tan \theta = \frac{R_y}{R_x} \quad (4)$$

or

$$\theta = \tan^{-1}\left(\frac{R_y}{R_x}\right)$$

(resultant, magnitude, and angle)

The vector sum of any number of vectors can be obtained by using the component method. This is conveniently done by having all the vectors originate from the origin and resolving each into x and y components, as shown in ● Fig. 4 for $\mathbf{R} = \mathbf{A} + \mathbf{B} + \mathbf{C}$.

The procedure is to add vectorially all of the x components together and all of the y components together. The $\mathbf{R}_x$ and $\mathbf{R}_y$ resultants are then added together to get the total resultant **R**. Doing this for the vectors in Fig. 4, we have

$$\mathbf{R}_x = \mathbf{A}_x + \mathbf{B}_x + \mathbf{C}_x$$
$$= 6.0 \cos 60° + 0 - 10 \cos 30°$$
$$= -5.7 \text{ N}$$

$$\mathbf{R}_y = \mathbf{A}_y + \mathbf{B}_y + \mathbf{C}_y$$
$$= 6.0 \sin 60° + 5.0 - 10 \sin 30°$$
$$= 5.2 \text{ N}$$

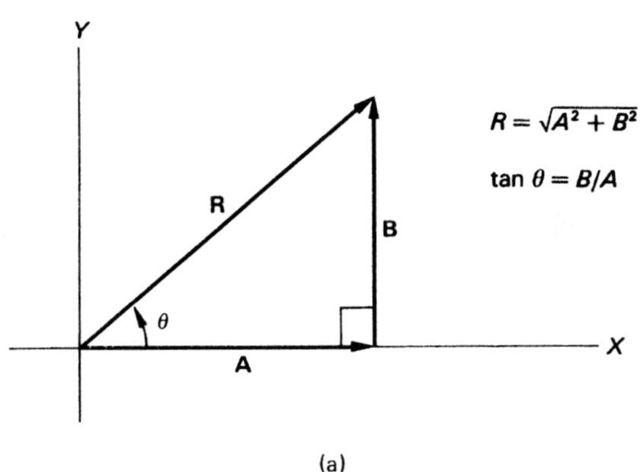

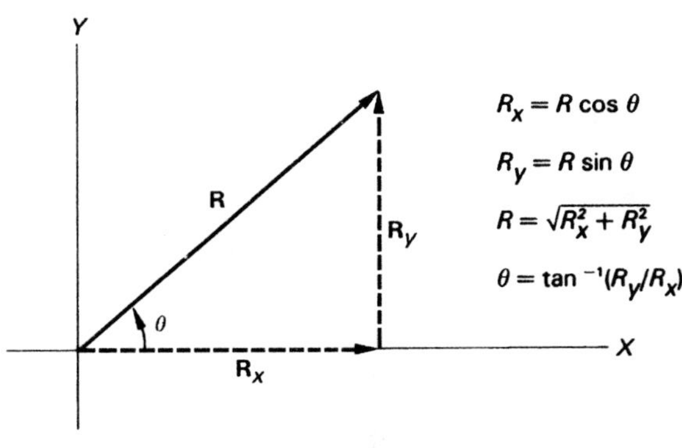

Figure 3 Vector resultant and components. (a) The vector addition of **A** and **B** gives the resultant **R**. (b) A vector, such as **R**, can be resolved into x and y (rectangular) components $\mathbf{R}_x$ and $\mathbf{R}_y$, respectively.

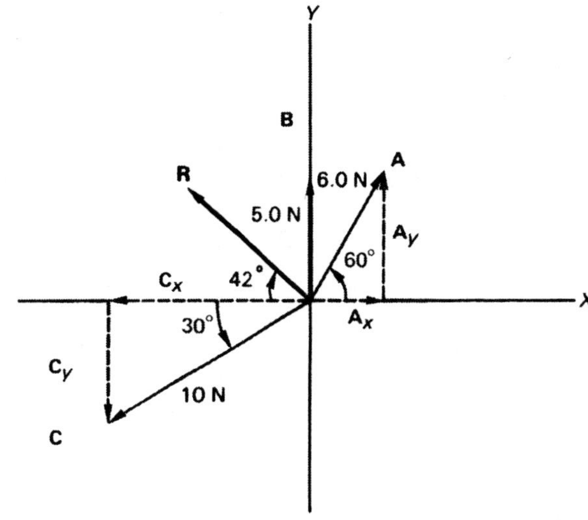

Figure 4 Component method. Rather than using the head-to-tail method of vector addition, it is generally more convenient to use the component method, in which all vectors are drawn originating from the origin and resolved into components.

where the component directions are indicated by the positive and negative signs (arbitrary units). Note that **B** has no x component and that $\mathbf{C}_x$ and $\mathbf{C}_y$ are in the negative x and y directions, as indicated by the minus signs. Then the magnitude of **R** is (Eq. 3):

$$R = \sqrt{R_x^2 + R_y^2} = \sqrt{(5.7)^2 + (5.2)^2} = 7.7 \text{ N}$$

and, by Eq. 4,

$$\theta = \tan^{-1}\left|\frac{R_y}{R_x}\right| = \tan^{-1}\left(\frac{5.2}{5.7}\right) = 42°$$

relative to the $-X$ axis (or $180° - 42° = 138°$ relative to the $+X$ axis). It is convenient to measure all component angles as acute angles from the X axis. The minus R_x and positive R_y indicate that the resultant is in the second quadrant.*

C. *Methods of Vector Addition: Experimental*

The Force Table

The **force table** is an apparatus that makes possible the experimental determination of the resultant of force vectors (● Fig. 5). The rim of the circular table is calibrated in degrees. Weight forces are applied to a central ring by means of strings running over pulleys and attached to weight hangers. The magnitude (mg) of a force (vector) is varied by adding or removing slotted weights, and the direction is varied by moving the pulley.

(a)

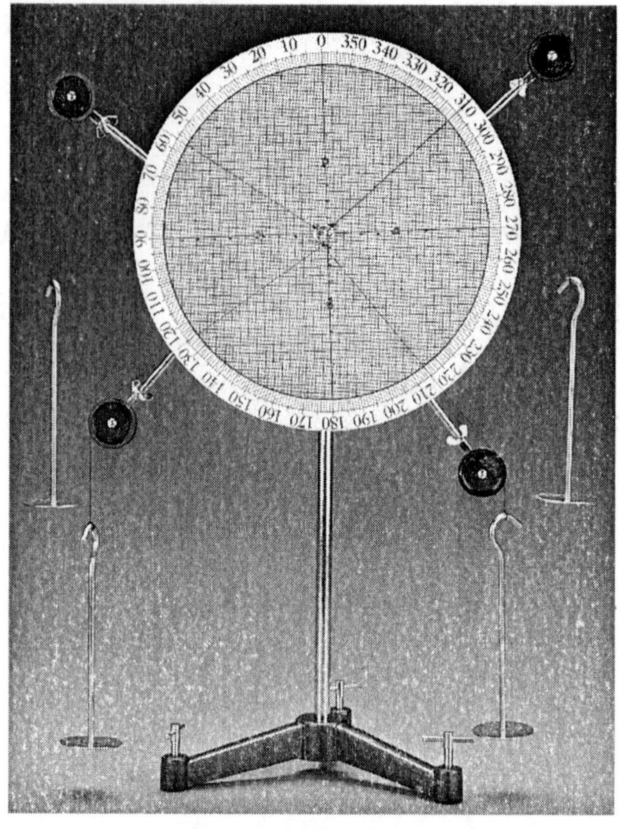

(b)

(c)

Figure 5 Force tables. Various types of force tables. The table in (c) may be used vertically for demonstration (b), or horizontally in the laboratory. [Courtesy of Sargent-Welch.]

* Although it is customary to measure angles counterclockwise from the positive X axis, this procedure is convenient in eliminating the need for double-angle equations.

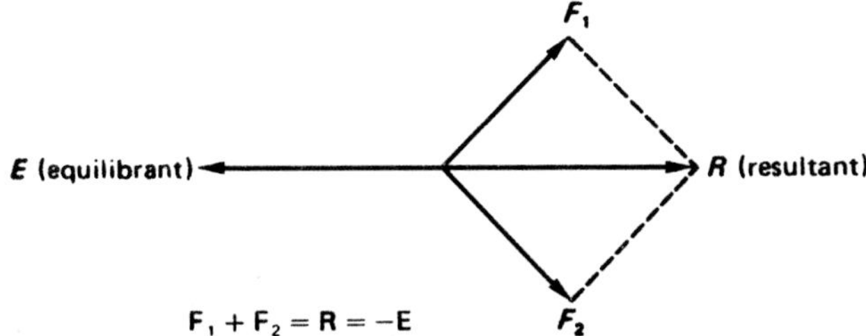

Figure 6 Resultant and equilibrant. On a force table, the magnitude and direction of the equilibrant **E** are measured, rather than those of the resultant **R**, and **R** = −**E**.

The resultant of two or more forces (vectors) is found by balancing the forces with another force (weights on a hanger) so that the ring is centered around the central pin. The balancing force is *not* the resultant **R** but rather the *equilibrant* **E**, or the force that balances the other forces and holds the ring in equilibrium.

The equilibrant is the vector force of equal magnitude, but in the *opposite direction,* to the resultant (i.e., **R** = −**E**). See ● Fig. 6. For example, if an equilibrant has a magnitude of $(0.30)g$ N in a direction of 225° on the circular scale, the resultant of the forces has a magnitude of $(0.30)g$ N in the opposite direction, 225° − 180° = 45°. It should be evident that the resultant cannot be determined directly from the force table. (Why?)*

EXPERIMENTAL PROCEDURE

1. Set up the force table with strings and suspended weights and perform the following cases of vector addition.

2. *Vector addition 1.* Given two vectors with magnitudes $F_1 = (0.200)g$ N and $F_2 = (0.200)g$ N at 30° and 120°, respectively, find their vector sum or resultant $\mathbf{F} = \mathbf{F}_1 + \mathbf{F}_2$ by each of the following procedures. (*Note:* Orientation angles of vectors are given relative to the 0° reference line or positive *X* axis.)
   (a) *Graphical.* Using the parallelogram method of vector addition, draw a vector diagram to scale. Use a scale such that the finished vector diagram fills about half a sheet of graph paper. Measure the magnitude and direction of the resultant (with ruler and protractor) and record the results in the data table. Save your graphical sheets to attach to the Laboratory Report.
   (b) *Analytical.* Using the law of cosines, compute the magnitude of the resultant force. Compute the angle of orientation from the relationship $\tan\theta = F_2/F_1$. (Why can you use $\tan\theta$? Remember that θ is the angle between **F** and $\mathbf{F}_1$.) Record the results in the data table.
   (c) *Experimental.* On the force table, clamp pulleys at 30° and 120° and add enough weights to each weight hanger to total 0.200 kg, so as to give weight forces of $F_1 = F_2 = (0.200)g$ N in these directions. (The weight hangers usually have masses of 50 g, or 0.050 kg.)

   Using a third pulley and weights, determine the magnitude and direction of the equilibrant force that maintains the central ring centered in equilibrium around the center pin. Record the magnitude and direction of the resultant of the two forces in the data table. Remember, the resultant has the same magnitude as the equilibrant but is in the opposite direction.

   (*Note:* The string knots on the central ring should be of a nontightening variety so that the strings will slip freely on the ring and allow the strings to pull directly away from the center. Pulling the center ring straight up a short distance and releasing it helps adjust the friction in the pulleys as the ring vibrates up and down so that it can settle into an equilibrium position involving only the applied forces. When the forces are balanced, the pin may be carefully removed to see whether the ring is centered around the central hole.)

3. *Vector addition 2.* Repeat procedure 2 for $F_1 = (0.200)g$ N at 20° and $F_2 = (0.150)g$ N at 80°. Use the other half of the sheet of graph paper used in procedure 2(a) for the graphical analysis. Be careful in the analytical analysis. Can you use $\tan\theta = F_2/F_1$ in this case?

4. *Vector addition 3.* Repeat procedure 2 with $F_1 = F_x = (0.200)g$ N (at 0°) and $F_2 = F_y = (0.150)g$ N (at 90°). In this case, $\mathbf{F} = \mathbf{F}_x + \mathbf{F}_y$, where $\mathbf{F}_x$ and $\mathbf{F}_y$ are the *x* and *y* components of **F**, respectively. That is, the resultant can be resolved into these components. Use half of another sheet of graph paper for the graphical method.

5. *Vector resolution.* Given a force vector of $F = (0.300)g$ N at 60°, resolve the vector into its *x* and *y* components and find the magnitudes of $\mathbf{F}_x$ and $\mathbf{F}_y$ by the following procedures:
   (a) *Graphical.* Draw a vector diagram to scale (on the other half of the sheet of graph paper used in procedure 4) with the component vectors (see Fig. 3b) and measure the magnitudes of $\mathbf{F}_x$ and $\mathbf{F}_y$. Record the results in the data table.

* The magnitude of the (weight) force vectors are in general given in the form $R = mg = (0.150)g$ N, for example, where it is understood that the mass is in kilograms and g is the acceleration due to gravity. It is convenient to leave g in symbolic form so as to avoid numerical calculations until necessary. This is similar to carrying along π in symbolic form in equations. Also, note that the masses of the laboratory "weights" usually have values stamped in grams. Don't forget to change grams to kilograms when working in the SI: for example, 150 g = 0.150 kg.

(b) *Analytical.* Compute the magnitudes of $\mathbf{F}_x$ and $\mathbf{F}_y$ (see the Theory section). Record the results in the data table.

(c) *Experimental.* Clamp pulleys at 240°, 90°, and 0° on the force table. Place a *total* of 0.300 kg on the 240° pulley string using a weight hanger. This force is then the equilibrant of $F = (0.300)g$ N at 60° (since 60° + 180° = 240°), which must be used on the force table rather than the force itself. Add weights to the 0° and 90° hangers until the system is in equilibrium. The 0° and 90° forces are then the $\mathbf{F}_x$ and $\mathbf{F}_y$ components, respectively, of $\mathbf{F}$. Record their magnitudes in the data table.

6. *Vector addition 4.* Given the force vectors $F_1 = (0.100)g$ N at 30°, $F_2 = (0.200)g$ N at 90°, and $F_3 = (0.30)g$ N at 225°, find the magnitude and direction of their resultant $\mathbf{F} = \mathbf{F}_1 + \mathbf{F}_2 + \mathbf{F}_3$ by the following procedures:

(a) *Graphical.* Use the polygon method.

(b) *Analytical.* Use the component method.

(c) *Experimental.* Use the force table. Record the results in the data table.

7. *Vector addition 5.* Instructor's choice (optional). Your instructor will give you a set of vectors to add. Record the results in the data table as you did for previous procedures.

Name ______________________ Section ______________ Date ______________

Lab Partner(s) ____

EXPERIMENT 3

The Addition and Resolution of Vectors: The Force Table

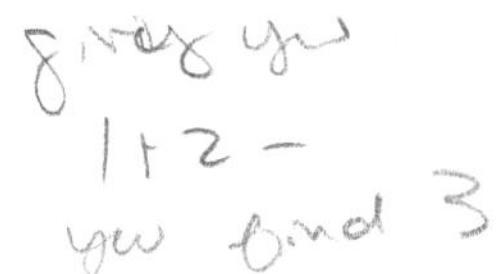

TI Laboratory Report

Note: Attach graphical analyses to Laboratory Report.

DATA TABLE

Purpose: To analyze results of different methods of vector addition.

	Forces ( )	Resultant R (magnitude and direction)		
		Graphical	Analytical*	Experimental
Vector addition 1	$F_1 = (0.200)g$ N, $\theta_1 = 30°$ $F_2 = (0.200)g$ N, $\theta_2 = 120°$			
Vector addition 2	$F_1 = (0.200)g$ N, $\theta_1 = 20°$ $F_2 = (0.150)g$ N, $\theta_2 = 80°$			
Vector addition 3	$F_1 = F_x = (0.200)g$ N, $\theta_1 = 0°$ $F_2 = F_y = (0.150)g$ N, $\theta_2 = 90°$			
Vector resolution	$F = (0.300)g$ N, $\theta = 60°$	F_x F_y	F_x F_y	F_x F_y
Vector addition 4	$F_1 = (0.100)g$ N, $\theta_1 = 30°$ $F_2 = (0.200)g$ N, $\theta_2 = 90°$ $F_3 = (0.300)g$ N, $\theta_3 = 225°$			
Vector addition 5				

*Show analytical calculations below.

Calculations
(attach additional sheet if necessary)

Don't forget units

(continued)

TI QUESTIONS

1. Considering the graphical and analytical methods for obtaining the resultant, which method is more accurate? Give the probable sources of error for each method.

2. Vector subtraction (**A** − **B**) is a special case of vector addition, since **A** − **B** = **A** + (−**B**). Suppose that the cases of vector addition 1, 2, and 3 in this experiment were vector subtraction ($\mathbf{F}_1 - \mathbf{F}_2$).
   (a) What effect would this have on the directions of the resultants? (Do not calculate explicitly. Simply state in which quadrant the resultant would be in each case.)

   (b) Would the magnitude of the resultant be different for vector subtraction than for vector addition in each case? If so, state whether the subtractive resultant would be greater or less than the additive resultant.

3. A picture hangs on a nail as shown in ● Fig. 7. The tension T in each string segment is 3.5 N.
   (a) What is the equilibrant or the upward reaction force of the nail?
   (b) What is the weight of the picture?

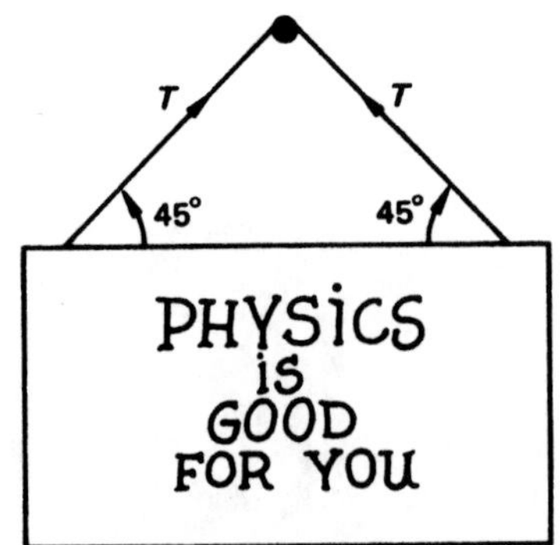

Figure 7 See Question 3.

Name ______________________ Section ______________ Date ______________

Lab Partner(s) ____

EXPERIMENT 4

Newton's Second Law: The Atwood Machine

TI Advance Study Assignment

Read the experiment and answer the following questions.

1. Write Newton's second law in mathematical form, and describe how the acceleration of an object or system varies with the unbalanced force and mass of the system.

2. What are F and m in Newton's second law in terms of the Atwood machine?

3. Explain how F and m are individually varied while the other is held constant. Why is this done?

(continued)

4. How can the frictional force be experimentally determined, and how is it used in the calculations?

5. What is measured in the experiment, and how is this used to compute the acceleration of the system?

CI Advance Study Assignment

Read the experiment and answer the following questions.

1. When the Atwood machine is moving, what is the shape of a velocity-versus-time plot for the motion? Why?

2. The photogate will measure the tangential speed of the pulley. Why is this speed the same as the speed of the ascending and descending masses?

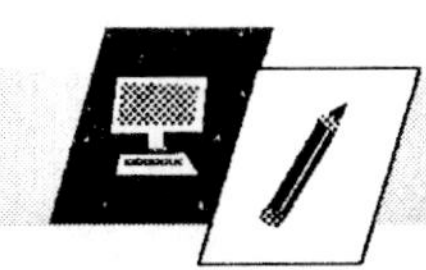

EXPERIMENT 4

Newton's Second Law: The Atwood Machine

Overview

Experiment examines Newton's second law using the Atwood machine by TI procedures and/or CI procedures. Both procedures apply the second law by (1) varying the total mass while keeping the unbalanced force constant and (2) varying the unbalanced force while keeping the total mass constant.

The TI procedure determines the accelerations of the system using distance-time measurements. In the CI procedure, speed-time measurements are used by electronically observing the motion of the pulley.

Introduction and Objectives

Newton's second law of motion states that the acceleration **a** of an object or system is directly proportional to the vector sum of the forces acting on the object, $\Sigma \mathbf{F}_i$ or the unbalanced or net force $\mathbf{F}_{net}$, and inversely proportional to the total mass m of the system ($\mathbf{a} \propto \mathbf{F}_{net}/m$). In equation form with standard units, $\mathbf{a} = \mathbf{F}_{net}/m$ or, more commonly, $\mathbf{F} = m\mathbf{a}$.

This relationship will be investigated using an Atwood machine, which consists of two masses connected by a string looped over a pulley (● TI Fig. 1). The Atwood machine is named after the British scientist George Atwood (1746–1807), who used the arrangement to study motion and measure the value of g, the acceleration due to gravity.

In this experiment, the relatively slow, uniform acceleration of the masses will be used to investigate Newton's second law. Since the acceleration a of the system depends on two variables (F_{net} and m, where $a = F_{net}/m$), one of the variables will be held constant while the other is varied. This is common experimental procedure. By varying the unbalanced weight force and the total mass of the system, we can determine the resulting accelerations experimentally from distance and time measurements and compare them with the predictions of Newton's second law.

After performing this experiment and analyzing the data, you should be able to do the following:

TI Objectives

1. Tell how the acceleration of a system varies with changes in net force or mass—in particular, for
   a. mass variations with a constant (unbalanced) force, and
   b. force variations with constant mass.
2. Articulate the precise meanings of the variables (F, m, and a) in Newton's second law.
3. Explain how the acceleration of the masses of an Atwood machine may be determined experimentally.

CI Objectives

Experimentally verify Newton's second law of motion in two ways:

1. by keeping the net force on a system constant and varying the mass, and
2. by keeping the mass of the system constant and varying the net force.

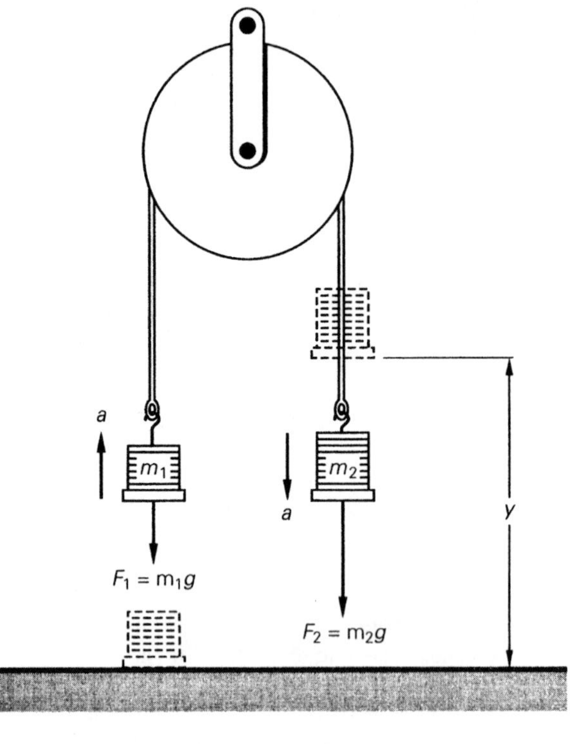

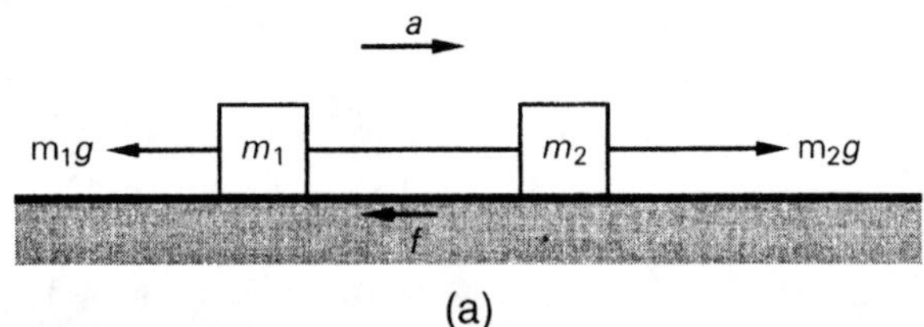

(a)

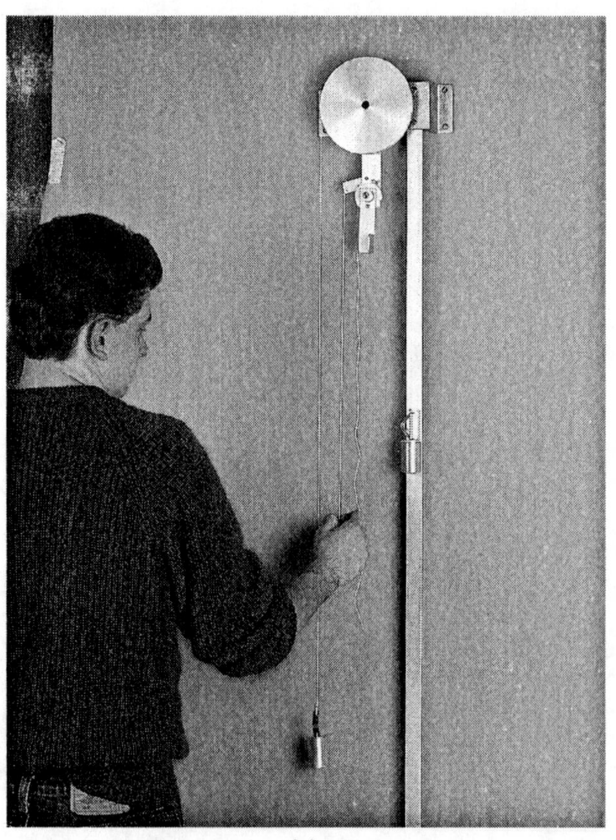

(c)

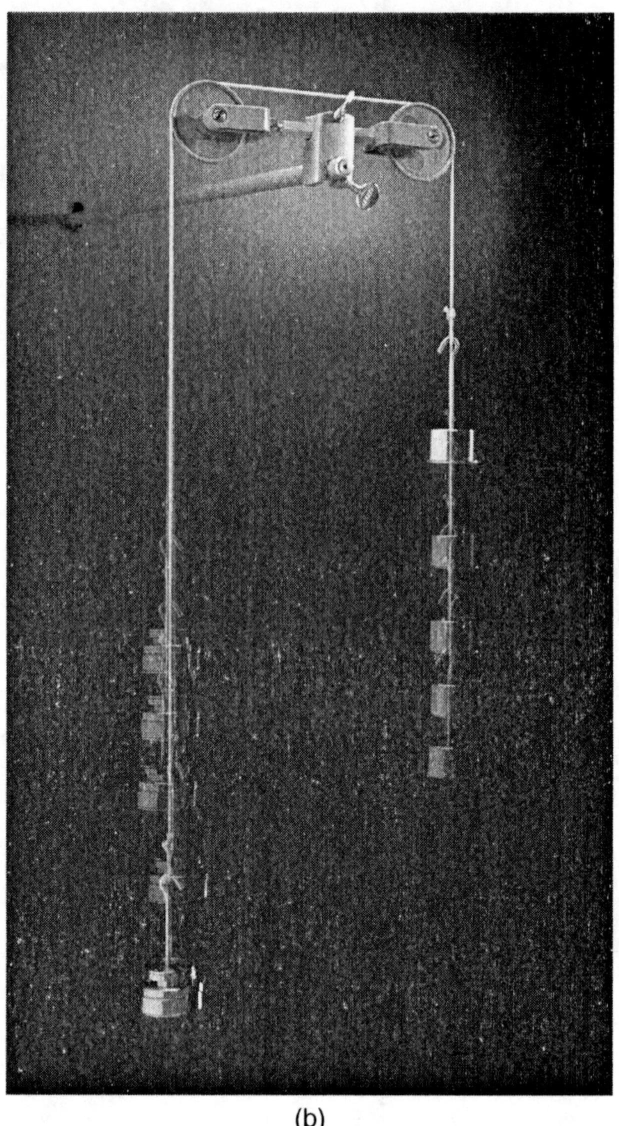

(b)

TI Figure 1 The Atwood machine. (a) The dynamics of the Atwood machine. A single (or double) pulley system is simply a "direction changer," and it is sometimes convenient to draw a horizontal diagram for analysis. (b) A double-pulley system eliminates the possibility of the passing weights hitting each other, which may occur with a single pulley of small diameter. (c) A wall-mounted precision Atwood machine. A trip platform supports the upper weight before the start of each run and is released and reset by control cords. (Photos courtesy of Sargent-Welch.)

TI EXPERIMENT 4

Newton's Second Law: The Atwood Machine

TI EQUIPMENT NEEDED

- Pulley (preferably low-inertia, precision ballbearing type)
- Clamps and support rods
- Two weight hangers
- Set of slotted weights, including small 5-, 2-, and 1-g weights
- Paper clips
- String
- Laboratory timer or stopwatch
- Meterstick
- 2 sheets of Cartesian graph paper

TI THEORY

The light string is considered to be of negligible mass. With masses m_1 and m_2 as the ascending and descending sides of the system, respectively (Fig. TI 1), the unbalanced (net) force is (taking the more massive hanger to be moving in the positive direction)

$$F_{net} = m_2 g - m_1 g = (m_2 - m_1)g \qquad \textbf{(TI 1)}$$

where the friction and inertia of the pulley can be neglected without appreciably affecting the results.

By Newton's second law,

$$F_{net} = ma = (m_1 + m_2)a \qquad \textbf{(TI 2)}$$

where $m = m_1 + m_2$ is the total mass of the moving system. Then, equating Eqs. TI 1 and TI 2, we have

$$(m_2 - m_1)g = (m_1 + m_2)a$$

or

$$\boxed{a = \frac{(m_2 - m_1)g}{m_1 + m_2}} \qquad \textbf{(TI 3)}$$

(acceleration, theoretical)

(*Optional*) In the experimental arrangement, there may be an appreciable frictional force f associated with the pulley that opposes the motion. Also, the pulley has inertia. In an attempt to take this inertia into account, we will add an equivalent mass m_{eq} to the total mass being accelerated. Hence, for better accuracy, the equation for the acceleration of the system should be modified as follows:

$$F_{net} = ma$$

$$F - f = (m_1 + m_2 + m_{eq})a$$

$$(m_2 + m_1)g - f = (m_1 + m_2 + m_{eq})a$$

or

$$a = \frac{(m_2 - m_1)g - f}{m_1 + m_2 + m_{eq}} \qquad \textbf{(TI 4)}$$

If the masses of the Atwood machine move with a constant speed, the magnitude a of the acceleration of the system is zero, and

$$a = 0 = \frac{(m_2 - m_1)g - f}{m_1 + m_2 + m_{eq}}$$

or

$$f = (m_2 - m_1)g = m_f g \qquad \textbf{(TI 5)}$$

(uniform speed)

which provides a method for determining the magnitude of the frictional force of the pulley, or the mass m_f needed to provide the weight to balance the frictional force.

Hence, the expression for the theoretical acceleration of the system (Eq. TI 4) may be written

$$\boxed{a_t = \frac{(m_2 - m_1 - m_f)g}{m_1 + m_2 + m_{eq}}} \qquad \textbf{(TI 6)}$$

(acceleration, theoretical)

where a_t is used to distinguish the theoretical acceleration from the experimentally measured acceleration a_m.

Thus, part of the weight of m_2 goes into balancing or canceling the frictional force of the pulley. In the experimental acceleration trials, the m_f determined in each case is left on the descending hanger as part of m_2 to compensate for the frictional force.

To determine the acceleration of the system experimentally so that it may be compared to that predicted by theory, we measure the time t for the descending mass to fall through a given distance y. Then, using the kinematic equation

$$y = v_o t + \tfrac{1}{2}at^2$$

with the mass starting from rest ($v_o = 0$), and $y_o = 0$, $t_o = 0$, we have

$$y = \tfrac{1}{2}at^2$$

or

$$\boxed{a_m = \frac{2y}{t^2}} \qquad \textbf{(TI 7)}$$

(acceleration, measured)

where a_m is the experimentally measured acceleration.

When a_m is determined experimentally using distance and time measurements, friction and pulley inertia are involved. These are taken into account in the theoretical expression (Eq. TI 6) so that the experimental and theoretical values of a will be more comparable. Even so, keep in mind that these are approximations and the percent differences may be large. The main purpose of the experiment is to demonstrate how the acceleration of a system depends on the net force and total mass.

TI EXPERIMENTAL PROCEDURE*

1. Set up the Atwood machine as shown in Fig. TI 1. Use enough string so that the distance of travel (y) is slightly less than 1 m for convenient measuring. (To measure y, hold one hanger against the floor and measure from the floor to the bottom of the other hanger.) Measure and record y in TI Data Table 1.

A. *Varying the Total Mass (Unbalanced Force Constant)*

2. (If using inertia and friction corrections, go to procedure 2a below.) Begin by placing 10 g on the descending hanger so as to create an unbalanced force that should cause the system to accelerate from rest. Make a trial run to see if the system moves at an acceleration suitable for timing. If not, adjust the mass accordingly.

   Taking the descending mass as m_2, record m_1 and m_2 in TI Data Table 1 as Trial 1. [Ignore the columns headed with asterisks and the m_{eq} and m_f symbols.]

3. Make three independent measurements of the time it takes for m_2 to travel the distance y from rest. Record the time in TI Data Table 1.† (See "Comments on Experimental Technique" at the end of the Procedure section.)

4. Add 100 g to each hanger. Repeat procedure 3 (measurement of time with a 10-g mass imbalance). Record the data in the Trial 2 column. *Note:* The value of y should be remeasured for each trial. The length of the string (and y distance) may vary noticeably because of stretching.

5. Repeat procedure 3 for two more trials with another 100 g being added for each trial.

(Procedure using inertia and friction corrections.)

2a. As noted in the Theory section, the pulley contributes to the inertia of the system as though an "equivalent mass" m_{eq} were part of the total mass being accelerated. The instructor will provide the value of m_{eq} or tell you how to measure it (*Instructor's Resource Manual*). Record the value of m_{eq} in the data tables.

3a. Begin with the descending mass (m_2) and the ascending mass (m_1) each equal to 50 g (i.e., the masses of the hangers alone). With $m_1 = m_2$, the system is in equilibrium—equal forces, $m_1 g = m_2 g$. In the absence of friction, a slight tap or momentary force applied to m_2 should set the system in uniform motion (constant speed). Why? However, because of the opposing frictional force, the motion will not persist.

4a. Add small masses to m_2 until a downward push causes m_2 to descend with a uniform (constant) velocity. (See "Comments on Experimental Technique" at the end of the Procedure section.) Apply a sufficient push so the masses move at a reasonable speed; they should not move too slowly. You may find it easier to recognize uniform motion by observing the rotating pulley rather than the masses.

Record m_1 and m_2 in TI Data Table 1 in the first column marked with an asterisk. These values are used to calculate the frictional mass, $m_f = m_2 - m_1$, needed in the theoretical calculation of the acceleration of the system (Eq. TI 6).

5a. (i) Add 10 g to m_2, leaving m_f in place. This creates an unbalanced force that should cause the system to accelerate from rest. Measure the distance y. Record y, m_1, and the new value of m_2 in TI Data Table 1 (Trial 1).

* Refinements in the Experimental Procedure section were developed by Professor I. L. Fischer, Bergen Community College, New Jersey.

† The data tables are arranged to facilitate data taking and analysis. The upper (seven) rows include all the experimental measurements, and the lower (six) rows are for calculations based on these measurements.

(ii) Make three independent measurements of the time it takes for m_2 to travel the distance y from rest. Record the data as Trial 1. (See "Comments on Experimental Technique" at the end of the Procedure section.)

(iii) Remove m_f and the 10-g mass before proceeding to the next trial.

6a. (i) Add 100 g to each hanger for a total of 150 g each.

(ii) Repeat procedure 4a (measurement of frictional mass) and record data in the next asterisked column in TI Data Table 1.

(iii) Repeat timing measurements procedure 5a (measurement of acceleration with a net 10-g mass imbalance). Record the data in the Trial 2 column. The calculations for Trial 2 should utilize the value of m_f obtained for the immediately preceding asterisked column. *Note:* The values of m_f and y should be remeasured for each of the trials in TI Data Table 1. As the total mass is changed, the friction will change likewise. Even the length of the string (y distance) may vary noticeably because of stretching.

7a. Repeat procedures 4a and 5a for two more trials with another 100 g being added for each trial.

B. Varying the Unbalanced Force (Total Mass Constant)

1. (If using inertia and friction corrections, go to procedure 1b below.) Begin with an ascending mass m_1 = 260 g (50-g hanger + 200 + 5 + 2 + 2 + 1-g masses) and a similar descending mass m_2 = 260 g (50-g hanger + 200 + 10-g masses.)*

2. Transfer 1 g from m_1 to m_2 in order to create an unbalanced force without affecting the total mass. Make three measurements of the travel time as done previously in procedure A3. Record the data as Trial 5 in TI Data Table 2.

3. Leaving the previously transferred 1-g mass in place,
(a) Transfer an additional 2 g for Trial 6.
(b) Transfer an additional 2 g for Trial 7.
(c) Transfer an additional 5 g for Trial 8.

(Procedure using inertia and friction corrections.)

1b. Begin with an ascending mass m_1 = 260 g (50-g hanger + 200 + 5 + 2 + 2 + 1-g masses) and a similar descending mass m_2 = 260 g (50-g hanger + 200 + 10-g masses).*

* Mass increments larger than 1 and 2 g may have to be used, depending on the pulley friction. Friction may not be uniform, so a greater mass difference may be needed to initiate motion.

2b. Measure the frictional mass as done previously in procedure A4a. Record the data in the asterisked column in TI Data Table 2. The value of m_f from these data may be used in the calculations for all trials in TI Data Table 2, since the total mass (and presumably the friction) will now be constant.

3b. Leaving m_f in place, transfer 1 g from m_1 to m_2 in order to create a net unbalanced force without affecting the total mass. Make three measurements of the travel time as in procedure 5a. Record all pertinent data in the Trial 5 column.

4b. Leaving m_f and the previously transferred 1-g mass in place,
(a) Transfer an additional 2 g for Trial 6.
(b) Transfer an additional 2 g for Trial 7.
(c) Transfer an additional 5 g for Trial 8.

C. Comments on Experimental Technique

1. Measure the frictional mass to a precision of $\pm\frac{1}{2}g$. Fine adjustment of the descending mass may be made by using small "custom" masses (paper clips) as needed. These paper clips can be attached to the cord just above the m_2 hanger. Good precision is necessary for good results because the frictional force is comparable in magnitude to the accelerating force. Small errors in the frictional masses may create large experimental errors.

2. The masses must start from rest during the acceleration trials. A good technique is as follows:
(a) Hold m_1 down against the floor.
(b) Simultaneously release m_1 and start the timer.
(c) Stop the timer at the instant m_2 strikes the floor.
The best results are obtained when the same person releases m_1 and operates the timer.

3. Some of the masses may be jolted off the hangers by the impact on hitting the floor. It may be helpful to place a shock-absorbing pad on the floor. Also one lab partner should attend to the upper weight to prevent it, or some of it, from falling.

4. Take turns at each task.

Name ______________________ Section ______________ Date ______________

Lab Partner(s) ____

TI EXPERIMENT 4

Newton's Second Law: The Atwood Machine

TI Laboratory Report

TI DATA TABLE 1

Purpose: To investigate $a = F/m$ by holding F constant. (If not considering pulley inertia and friction, ignore (*) columns and m_{eq} and m_f symbols.)

m_{eq} ________ ( )		Trial							
		*	1	*	2	*	3	*	4
Descending mass m_2 ( )									
Ascending mass m_1 ( )									
Distance of travel y ( )									
Time of travel t ( )	Run 1								
	Run 2								
	Run 3								
	Average								
Measured acceleration $a_m = 2y/t^2$ ( )									
Total mass $= m_1 + m_2 + m_{eq}$ ( )									
Measured frictional mass $m_f = m_2 - m_1$									
Net force $= (m_2 - m_1 - m_f)g$ ( )									
Theoretical acceleration $a_t = \frac{\text{net force}}{\text{total mass}}$									
Percent difference between a_m and a_t									

* Measurement of frictional mass m_f. Masses move with constant velocities when given an initial push.

Calculations
(show work)

Don't forget units

(continued)

Calculations
(show work)

TI DATA TABLE 2

Purpose: To investigate $a = F/m$ by holding m constant. (If not considering pulley inertia and friction, ignore (*) columns and m_{eq} and m_f symbols.)

m_{eq} ______ ( )		Trial				
		*	5	6	7	8
Descending mass m_2 ( )						
Ascending mass m_1 ( )						
Distance of travel y ( )						
Time of travel t ( )	Run 1					
	Run 2					
	Run 3					
	Average					
Measured acceleration $a_m = 2y/t^2$ ( )						
Total mass $= m_1 + m_2 + m_{eq}$ ( )						
Measured frictional mass $m_f = m_2 - m_1$						
Net force $=$ $(m_2 - m_1 = m_f)g$ ( )						
Theoretical acceleration $a_t = \frac{\text{net force}}{\text{total mass}}$						
Percent difference between a_m and a_t						

* Measurement of frictional mass m_f. Masses move with constant velocities when given an initial push.

Name ______________________ Section ______________ Date ______________

Lab Partner(s) ____

Calculations
(show work)

TI QUESTIONS

1. In the experiment, should the mass of the string be added to the total mass moved by the unbalanced force for better accuracy? Explain.

2. Complete the following sentences:
   (a) When the unbalanced force increases (total mass remaining constant), the acceleration of the system ______________.
   (b) When the total mass that is accelerating increases (unbalanced force remaining constant), the acceleration of the system ______________.

3. How can the value of g, the acceleration due to gravity, be determined using an Atwood machine?

4. Using the data in TI Data Table 2 (constant total mass), plot a_m versus $(m_2 - m_1)$ for each trial and draw a straight line that best fits the data. Find the slope and intercept of the line and enter the values below.

   Rewrite Eq. TI 6 in slope-intercept form ($y = mx + b$) and, using the data in Trial 6, compute the slope and intercept. (Show calculations.) Compare and comment on your results.

	From graph	From Eq. TI 6
Slope	______________ (units)	______________ (units)
Intercept	______________ (units)	______________ (units)

CI EXPERIMENT 4

Newton's Second Law: The Atwood Machine

CI Equipment Needed

- Photogate/Pulley System (PASCO ME-6838) (Smart Pulley)
- Mass set that includes 1-g, 2-g, and 5-g weights (Suggested: PASCO ME-8967)
- 2 mass hangers
- Clamps and support rods
- Graph paper

CI Theory

When the Atwood machine is unbalanced, the masses move, one ascending, the other descending. As they move, the string makes the pulley rotate. As discussed before, with masses m_1 and m_2 as the ascending and descending sides of the system, respectively, the acceleration of the Atwood machine is given by

$$a = \frac{F_{\text{net}}}{M_{\text{total}}} = \frac{(m_2 - m_1)g}{m_2 + m_1} \qquad \textbf{(CI 1)*}$$

where the friction and inertia of the pulley have been ignored.

In this part of the experiment, we are going to analyze the motion of the ascending and descending masses by using a motion sensor to look at the motion of the pulley. The main idea is that all the objects in the system—the ascending mass, the descending mass, and the pulley—must be moving with the same linear speed at any moment. The linear speed of the pulley is measured as the speed of a point on the rim. The sensor detects how many revolutions per second the pulley is making (the angular speed). For a known radius of pulley, the linear speed on the rim is easily determined:

$$v = r\omega$$

where ω is the angular speed.

The sensor performs this calculation automatically. Notice that by measuring the linear speed of the pulley, we are also measuring the ascending speed of mass m_1 and the descending speed of mass m_2.

The measured speeds will then be plotted as a function of time. Because the acceleration of the system is constant, the plot of speed versus time will be a straight line with slope equal to the acceleration of the system. The experimental acceleration of the system will be determined by finding the slope of the graph. It will then be compared to the theoretical value predicted by Eq. CI 1.

* see Eq. TI 3 development

Setting Up Data Studio

1. Open Data Studio and choose "Create Experiment."
2. From the sensor list, choose the Smart Pulley. An icon for velocity should appear on the data list, to the left of the screen.
3. Connect the Smart Pulley to the interface as shown in the computer screen.
4. Create a graph by dragging the velocity data icon from the data list and dropping it on top of the graph icon of the displays list. A graph of velocity versus time will open. The window will be called Graph 1.
5. ● CI Figure 1 shows what the screen should look like once the setup is complete.

CI Experimental Procedure

A. *Varying the Total Mass (Unbalanced Force Constant)*

1. Set up the Atwood machine using the Photogate/Pulley System (Smart Pulley) instead of a conventional pulley. The ascending mass should begin close to, but not touching, the floor. The descending mass will start at the top. ● CI Fig. 2 shows the experimental setup. Make the string long enough, and install the pulley high enough, so that the masses can move at least half a meter.
2. If using the PASCO ME-8967 mass and hanger set, begin by placing 50 g on each hanger. This added

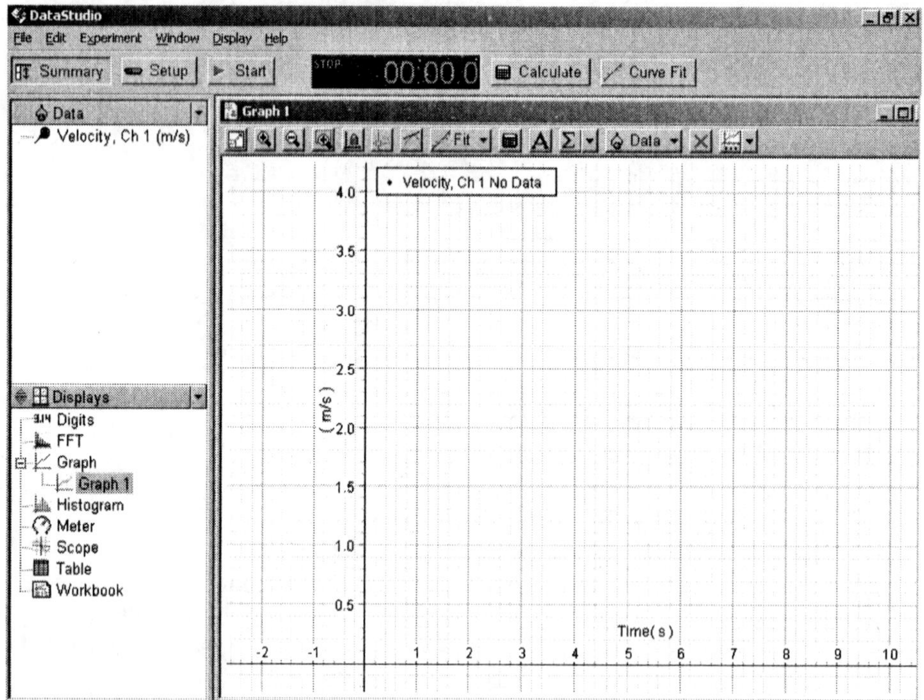

CI Figure 1 Data Studio setup. A graph of velocity versus time was created by dragging the "Velocity" icon from the data list and dropping it on the "Graph" icon in the displays list below. In this picture, the graph window has been resized to occupy most of the screen. (Data displayed using DataStudio Software. Reprinted courtesy of PASCO scientific.)

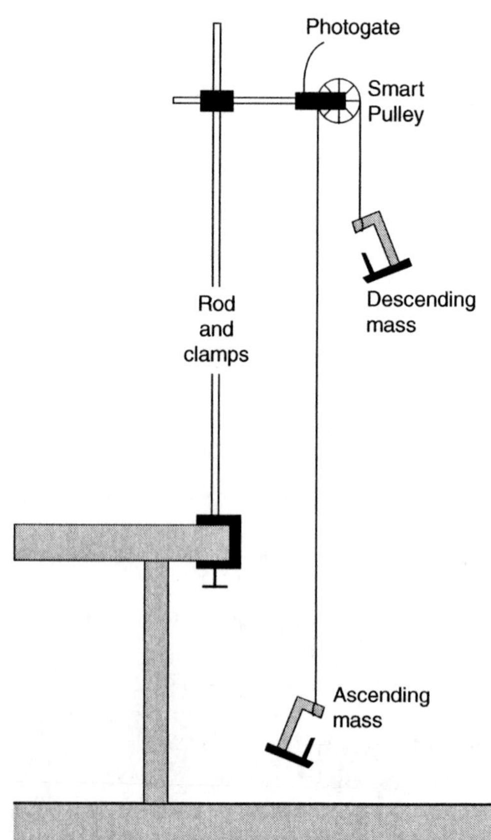

CI Figure 2 Experimental setup. A Photogate/Pulley System (Smart Pulley) is used instead of a conventional pulley to set up the Atwood machine. The ascending mass starts near the bottom, close to, but not touching, the floor. The descending mass starts from rest at the top. The Smart Pulley measures the speed of the system as it moves.

weight will prevent the system from moving too fast, and data collection will be easier. If you are using a conventional mass and hanger set, a 50-g hanger will work fine with no added mass. For all data collection and calculations, keep track of the total ascending and descending masses, including the mass of the hanger.

3. When the ascending and descending masses are equal, the system should not move. If it does, check that the pulley is level.
4. Trial 1: Add a 5-g piece to the descending mass to unbalance the system. Make a note of the ascending and descending masses in CI Data Table 1. Do not forget to account for the mass of the hangers.
5. Place the ascending mass at the bottom and the ascending mass at the top, as shown in CI Fig. 2. Gently hold the pulley to prevent the system from moving.
6. Let the system start from rest by letting go of the pulley. Once it starts moving, press the START button. Keep your eyes on the system, and press the STOP button before the masses reach the end of their line and bounce. If the hangers collide while passing each other, try making the strings longer and pressing STOP just before they collide.
7. A straight-line graph should have appeared on the screen. To see it better, press the Scale-to-Fit button on the graph toolbar. (It is the leftmost button of the toolbar.)
8. On the graph toolbar there is also a drop menu called Fit. Choose to do a "Linear Fit" for the graph. A box will pop up with information about the fit. Make a note of the slope of the line. This is the measured, experimental acceleration. Enter it in CI Data Table 1.
9. Clear the fit information by going to the Fit menu and deselecting the linear fit.
10. Trial 2: Add 10 g to each hanger. The descending mass should still have the 5-g unbalance. Note that this increases the overall total mass of the system but keeps the unbalanced force the same. Repeat the data collection process and enter the data in CI Data Table 1.
11. Trials 3 and 4: Repeat two more times, each time adding an extra 10 g to each hanger.
12. Clear the graph window of all fit information and then print the graph. Label each of the plots with the total mass of the system corresponding to each trial. Paste the graph to the laboratory report.
13. Calculate the net unbalanced force, in newtons.
14. Calculate the theoretical acceleration for each trial, using Eq. CI 1. Compare the theoretical value with the experimental value by taking a percent error.

B. *Varying the Unbalanced Force (Total Mass Constant)*

1. Erase all previous data by going to the main menu and, under "Experiment," choosing "Delete all data runs."
2. Place the following mass pieces on the ascending hanger: 5 g, 2 g, 2 g, 1 g. If you are using the PASCO mass and hanger set, the hangers should also have a 50-g piece, as discussed previously. If you are using a conventional 50-g hanger, no extra weight is needed. ● CI Fig. 3 shows the ascending and descending masses for the PASCO mass and hanger set.
3. Place a 10-g piece on the descending hanger. Again, with the PASCO mass and hanger set, the hanger should also have a 50-g piece, but with a conventional 50-g hanger, no extra weight is needed.
4. Trial 1: Unbalance the system by transferring the 1-g piece from the ascending to the descending hanger. At this time make a note of the ascending and the descend-

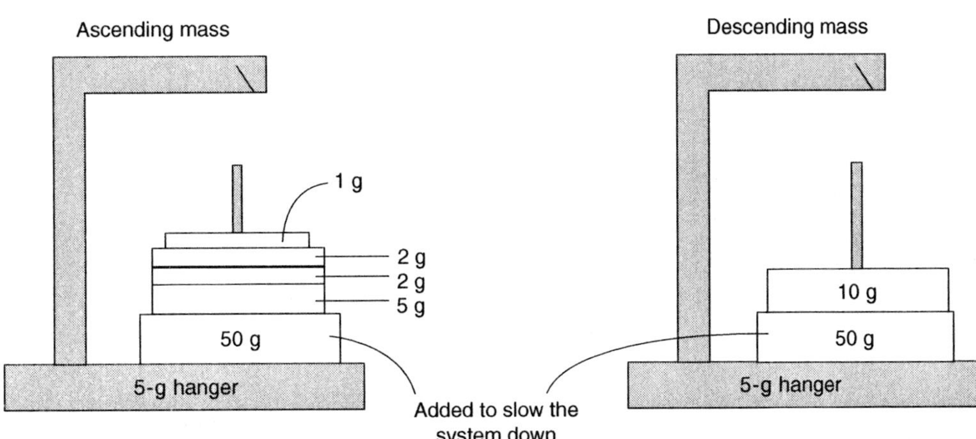

CI Figure 3 Ascending and descending masses using PASCO mass and hanger set ME-8967. A 50-g piece is added to each of the small 5-g hangers to prevent them from moving too fast. The ascending mass has a combination of small pieces (5 g, 2 g, 2 g, 1 g) that add to 10 g. A 10-g piece is placed in the descending mass hanger. To unbalance the system, small pieces from the ascending hanger are moved to the descending hanger.

ing masses and enter the values in CI Data Table 2. Do not forget to include the mass of the hangers!

5. Collect the data as before and determine the experimental acceleration.
6. Trial 2: Move one of the 2-g pieces from the ascending to the descending hanger and repeat the data collection process. Note that this changes the amount of unbalanced force without changing the total mass of the system.
7. Trial 3: Move the other 2-g piece from the ascending to the descending hanger and repeat the data collection process.
8. Trial 4: Move the 5-g piece from the ascending to the descending hanger and repeat the data collection process.
9. Calculate the net unbalanced force, in newtons, of each trial, and enter the results in CI Data Table 2.
10. Clear the graph window of any fit information and print the graph. Label each of the plots with the unbalanced force corresponding to each trial. Paste the graph to the laboratory report.
11. Calculate the theoretical acceleration for each trial, using Eq. CI 1. Compare the theoretical value with the experimental value by taking a percent error.

Name ______________________ Section ______________ Date ______________

Lab Partner(s) ____

C I EXPERIMENT 4

Newton's Second Law: The Atwood Machine

CI Laboratory Report

CI DATA TABLE 1

Purpose: To investigate how the acceleration of a system varies as the mass of the system increases, without changing the net applied force.

Trial	Ascending m_1	Descending m_2	Total mass $m_1 + m_2$	Measured acceleration (from graph)	Unbalanced force $(m_2 - m_1)g$	Theoretical acceleration	% error
1							
2							
3							
4							

CI DATA TABLE 2

Purpose: To investigate how the acceleration of a system varies as the net applied force on the system increases, while the mass remains constant.

Trial	Ascending m_1	Descending m_2	Total mass $m_2 + m_1$	Measured acceleration (from graph)	Unbalanced force $(m_2 - m_1)g$	Theoretical acceleration	% error
1							
2							
3							
4							

Don't forget units

(continued)

CI QUESTIONS

1. What happens to the acceleration of a system when the mass of the system increases but the net force stays constant?

2. What happens to the acceleration of a system when the net applied force increases but the mass of the system does not change?

3. Refer to the data in CI Data Table 2. Make a one-page graph of unbalanced force versus measured acceleration, and draw the best-fitting straight line. Determine the slope of this line. Show the details of the calculation on the graph, and attach the graph to the lab report.

4. What are the units of the slope of your graph?

5. What physical quantity of the system is represented by the slope of the force versus acceleration graph? How well does it match the experimental setup?

6. Looking at the results, was there a good agreement between the experimental acceleration and the theoretical (expected) acceleration? What causes the difference? Discuss sources of experimental uncertainty for this experiment.

Name ______________________ Section ______________ Date ______________

Lab Partner(s) ______________________________

EXPERIMENT 5

Friction

TI Advance Study Assignment

Read the experiment and answer the following questions.

1. State the three general empirical rules used to describe friction.

2. What is the normal force, and why is it used instead of the load?

3. Why is it important to have the string parallel to the horizontal surface in the procedures where suspended weights are used?

4. What is the coefficient of friction, and in what units is it expressed? Distinguish between μ_s and μ_k. Which is generally greater?

(continued)

5. Explain how graphs of weight versus normal force in procedures A and B give the coefficients of friction.

CI *Advance Study Assignment*

Read the experiment and answer the following question.

1. Under what conditions is the tension in the string pulling horizontally on the cart equal in magnitude to the frictional force?

Friction

OVERVIEW

Experiment examines friction using complementary TI and CI approaches. The TI procedures are concerned with determination of the coefficients of friction, μ_s and μ_k, with an option of investigating the dependence of μ on various parameters, such as different materials, lubrication, and so on.

The CI procedures extend the investigation by examining the effect of speed on sliding friction.

INTRODUCTION AND OBJECTIVES

In general, the term **friction** refers to the force or resistance to motion between contacting material surfaces. (Internal friction occurs in liquids and gases.) The friction between unlubricated solids is a broad and complicated topic, because it depends on the contacting surfaces and the material properties of the solids. Three general empirical "rules" are often used to describe friction between solid surfaces. These are that the frictional force is

1. Independent of the surface area of contact.
2. Directly proportional to the **load,** or the contact force that presses the surfaces together.
3. Independent of the sliding speed.

Let's take a look at these rules:

1. Intuitively, one would think that friction would depend on the roughness or irregularities of the surfaces or, more specifically, on the *actual* area of contact of the irregularities of the surfaces. This would seem to contradict rule 1.
2. The contact area of the surfaces, however, should depend on the force that presses the surfaces together, or the load. Increasing this force should increase the amount of contact surface and hence the friction. Rule 2 then seems logical.
3. Is it consistent that the friction between a sliding object and a surface be independent of the sliding speed? It would seem that the rate at which the surface irregularities met, which is dependent on the sliding speed, should have some effect.

With such thoughts in mind, in this experiment we will investigate the validity of the foregoing empirical rules. Although we apply these rules in analyzing friction, you might find experimentally that they are very general and, at best, approximations when applied to all materials and all situations.

After performing the experiment and analyzing the data, you should be able to do the following:

TI OBJECTIVES

1. Comment on the validity of the empirical rules of friction.
2. Describe how coefficients of friction are determined experimentally.
3. Tell why the normal reaction force of a surface on an object is used to determine the frictional force rather than the weight of the object.

CI OBJECTIVES

1. Verify that friction is proportional to the normal force.
2. Indicate whether or not friction is independent of sliding speed.

Friction

TI EQUIPMENT NEEDED

- Board with attached pulley
- Rectangular wooden block with hook (e.g., piece of 2 × 4 lumber or commercially available block)
- Weight hanger and set of weights
- String
- Protractor
- Laboratory balance
- Table clamp and support
- Meterstick
- Masking tape
- 2 sheets of Cartesian graph paper

(*Optional*)

- Plastic block
- Aluminum block
- Wheel cart
- Lubricating powder

TI THEORY (general, TI and CI)

It is sometimes assumed that the *load,* or the contact force that presses the surfaces together, is simply the weight of the object resting on a surface. Consider the case of a block resting on a horizontal surface as illustrated in ● TI Fig. 1a. The force that presses the surfaces together is the downward weight force of the block (magnitude mg), which is the load. However, on an inclined plane, only a component of the weight contributes to the load, the component perpendicular to the surface. (See TI Fig. 3, where the magnitude of the load is $mg \cos \theta$.)

In order to take such differences into account, the frictional force f is commonly taken to be directly proportional to the normal force N, which is the force of the surface *on* the block—that is, $f \propto N$ (see TI Fig. 1). In the absence of other perpendicular forces, the normal force is equal in magnitude to the load, $N = mg$ in TI Fig. 1 and $N = mg \cos \theta$ in TI Fig. 3, which avoids any confusion between weight and load.

With $f \propto N$, we may write in equation form

$$f = \mu N$$

or

$$\mu = f/N \qquad \textbf{(TI 1)}$$

where the Greek letter mu (μ) is a dimensionless constant of proportionality called the **coefficient of friction.**

When a force F is applied to the block parallel to the surface and no motion occurs, we say that the applied force is balanced by an opposite force of static friction f_s that is exerted on the block by the table along the surface of contact (TI Fig. 1b, $\Sigma F_x = F - f_s = ma = 0$). As the magnitude of the applied force is increased, f_s increases to a *maximum* value given by (TI Fig. 1c)

$$f_{s_{max}} = \mu_s N \qquad \textbf{(TI 2)}$$

(static friction)

where μ_s is the coefficient of static friction.* The maximum force of static friction is experimentally approximated by the smallest force applied parallel to the surface that will just set the block into motion.

At the instant the applied force F becomes greater than $f_s = \mu_s N$, however slightly, the block is set into motion, the motion is opposed by the force of kinetic (sliding) friction f_k, and (TI Fig. 1d)

$$f_k = \mu_k N \qquad \textbf{(TI 3)}$$

(kinetic friction)

where μ_k is the coefficient of kinetic (sliding) friction.

In general, $\mu_k N < \mu_s N$, and the unbalanced force causes the block to accelerate ($\Sigma F_x = F - f_s = ma$). However, if the applied force is reduced so that the block moves with a uniform velocity ($a = 0$), then $F = f_k = \mu_k N$.

Usually, for a given pair of surfaces, $\mu_k < \mu_s$. That is, it takes more force to overcome static friction (get an object moving) than to overcome kinetic friction (keep it moving).

* These conditions of f_s are sometimes written $f_s \leq \mu_s N$; that is, f_s is less than or equal to the maximum value of $\mu_s N$. (See TI Fig. 1.)

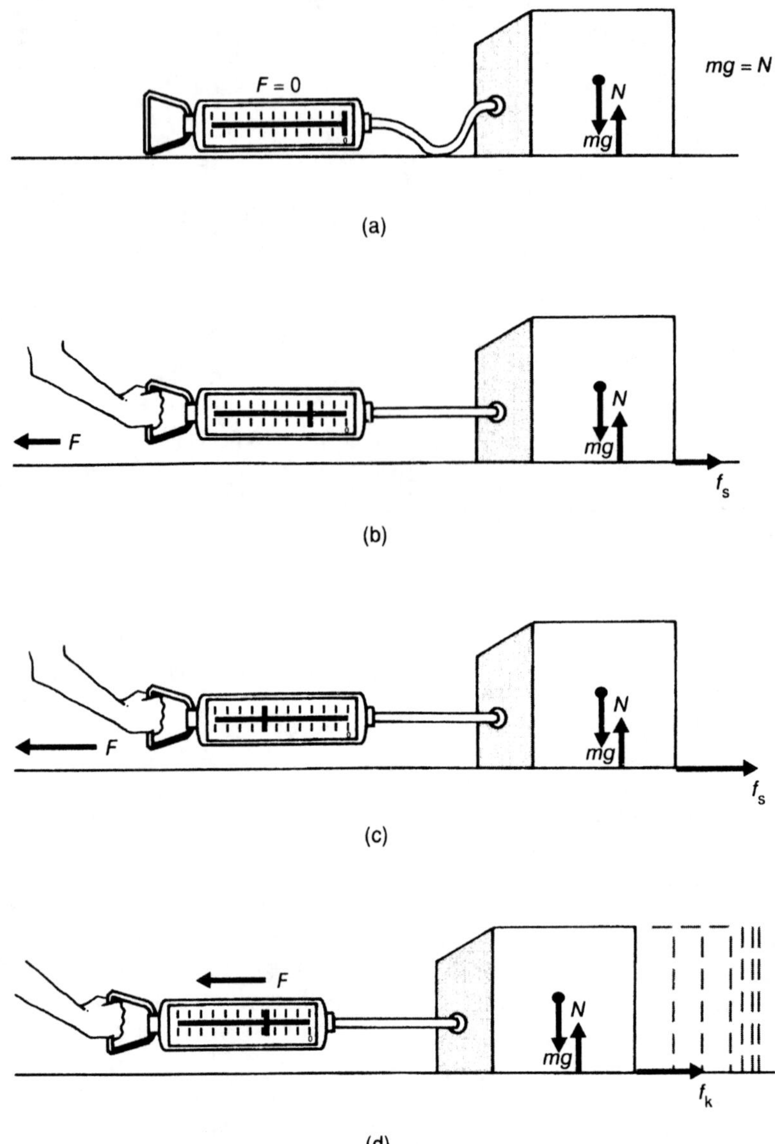

TI Figure 1 Friction. The applied force is balanced by the force of static friction f_s (a–c, $\Sigma F_x = F - f_s = ma = 0$) until a maximum value is reached. A slightly greater force (d) sets the block into motion ($\Sigma F_x = F - f_k = ma$), with the applied force being opposed by the force of kinetic friction, f_k.

Both coefficients may be greater than 1, but they are usually less than 1. The actual values depend on the nature and roughness of the surfaces.

TI EXPERIMENTAL PROCEDURE

A. Determination of μ_s

1. Determine the mass of the wooden block on a laboratory balance, and record it in the Laboratory Report.

2. Clean the surfaces of the board and block so they are free from dust and other contaminants. Place the board with the pulley near the edge of the table so that the pulley projects over the table's edge (● TI Fig. 2). Attach one end of a length of string to the wooden block and the other end to a weight hanger. Place the block flat on the board, and run the string over the pulley so that the weight hanger is suspended over the end of the table. Be sure that the string is parallel to the board.

3. With the rectangular block lying on one of its sides of larger area, add weights to the hanger until the block just begins to move. (*Note:* If the 50-g hanger causes the block to move, add some weights to the block and

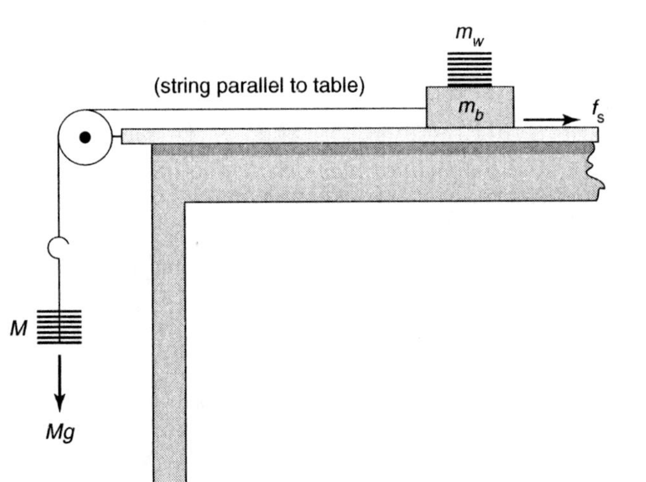

TI Figure 2 Coefficient of static friction. Experimental setup to determine μ_s. See text for description.

add this mass to the mass of the block, m_b.) Determine the required suspended mass within 1 gram. Record the weight force (Mg) required to move the block in TI Data Table 1. This is equal in magnitude to the frictional force, $f_{s_{max}}$.

Suggested experimental technique:

(a) Keep the block in the middle of the plane.

(b) Lift the block, gently lower it onto the plane, *restrain* it from moving for a count of five (*do not* press it against the plane), and then release the block. If the block moves, the suspended mass M is too large; if it doesn't move, M is too small; if the block moves about half the time, M is about right.

4. Repeat procedure 3 with m_w = 100-, 200-, 300-, 400-, and 500-g masses, respectively, added to the block. Record the results in TI Data Table 1.

5. Plot the weight force just required to move the block (or the maximum force of static friction, $F = f_s$) versus the normal force N of the surface on the block [$N = (m_b + m_w)g$]. Draw a straight line that best fits the data. Include the point (0, 0). Why?

Since $f_s = \mu_s N$, the slope of the straight line is μ_s. Determine the slope and record it in TI Data Table 1.

B. *Determination of μ_k*

Horizontal Board

6. When the block moves with a uniform speed, its acceleration is zero. The weight force F and the frictional force f_k are then equal and opposite ($\Sigma F_x = F - f_k = ma = 0$, and $F = f_k$).

7. Using the larger side (surface area) of the block and the series of added masses as in part A, add mass to the weight hanger until a slight push on the block will cause it to move with a uniform speed. It may be helpful to tape the weights to the block. The required weight force for the motion in each case should be less than that for the corresponding case in part A. Why? Record the data in TI Data Table 2.

Suggested experimental technique:

(a) Begin with the block at one end of the plane, and give it a push so that it slides across the entire plane.

(b) Observe the behavior of the block in the same region as before, namely in the middle of the plane. This is where the block should be observed for constant speed.

8. Plot the weight force (or the force of kinetic friction, $F = f_k$) versus the normal force N for these data on the same graph as for part A. Draw a straight line that best fits the data.

Since $f_k = \mu_k N$, the slope of the straight line is μ_k. Determine the slope and record it in TI Data Table 2. Calculate the percent decrease of μ_k from the μ_s value.

Elevated Board (Inclined Plane)

9. Elevate the pulley end of the board on a support to form an inclined plane (● TI Fig. 3, see Fig. 10.3 for a similar setup). Note in the figure that the magnitude of the normal force is equal to a *component* of the weight force.

With the block lying on a *side* of its larger surface area, determine the angle θ of incline that will allow the block to slide down the plane with a constant speed after being given a slight tap. (No suspended weight is used in this case.) *Note:* The maximum angle before slipping *without* tapping gives μ_s, whereas the angle of constant velocity *with* tapping gives μ_k.

10. Using a protractor, measure the angle θ and record it in TI Data Table 3. Also, with a meterstick, measure the length L of the base (along the table) and the height h of the inclined plane. Record the ratio h/L in TI Data Table 3.

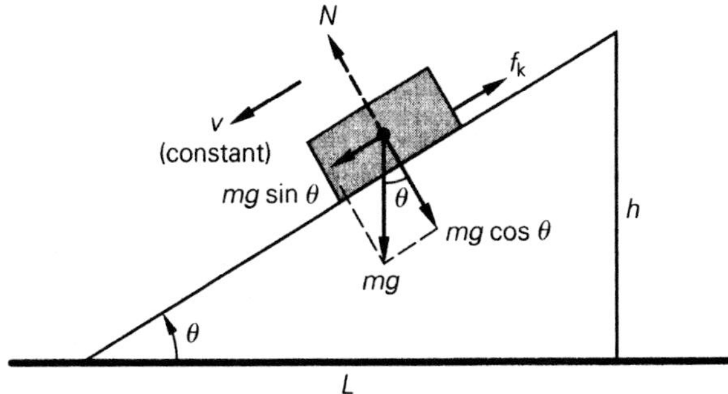

TI Figure 3 Coefficient of kinetic friction. Experimental setup to determine μ_k. See text for description.

11. Repeat this procedure for the block with the series of added masses as in the previous procedure for the horizontal board and record in TI Data Table 3. It may be helpful to tape the masses to the block.

12. Using your calculator, find the tangents of the θs, and record. Compute the average of these values and the average of the ratios h/L. These averages should be similar. Why?

13. Compare the average value of tan θ with the value of μ_k found in the procedure for the horizontal board. It can be shown theoretically (Question 3) that tan $\theta = \mu_k$ in this case. Compute the percent difference of the experimental values.

C. *Dependences of μ (optional)**

14. Use the *inclined plane method* to investigate the dependence of μ on area, material, velocity, rolling, and lubrication. The experimental setups are described in TI Data Table 4. Answer the questions listed after the data table.

* This experimental procedure and modifications were suggested by Professor I. L. Fischer, Bergen Community College, New Jersey.

Name ______________________ Section ______________ Date ______________

Lab Partner(s) ____

T I EXPERIMENT 5

Friction

TI Laboratory Report

Note: Attach graphs to Laboratory Report

Mass of block m_b ______________

A. *Determination of* μ_s

TI DATA TABLE 1

Purpose: To investigate $f_s = \mu_s N$, where N depends on $m_b + m_w$, by measuring μ_s on a level plane (see TI Fig. 2).

m_w	0					
$N = (m_b + m_w)g$*						
$f_s = F = Mg$						

* It is convenient to express the force in terms of mg, where g is left in symbol form [e.g., $(0.250)g$ N], even when graphing.

Calculations
(show work)

μ_s ______________ (from graph)

Don't forget units

(continued)

B. Determination of μ_k

TI DATA TABLE 2

Purpose: To investigate $f_k = \mu_k N$, where N depends on $m_b + m_w$, by measuring μ_k on a level plane.

m_w	0					
$N = (m_b + m_w)g$						
$f_k = F = Mg$						

Calculations
(show work)

μ_k ________________ (from graph)

Percent decrease of μ_k relative to μ_s ________________

TI DATA TABLE 3

Purpose: To investigate $\mu_k = \tan\theta$, where θ is independent of $m_b + m_w$, by measuring μ_k by the inclined plane method (see TI Fig. 3).

m_w	0						
θ							Average
h/L							
$\tan\theta$							

Calculations
(show work)

Percent difference between $\tan\theta = \mu_k$ and μ_k from TI Data Table 2 ________________

Name ______________________ Section ____________ Date ____________

Lab Partner(s) ______________________

C. Dependences of μ (optional)

TI DATA TABLE 4

Purpose: To investigate dependences of μ by various measurements using the inclined plane method and other materials (if available).

No.	Conditions	θ	$\mu = \tan\theta$
1	Wooden block on larger area, static (μ_s)		
2	Wooden block on smaller area, static (μ_s)		
3	Wooden block on smaller area, kinetic (μ_k)		
Other materials			
4	Plastic block		
5	Aluminum block, moving slowly		
6	Aluminum block, moving faster		
7	Wheeled cart		
8	Aluminum block with dry lubricating powder		
9	Plastic block with dry lubricating powder		

Answer the following questions on a separate sheet of paper and attach it to the TI Laboratory Report.

(a) Compare No. 1 with TI Data Table 1: Is the inclined plane method valid for μ_s?
(b) Compare No. 2 with No. 1 and No. 3 with TI Data Table 3: Does μ depend on area?
(c) Compare Nos. 3, 4, and 5: Does μ_k depend on material?
(d) Compare No. 5 with No. 6: Does μ_k depend on velocity?
(e) Compare No. 7 with anything: How does rolling friction compare with other types of friction?
(f) Compare Nos. 8 and 9 with Nos. 5 and 4: What is the effect of adding the lubricant?

TI QUESTIONS

1. Explain why $f_s \leq \mu_s N$; that is, why is f_s less than or equal to $\mu_s N$?

(continued)

2. Speculate, in terms of the microscopic surface irregularities, about why $\mu_k < \mu_s$ and what effect a lubricant has on the coefficient of friction.

3. (a) Prove that tan θ is equal to μ_k when the block slides down the incline with a constant speed. (Use symbols, not numbers.)

   (b) If θ is the maximum angle of incline just before the block moves, what is μ_s in terms of θ?

4. Suppose that the block were made to move up the inclined plane with a uniform speed by suspending masses on a string over the pulley. Derive an equation for the coefficient of kinetic friction for this case in terms of the suspended masses, the mass of the block, and the angle of decline. (Neglect any friction and mass effects of the pulley.)

5. On the basis of your experimental results, draw and justify conclusions about the validity of the empirical rules for friction. What does this tell you about applying general rules to all materials and about the nature of friction?

Friction

EQUIPMENT NEEDED

- 1 wooden block (The block used in the TI procedure can be used here also. Another option is the "Friction Block" included in the PASCO Classic Dynamics System.)
- Additional blocks as needed to make the string horizontal when connected to the force sensor (Two PASCO cars (ME–9430 or 9454), stacked upside down on top of each other and on top of the friction block will make a tower of the correct height.)
- 1 straight, smooth track (PASCO dynamics track)
- 1 force sensor (PASCO CI-6537)
- 1 constant-speed motorized car (PASCO ME-9781)
- Extra weights to load the sliding object (200-g or 500-g pieces will work fine) (The PASCO Classic Dynamics System includes mass bars that can be used in this part.)
- Graph paper

THEORY

In this experiment, we will study two of the general empirical rules used to describe the friction between solid surfaces. In the first part, we will examine the relationship between friction and the normal force to verify that they are proportional to each other. In the second part, we will examine the effect of the speed of the object on the amount of frictional force. In both cases, a force sensor will be used to measure the frictional force between a sliding wooden block and a track.

● CI Figure 1 illustrates the experimental situation. The sliding object is a wooden block. Other blocks are shown added as needed so that the string is *horizontal* when connected to a force sensor riding on a motorized car. As an alternative, the figure also shows the setup using the suggested PASCO equipment, where a stack of cars is used to make the object the correct height. Other alternatives include using a single 2 × 4 board with a nail that makes it possible to attach the string at the proper height (not pictured).

● CI Figure 2 shows a free-body diagram of a block as it slides with constant speed along a level track. The horizontal forces are F, the tension of the string, and f, the frictional force provided by the track. With the speed constant, there is no acceleration. From Newton's second law, we have

$$\Sigma F_x = F - f = ma = 0$$

or

$$F = f$$

In this experiment, the force sensor will directly measure F, the tension in the string. Notice that as long as the car moves at a constant speed, the magnitude of F is equal to the magnitude of the frictional force acting on the sliding block.

On the other hand, the vertical forces balance each other out, so the magnitude of the normal force N can be determined as the magnitude of the weight of the object: $N = mg$.

SETTING UP DATA STUDIO

Note: The force sensor needs to be calibrated before use. Refer to the user's manual for instructions on how to calibrate the sensor. The procedures described below assume that the force sensor has been properly calibrated.

1. Open Data Studio and choose "Create Experiment."
2. From the list of sensors, choose a Force Sensor. Connect the force sensor to channel A of the interface, as shown on the screen.
3. Double-click on the Force Sensor icon. The Sensor Properties window will open. Under "General," set the

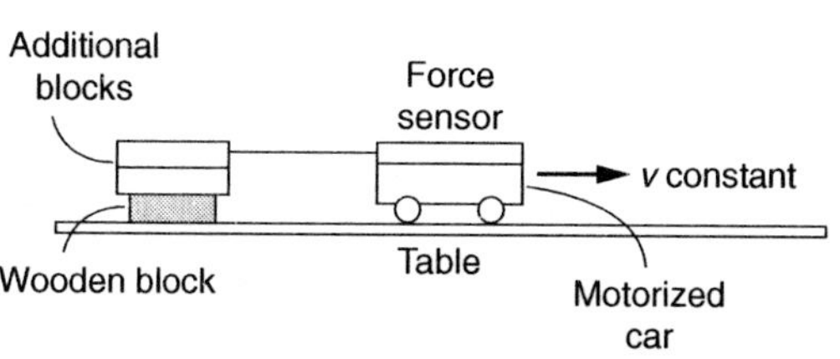

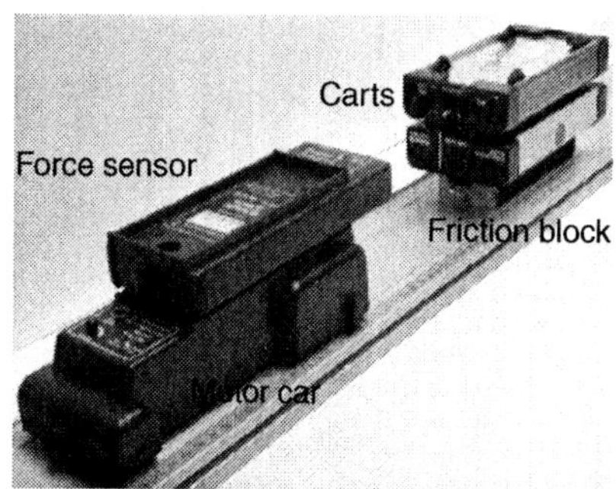

CI Figure 1 The experimental setup. A wooden block slides on a flat surface while being pulled by a motorized car that moves at a constant speed. Additional blocks can be added as necessary on top of the wooden block so that the string is horizontal when connected to the force sensor. The force sensor rides on the motorized car. As an alternative, PASCO dynamic cars can be stacked on top of a friction block to achieve the same effect.

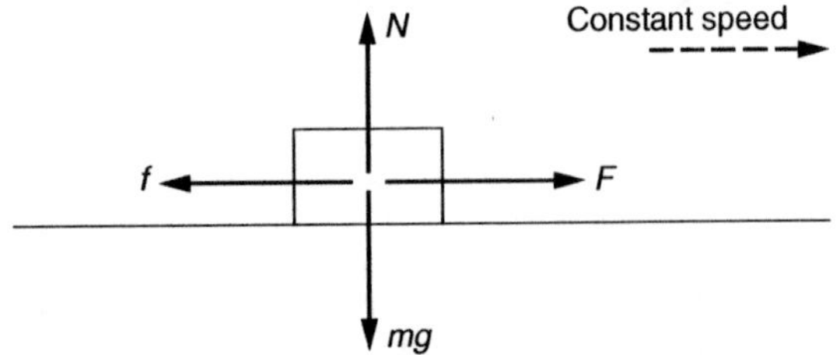

CI Figure 2 Free-body diagram of the sliding block. The horizontal forces are F, the tension on the string, and f, the friction from the surface. The force sensor measures F. At constant speed, the horizontal force vectors are equal and opposite, and $F = f$. The force sensor readings can be taken to be the friction as long as the block slides at constant speed.

sample rate to 200 Hz, fast. Click OK to get back to the main window.

4. Create a digits display by double-clicking on "Digits" in the displays list (lower left of the screen). The display window that opens will show the force readings from the sensor when data are collected.
5. On the digits display's toolbar there is a drop menu with the sigma symbol (Σ). Press it and choose "Mean." This will show the average of a series of measurements on the display.
6. The size of the display window can be adjusted for easier viewing, if needed. The bigger the screen, the more digits you will be able to see once data are collected. For the purpose of this experiment, keep the size such that only two decimal places are shown. (Wait until data are collected to adjust this. There have to be data on the display before any change can be noticed.)
7. ● CI Figure 3 shows what the screen will look like after the setup is complete and data are taken.

CI EXPERIMENTAL PROCEDURE

A. *The Effect of the Load*

1. Measure the mass of the wooden block and of any other block or car that will be placed on top of it to add height, as illustrated in CI Fig. 1. Record the total mass in Trial 1 of CI Data Table 1.

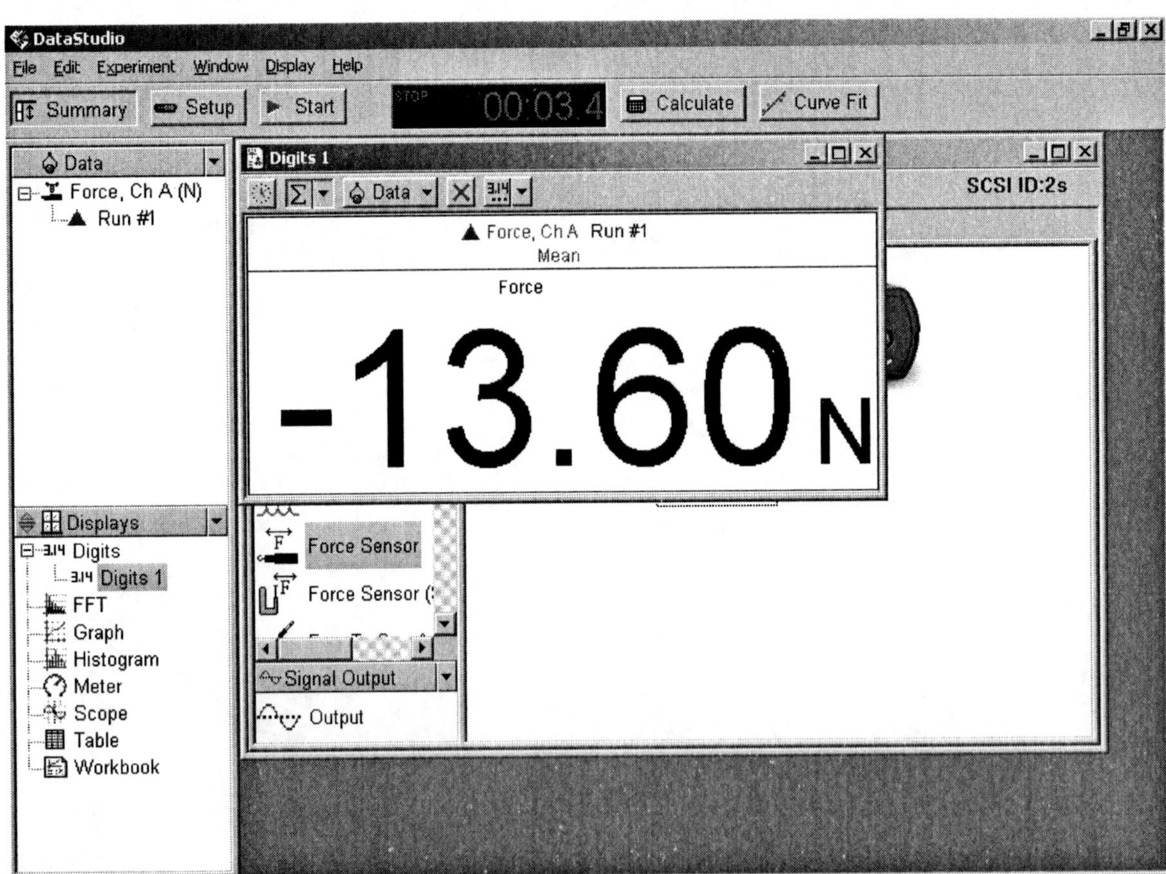

CI Figure 3 Data Studio setup. A digits display will show the force reading of the sensor. Once data are collected, the size of the display window is adjusted to show two decimal places. (Data displayed using DataStudio Software. Reprinted courtesy of PASCO scientific.)

2. Set up the equipment as shown in CI Fig. 1. It is important that the string connecting the force sensor to the pile of objects be *horizontal.* If using additional blocks instead of the PASCO cars, tape the blocks together so that they will not fall off.
3. Set the motorized car for a medium speed, and do not change it during the experiment.
4. ***Trial 1: The object with no extra load.***
   a. With the string slack, press the TARE button on the side of the force sensor to zero the sensor.
   b. Turn the motorized car on.
   c. Wait until the string tenses before pressing the START button to begin collecting data. Let the car move, pulling along the pile of blocks (the "object"), for about 20 cm, and then press the STOP button.
   d. Stop the car.
   e. Report the average fictional force reading in CI Data Table 1. Do not worry if the sensor reading is negative. That is a convention for direction (pull or push). In this experiment, we need only the magnitude.
5. ***Trials 2, 3, 4 and 5: The object with a load.***
   a. Place a load on top of the sliding object and record the new mass of the sliding object in CI Data Table 1.
   b. Repeat the data collection process as described in steps (a) to (e) for Trial 1.
   c. Repeat by continuing to add mass on top of the object until the table is complete.
6. Calculate the normal force for each trial by determining the weight of the object plus load in each case. Record the results in CI Data Table 1.
7. Use a full page of graph paper to make a plot of friction versus normal force. Determine the slope of the best-fitting line for the plot, and enter the result in the table. Attach the graph to the Laboratory Report.

B. The Effect of the Speed

1. Set up the equipment as shown in CI Fig. 1. It is important that the string connecting the force sensor to the pile of objects be *horizontal.* If using additional blocks instead of the PASCO cars, tape the blocks together so that they will not fall off.
2. Set the motorized car for a slow speed.
3. Turn on the motorized car. Wait until the string tenses before pressing the START button to begin collecting data. Let the car move, pulling along the block, for about 20 cm, and then press the STOP button.
4. Stop the car.
5. Report the average frictional force reading in CI Data Table 2.
6. Increase the speed of the motorized car, and measure the average frictional force again. Repeat by increasing the speed for each trial until the table is complete.

Name ______________________ Section ______________ Date ______________

Lab Partner(s) ____

CI EXPERIMENT 5

Friction

CI *Laboratory Report*

A. The Effect of the Load

CI DATA TABLE 1

Purpose: To investigate the effect of changing the load on an object (and thus changing the normal force) on the magnitude of the frictional force.

	Trial	Total mass of sliding object	Frictional force (sensor reading)	Normal force $N = mg$
The object with no load	1			
The object with increasing load	2			
	3			
	4			
	5			

Slope of graph = ______________

Don't forget units

(continued)

B. The Effect of Speed on Friction

CI DATA TABLE 2

Purpose: To investigate the effect of speed on the frictional force.

Different speed trials (from low speed to high)	Average frictional force
1	
2	
3	
4	
5	
6	
7	
8	
9	
10	

Name ______________________ Section ______________ Date ______________

Lab Partner(s) ____

EXPERIMENT 5 *Laboratory Report*

CI QUESTIONS

1. Is it true that the frictional force is directly proportional to the normal force? Discuss the experimental evidence.

2. What is the physical significance of the slope of the graph of friction versus normal force?

3. Is there a clear pattern for the frictional force as the speed of the object increases? (Compare to the pattern observed when increasing the load.) What can be concluded about the effect of the speed? Discuss.

4. Why was it so important that the string connecting the sensor and the object remain horizontal during the experiment? Discuss what would happen if it did not.

5. Refer to Step 3 of the Experimental Procedure for part A, which says, "Set the motorized car for a medium speed, and do not change it during the experiment." Given the results of part B of the experiment, discuss whether changing the speed would have made a difference in the results of experiment A.

Name ______________________ Section ______________ Date ______________

Lab Partner(s) ____

EXPERIMENT 6

Conservation of Linear Momentum

TI Advance Study Assignment

Read the experiment and answer the following questions.

1. What do we mean when we say that a quantity, such as linear momentum, is conserved?

2. What is the condition for the conservation of linear momentum of a system?

3. Is linear momentum conserved in common applications? Explain.

4. Is the conservation of linear momentum consistent with Newton's first and third laws of motion? Explain.

(continued)

5. In a system of particles for which the total linear momentum is conserved, is the linear momentum of the individual particles constant? Explain.

6. Suppose that a particle of mass m_1 approaches a stationary mass m_2 and that $m_2 >> m_1$.
   (a) Describe the velocity of m_2 after an elastic collision—that is, one in which both momentum and kinetic energy are conserved. Justify your answer mathematically.

   (b) What is the approximate momentum of m_1 after collision?

CI *Advance Study Assignment*

Read the experiment and answer the following questions.

1. What mechanism will be used to make the collision between the cars an elastic collision?

2. What mechanism will be used to make the collision between the cars an inelastic collision?

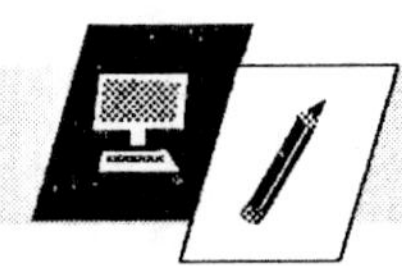

EXPERIMENT6

Conservation of Linear Momentum

OVERVIEW

Experiment examines the conservation of linear momentum by TI procedures and/or CI procedures. The TI procedure uses distance-time measurements to determine the velocities of air track cars before and after collisions to investigate the conservation of linear momentum.

The CI procedure measures the velocities electronically and graphs the data. The velocities, total momentum, and total kinetic energy are obtained from the graphs.

INTRODUCTION AND OBJECTIVES

The conservation of linear momentum ($\mathbf{p} = m\mathbf{v}$) is an important physical concept. However, the experimental investigation of this concept in an introductory physics laboratory is hampered by ever-present frictional forces.

An air track provides one of the best methods to investigate linear momentum (see Fig. 3.3). Aluminum cars or gliders riding on a cushion of air on the track approach frictionless motion—a necessary condition for the conservation of linear momentum.

In the absence of friction (and other external forces), the total linear momentum of a system of two cars will be conserved during a collision of the cars. That is, the total linear momentum of the system should be the same after collision as before collision. By measuring the velocities of cars of the same and different masses before and after collision, we can determine the total momentum of a system and investigate the conservation of linear momentum.

After performing this experiment and analyzing the data, you should be able to do the following:

TI OBJECTIVES

1. Explain when linear momentum is conserved and what this means in terms of force and motion.
2. Apply the conservation of linear momentum to a system.
3. Describe two-body collisions in terms of the conservation of linear momentum.

CI OBJECTIVES

1. Understand that momentum is conserved for both elastic and inelastic collisions.
2. Distinguish between elastic and inelastic collisions in terms of the conservation of kinetic energy.

TI EXPERIMENT 6

Conservation of Linear Momentum

TI EQUIPMENT NEEDED

- Air track
- Three cars (two of similar mass)
- Four laboratory timers or stopwatches*
- Laboratory balance
- Masking tape
- Meterstick (if no length scale on air track)
- Velcro (optional)

TI THEORY

The linear momentum **p** of a particle or object is defined as

$$\mathbf{p} = m\mathbf{v} \quad \text{(TI 1)}$$

where m is the mass of the object and **v** its velocity.[†] Since velocity is a vector quantity, so is linear momentum.

Newton's second law of motion, commonly expressed in the form $\mathbf{F} = m\mathbf{a}$, can also be written in terms of momentum:

$$\mathbf{F} = \frac{\Delta \mathbf{p}}{\Delta t} \quad \text{(TI 2)}$$

If there is no net or unbalanced external force acting on the object ($F = 0$), then

$$\mathbf{F} = \frac{\Delta \mathbf{p}}{\Delta t} = 0$$

or

$$\Delta \mathbf{p} = 0$$

That is, the change in the momentum is zero, or the momentum is conserved. By *conserved* we mean that the momentum remains constant (in time).

$$\Delta \mathbf{p} = \mathbf{p}_f - \mathbf{p}_i = 0$$

or

$$\mathbf{p}_f = \mathbf{p}_i \quad \text{(TI 3)}$$

and the "final" momentum $\mathbf{p}_f$ at any time t_f is the same as the initial momentum $\mathbf{p}_i$ at time t_i.

Notice that this is consistent with Newton's first law of motion, since

$$\mathbf{p}_f = \mathbf{p}_i \quad \text{or} \quad m\mathbf{v}_f = m\mathbf{v}_i$$

and

$$\mathbf{v}_f = \mathbf{v}_i$$

That is, an object remains at rest ($\mathbf{v}_i = 0$) or in uniform motion ($\mathbf{v}_i = \mathbf{v}_f$) unless acted on by some external force.

The previous development also applies to the total momentum of a system of particles or objects. For example, the total linear momentum (**P**) of a system of two objects m_1 and m_2 is $\mathbf{P} = \mathbf{p}_1 + \mathbf{p}_2$, and if there is no net external force acting on the system, then

$$\Delta \mathbf{P} = 0$$

In the case of a collision between two objects of a system (with only internal forces acting), the initial total momentum before the collision is the same as the final total momentum after the collision. That is,

$$\underset{\text{(before)}}{\mathbf{p}_{1_i} + \mathbf{p}_{2_i}} = \underset{\text{(after)}}{\mathbf{p}_{1_f} + \mathbf{p}_{2_f}} \quad \text{(TI 4)}$$

or

$$m_1\mathbf{v}_{1_i} + m_2\mathbf{v}_{2_i} = m_1\mathbf{v}_{1_f} + m_2\mathbf{v}_{2_f}$$

In one dimension, the directions of the velocity and momentum vectors are commonly indicated by plus and minus signs, i.e., $+v$ and $-v$.**

The internal forces do not change the total momentum because, according to Newton's third law, $\mathbf{F}_{12} = -\mathbf{F}_{21}$ (the force on object 1 due to object 2 is equal to and opposite in direction [minus] to the force on object 2 due to object 1). Thus the change in momentum for one object will be equal in magnitude and opposite in direction to the change in momentum for the other object, and the total momentum will be unchanged.

* If electronic photogates/timers and computer-assisted data analysis are available, your instructor will give you instruction on their use.* Boldfaced symbols indicate vectors (see Expt. 4).

† Boldfaced symbols indicate vectors (see Expt. 4).

** In two (or three) dimensions, the momentum is conserved in both (or all) directions. That is, $\mathbf{P} = \mathbf{P}_x + \mathbf{P}_y = 0$, and $\mathbf{P}_x = 0$ and $\mathbf{P}_y = 0$. Why? *Note:* $\mathbf{P}_x = \Sigma\mathbf{p}_x$ and $\mathbf{P}_y = \Sigma\mathbf{p}_y$.

TI EXPERIMENTAL PROCEDURES

1. Determine the mass of each car and record it in the TI Trial Data Table. Let the masses of the two cars of nearly equal mass be m_1 and m_2 and the mass of the third car be m_3.

2. Mark off two equal and convenient lengths (for example, $\frac{1}{2}$ or 1 m) on both sides of the center position of the air track. Make full use of the length of the track, but leave some space near the ends of the track. Place the four tape reference marks at the lower edges of the track so as not to interfere with the car motion. *Do not* mark the air track surface itself with tape or anything else.

3. *Time trials.* By measuring the time interval Δt it takes a car to move the reference mark length d, one can determine the magnitude of the velocity $v = d/\Delta t$ of the car, where $\Delta t = t_2 - t_1$. The actual timing of the motion of a car moving between the two sets of reference marks is done by either method (A), involving four observers, each with a timer and assigned to an individual reference mark, or method (B), involving two observers, each with a timer and assigned to one set of reference marks, as described below. Time trials will be done to determine the better method.*

   In addition to giving timing practice and determining the better method of timing, the time trials check out the experimental setup for possible systematic errors. The time intervals for the individual cars to travel the equal distances between the reference marks should be very similar for any one trial. If not, the air track may need leveling and/or there may be some frictional problem with part of the track. Should this be the case, call your instructor. *Do not* attempt to level the air track on your own.

   Experimentally carry out each of the following timing methods to determine which is better.

   Method A—Four Timers. Set one of the cars in motion with a *slight* push so that it moves with moderate speed up and down the track. (A few practice starts help.) As the car hits the bumper at one end of the track, all four observers should start their timers. As the leading edge of the car passes the reference marks, each respective observer stops his or her timer. (Making a dry run or two to become familiar with the timing sequence is helpful.) Carry out this procedure twice for each of the three cars, and record the data in the TI Trial Data Table.

   Method B—Two Timers. Set the car in motion. The two observers should start and stop their individual timers as the leading edge of the car passes their respective reference marks. Carry out this procedure twice for each of the three cars, and record the data in the TI Trial Data Table.

4. Compute the Δt's for each trial and calculate the percent difference for each trial set. From the data, decide which timing method should be used on the basis of consistency or precision.

CASE 1: COLLISION BETWEEN TWO CARS OF (NEARLY) EQUAL MASS, WITH ONE INITIALLY AT REST

5. With one of the cars (m_2) of nearly equal mass stationary at the center position of the air track, start the other car (m_1) moving toward the stationary car. See ● TI Fig. 1. (It may be more convenient to start m_1 moving away from m_2 and take measurements as m_1 returns from rebounding from the end of the track.) A trial run should show that m_1 remains at rest, or nearly at rest, after collision and that m_2 is in motion.

   Determine the time it takes for m_1 to travel between the reference marks as it approaches m_2 and the time it takes for m_2 to travel between the other set of reference marks after collision. Carry out this procedure three times and record the data in TI Data Table 1.

   Compute the velocities and the total momentum before and after collision and the percent difference in these values for each trial.

CASE 2: COLLISION BETWEEN TWO CARS OF UNEQUAL MASS, WITH THE MORE MASSIVE CAR INITIALLY AT REST

6. Repeat procedure 5 with m_2 replaced by m_3 (more massive than m_1 and m_2). See TI Fig. 1. In this case, m_1 will travel in the opposite direction after collision, as a trial run will show. Make appropriate adjustments

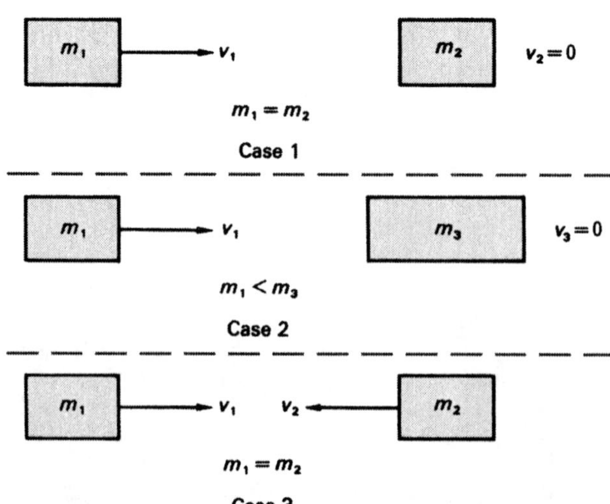

TI Figure 1 Experimental collision cases. See text for descriptions.

* If electronic photogate timers are available, your instructor will give you instruction in their use. Electronic timing greatly improves the accuracy and precision of the results. Why?

in the timing procedure to measure the velocity of m_1 before *and* after collision. Record the data and the required calculations in TI Data Table 2. Be careful with the directional signs of the velocities and momenta.

CASE 3: COLLISION BETWEEN TWO CARS OF (NEARLY) EQUAL MASS INITIALLY TRAVELING IN OPPOSITE DIRECTIONS

7. With m_1 and m_2 initially moving toward each other (TI Fig. 1), determine the total momentum before and after collision. (*Note:* Speeds do not have to be, and probably won't be, equal.)

Make appropriate adjustments in the timing procedure to measure the velocities of m_1 and m_2 before and after collision. Carry out the procedure three times and record the data in TI Data Table 3.

Compute the percent difference for the total momentum before and after collision for each trial.

(OPTIONAL PROCEDURE)

Another procedure, which may be done at the instructor's option, is as follows:

8. Attach pieces of Velcro to the collision bumpers of both cars, and repeat one or more of the preceding cases as directed by your instructor. Make up a data table, and analyze your results as done previously. (*Hint:* Read in your textbook about elastic and inelastic collisions—in particular, completely inelastic collisions.)

Name ______________ Section ______________ Date ______________

Lab Partner(s) ______________

T I EXPERIMENT 6

Conservation of Linear Momentum

TI Laboratory Report

Distance between marks ______________

TI TRIAL DATA TABLE

Purpose: To determine the better method of timing.

		Method A							Method B		
Car mass ( )		t_1 ( )	t_2 ( )	Δt_{12} ( )	t_3 ( )	t_4 ( )	Δt_{34} ( )	Percent diff.	Δt_{12} ( )	Δt_{34} ( )	Percent diff.
m_1											
m_2											
m_3											

TI DATA TABLE 1

Purpose: To analyze $m_1 = m_2$ case, with $v_{2_i} = 0$.

Trial	Before collision			After collision			
	m_1			m_2			
	Δt_1 ( )	v_{1_i} ( )	p_{1_i} ( )	Δt_2 ( )	v_{2_f} ( )	p_{2_f} ( )	Percent diff.
1							
2							
3							

Don't forget units

(continued)

TI DATA TABLE 2

Purpose: To analyze $m_3 > m_1$ case, with $v_{3_i} = 0$.

Trial	Before collision			After collision							Percent diff.
	m_1			m_1			m_3				
	Δt_{1_i} ( )	v_{1_i} ( )	Total momentum ( )	Δt_{1_f} ( )	v_{1_f} ( )	p_{1_f} ( )	Δt_{3_f} ( )	v_{3_f} ( )	p_{3_f} ( )	Total momentum ( )	
1											
2											
3											

TI DATA TABLE 3

Purpose: To analyze $m_1 = m_2$ case, initial motions in opposite directions.

Trial	Before collision						
	m_1			m_2			Total momentum ( )
	Δt_{1_i} ( )	v_{1_i} ( )	p_{1_i} ( )	Δt_{2_i} ( )	v_{2_i} ( )	p_{2_i} ( )	
1							
2							
3							

Trial	After collision							
	m_1			m_2			Total momentum ( )	Percent diff. ( )
	Δt_{1_f} ( )	v_{1_f} ( )	p_{1_f} ( )	Δt_{2_f} ( )	v_{2_f} ( )	p_{2_f} ( )		
1								
2								
3								

Name ______________________________ Section ______________ Date ______________

Lab Partner(s) ____

EXPERIMENT 6 *Laboratory Report*

TI QUESTIONS

1. Do the results of the experiment support the conservation of linear momentum? Consider possible sources of error.

2. Was it necessary to have equal length intervals in the experiment to investigate properly the conservation of momentum? Explain.

3. In Cases 1 and 2, one of the cars was initially at rest, so it must have received an acceleration. Is the car accelerating as it passes between the reference marks? Explain.

4. In each of the three cases, was kinetic energy conserved? Justify your answers with a sample calculation for a trial from each case. If the kinetic energy is not conserved, where did it go?

CI EXPERIMENT 6

Conservation of Linear Momentum

CI Equipment Needed

• 2 rotary motion sensors	PASCO CI-6538
• Brackets and pulley mounts:	
2 cart-string brackets	CI-6569
2 dynamics track mount accessories	CI-6692 (to mount the RMS to the track)
2 RMS/IDS adapters	ME-6569 (track pulley bracket)
• 2 collision carts	PASCO Classic Cars, ME-9454
• 1 track	
• Clay or Velcro strips	
• String	
• Optional: track end stop	

CI Theory

The purpose of this experiment is to investigate the momentum and kinetic energy for elastic and inelastic collisions. The momentum and kinetic energy before the collision of two cars are compared with the momentum and kinetic energy after the collision by looking at a plot of these quantities versus time.

In a collision between two objects, the total momentum at any time is found by adding the momentum of one of the objects to that of the other:

$$\vec{P}_{Total} = \vec{p}_1 + \vec{p}_2 = m_1\vec{v}_1 + m_2\vec{v}_2 \qquad \textbf{(CI 1)}$$

This is vector addition, which means the directions of motion of both objects must be taken into account. The sensor used to measure the speeds of the objects will also assign a positive or negative sign, depending on direction. In general, an object moving toward the sensor is assigned a positive velocity, and an object moving away from the sensor is assigned a negative velocity.

An object in motion also has kinetic energy. We can determine the total kinetic energy in a system by adding the kinetic energies of all objects in the system.

$$K_{Total} = K_1 + K_2 = \tfrac{1}{2}m_1v_1^2 + \tfrac{1}{2}m_2v_2^2 \qquad \textbf{(CI 2)}$$

The total momentum and the total kinetic energy just before and just after a collision are determined and compared. First, an elastic collision between two cars is considered. The cars have magnets that make them repel each other when they get close enough. The effect is that the cars bounce off each other (collide) without touching. Next, an inelastic collision is considered. The magnets are replaced by a piece of clay (or Velcro) that will make the cars stick to each other after the collision.

Before you Begin

1. Install a cart-string bracket on each of the collision carts. The cart-string bracket is mounted on the side of the cart, as shown in ● CI Fig. 1.
2. Choose one cart to be Car 1 and measure its mass, in kilograms, including the cart-string bracket. Report the mass of Car 1 in the laboratory report.
3. The other cart will be Car 2. Measure its mass and also record that mass in the laboratory report.
4. Do not lose track of which is Car 1 and which is Car 2. If needed, put a small tape label on the cars so that you will not confuse them later.

This information will be needed during the setup of Data Studio.

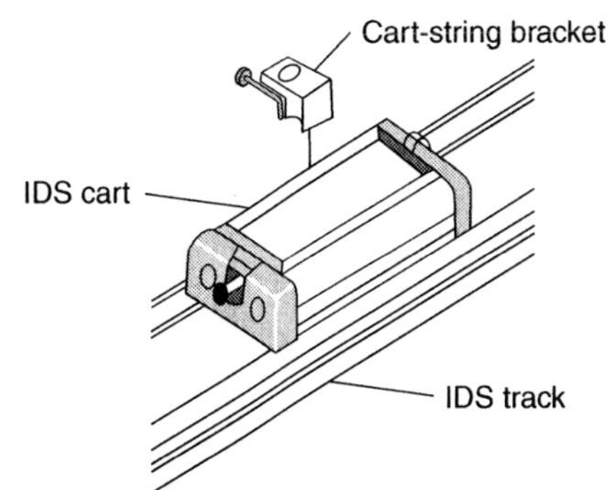

CI Figure 1 Installing cart-string brackets. The cart-string brackets are installed on top of the collision carts, secured with a side screw. The top screw is used to tie a string. When measuring the mass of the car, include the cart-string bracket.

Setting Up Data Studio

1. Open Data Studio and choose "Create Experiment."
2. From the sensor list, choose a Rotary Motion Sensor. Connect the sensor to the interface, as shown in the computer screen, to channels 1 and 2. This will be the sensor to track the motion of Car 1.
3. Choose a second rotary motion sensor from the sensor list. This one will be connected to channels 3 and 4. This will be the sensor to track the motion of Car 2.
4. Double-click on one of the Rotary Motion Sensor icons. The Sensor Properties window will open. Select the following:

   Under General: set the sample rate to 100 Hz, Fast.

   Under Measurement: choose Velocity (m/s) and deselect any others.

   Under Rotary Motion Sensor: set the Divisions/Rotations to 1440, and set the Linear Calibration to Large Pulley (Groove).

   Click OK to accept the choices and to close the Sensor Properties window.
5. Repeat this process with the other sensor.
6. Open the program's calculator by clicking on the Calculate button, on the top main menu. Usually a small version of the calculator opens, as shown in ● CI Fig. 2. Expand the calculator window by clicking on the button marked "Experiment Constants."
7. The expanded window (shown in ● CI Fig. 3) is used to establish values of parameters that will remain constant throughout the experiment. In this case, these are the masses m_1 and m_2 of the carts, which have already been measured. This is how to do it:
   a. Click on the lower New button (within the "Experiment Constants" section of the calculator window) and enter the name of the constant as m1, the value as the mass of Car 1 measured before, and the units as kg.
   b. Click the lower Accept button.
   c. Click on the New button again and enter the name of the constant as m2, the value as the mass of Car 2 measured before, and the units as kg.
   d. Click the lower Accept button.
   e. Close the experiment constants portion of the calculator window by pressing the button marked "Experiment Constants" again.
8. **Calculation of the total momentum of the system:**
   a. In the same calculator window, clear the definition box and enter the following equation: TotalP = m1 * smooth(10,v1) + m2 * smooth(10,v2)
   This is the calculation of the total momentum, $\vec{P}_{\text{Total}} = m_1\vec{v}_1 + m_2\vec{v}_2$, that we will call TotalP. The smooth function will help produce a cleaner graph.
   b. Press the top Accept button after entering the formula. Notice that the variables m1, m2, v1, and v2 will appear in a list. The masses were already assigned values, but v1 and v2 are waiting to be defined.
   c. To define variables v1 and v2, do them one at a time by clicking on the drop menu button on the left side of each variable. A list of options appears, asking what type of variable this is.
      - Define v1 as a Data Measurement and, when prompted, choose Velocity(Ch1&2).
      - Define v2 as a Data Measurement and, when prompted, choose Velocity(Ch3&4).
   d. Press the Accept button again.
   Please notice that channels 1&2 will keep track of Car 1 and that channels 3&4 will track Car 2. Make sure the equipment is set up accordingly.
9. **Calculation of the total kinetic energy of the system:**
   a. Still in the same calculator window, press the top New button again to enter a new equation.

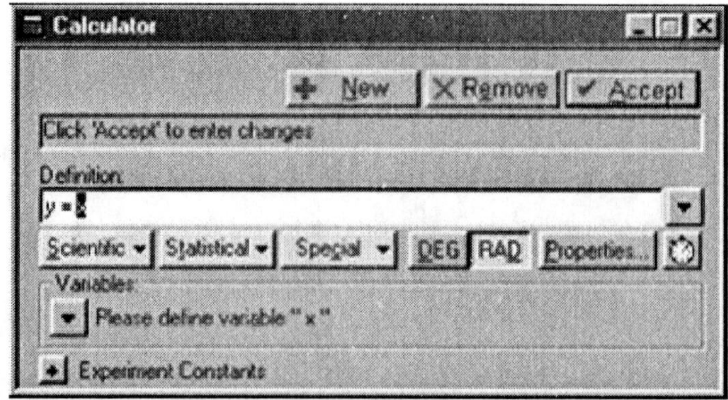

CI Figure 2 The calculator window. This small version of the calculator window opens when the Calculate button is pressed. The calculator will be used to enter formulas that handle the values measured by the sensor. The computer will perform the calculations automatically as the sensor takes data. (Data displayed using DataStudio Software. Reprinted courtesy of PASCO scientific.)

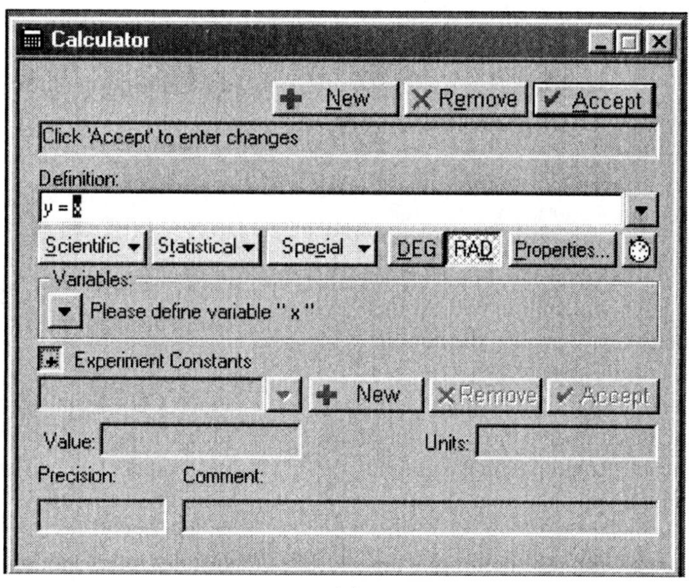

(a)

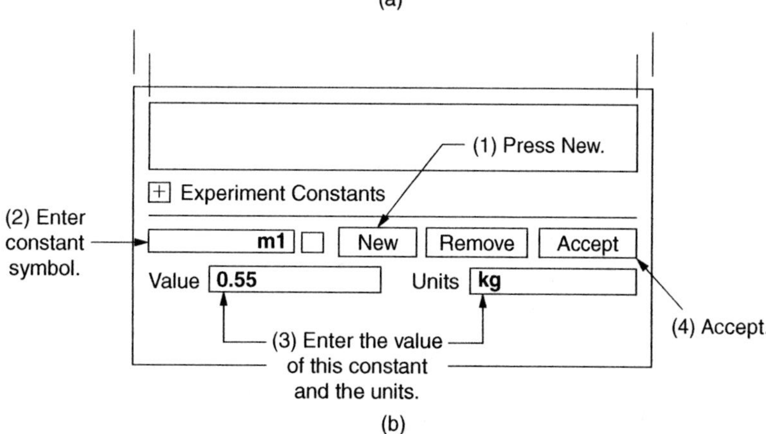

(b)

CI Figure 3 The expanded calculator window. (a) After the Experiment Constants button is pressed, the calculator window expands to full size. (b) The "Experiment Constants" section is the lower part of the expanded calculator. This section is used to define parameters that are to remain constant during the experiment. The diagram shows the steps needed to enter experimental constants into the calculator. (Data displayed using DataStudio Software. Reprinted courtesy of PASCO scientific.)

b. Clear the definition box and enter the following equation: TotalKE = 0.5* m1 * smooth(10,v1)^2 + 0.5* m2 * smooth(10, v2)^2
   This is the calculation of the total kinetic energy, $K_{\text{Total}} = \frac{1}{2}m_1v_1^2 + \frac{1}{2}m_2v_2^2$, that we will call TotalKE.
c. Press the Accept button after entering the formula. Notice that the variables will again appear in a list. Define them exactly as before.
d. Press the Accept button again.

10. Close the calculator window.
11. The data list at the top left of the screen should now have four items: Velocity from Ch1&2, Velocity from Ch3&4, TotalP, and TotalKE. A small calculator icon identifies the quantities that are calculated.
12. Create a graph by dragging the "Velocity Ch1&2" icon from the data list and dropping it on the "Graph" icon on the displays list. A graph of velocity versus time will open, in a window titled Graph 1.
13. Double-click anywhere on the graph. The Graph Settings window will open. Make the following changes and selections:
    Under the tab Appearance:
      Data:
        Connect data points in bold
        Deselect the buttons marked "Show Data Points" and "Show Legend Symbols"
    Under the tab Layout:
      Multiple graphs:
        Vertical

Layering:
Do not layer
Measurement adding:
Replace matching measurement
Group measurement:
Do not group

Click OK to accept the changes and to exit the graph settings window.

14. Drag the "Velocity Ch3&4" data icon and drop it in the middle of Graph 1. The graph will split in two. At the top you will see the Velocity Ch1&2 and at the bottom the Velocity Ch3&4, on separate Y axes.
15. Drag the "TotalP" icon and drop it on the split graph. The graph will split again, this time into three sections.
16. Drag the "TotalKE" icon and also drop it on the graph. The result should be a graph split into four sections, one section for each of the quantities.
17. Press the "Align Matching X Scales" button on the graph's toolbar. (It is a button with a picture of a padlock.) This will make all graphs aligned to a common $t = 0$ on the X axis.
18. ● CI Fig. 4 shows what the screen should look like after all setup is complete. The size of the graph window can be maximized so that you can observe the plots better.

CI EXPERIMENTAL PROCEDURE

The complete experimental setup is shown in ● CI Fig. 5. Each car is connected to its own sensor and pulley system, one on each side of the track. Here are the instructions for setting up the carts:

1. Place Cars 1 and 2 (with the cart-string brackets attached) on the track with the magnetic sides facing each other. The cart-string brackets may need repositioning so that they face the outside of the track, as shown in CI Fig. 5.
2. Install a rotary motion sensor (RMS) on each side of the track, with the pulleys facing the inside of the track.
3. On the opposite side of the track, install the RMS/IDS adapters (small pulleys). See ● CI Fig. 6 for reference.

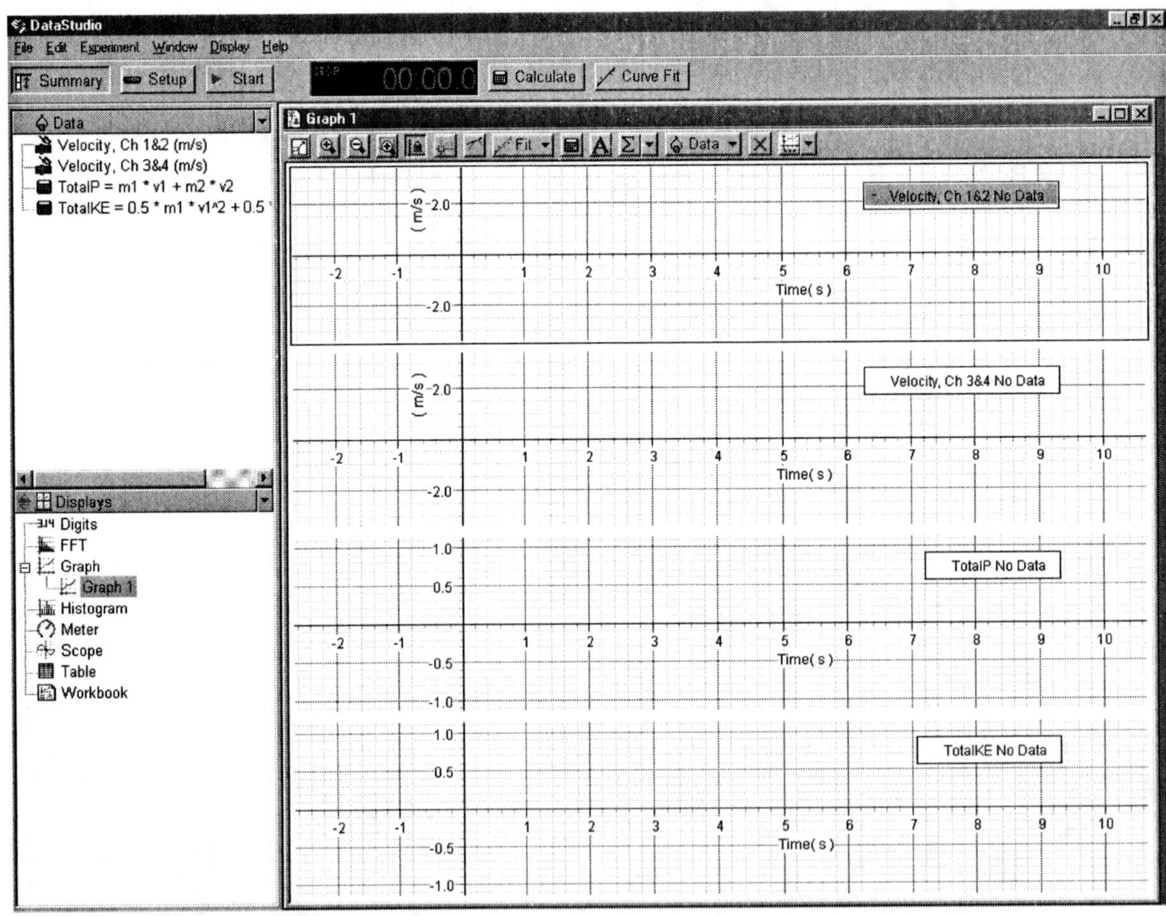

CI Figure 4 Data Studio setup. Data for velocity of each car, total momentum, and total kinetic energy will appear simultaneously on four plots, with matching time axes. The graph window may be maximized to occupy the whole screen in order to display the experimental results better. (Data displayed using DataStudio Software. Reprinted courtesy of PASCO scientific.)

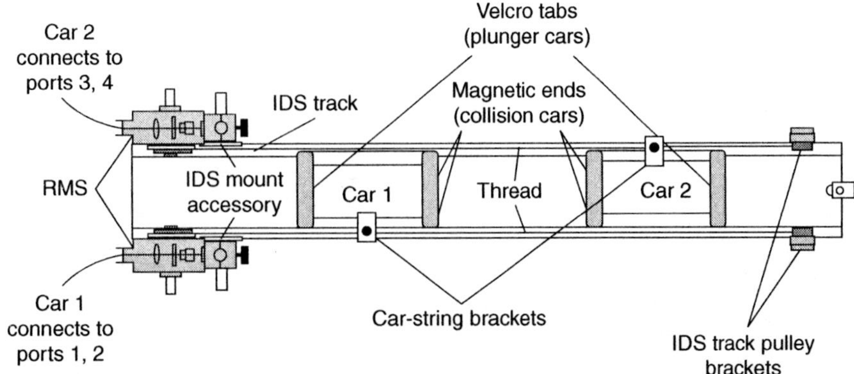

CI Figure 5 Experimental setup. Two collision carts are installed on the same track. Each cart is connected to its own rotary motion sensor on one side and to its own IDS-RMS adapter (track pulley bracket) on the other side. An elastic collision can be performed by having the magnetic ends of the cars face each other. An inelastic collision can be performed by having the nonmagnetic sides face each other and putting clay or Velcro on the ends of the cars.

4. A string will make a loop starting from the cart-string bracket on top of the car, to the large pulley of the RMS, to the small pulley of the RMS/IDS adapter and back to the cart, as shown in ● CI Fig. 7. Do this for both cars, as shown in the complete set up of CI Fig. 5. Adjust the height of the pulleys so that the strings are tense, not sagging, but the cars are able to move freely.

Case 1: Elastic Collision Between two Cars of (Nearly) Equal Mass, with one Initially at Rest

5. Set Car 2 somewhere on the middle of the track, at rest.
6. Set Car 1 all the way to the end of the track.
7. Press the START button and then give Car 1 a good push toward Car 2.
8. Press the STOP button after the collision, before Car 2 bounces at the end of the track. (Several practice runs, and the help of a partner, may be needed.)
9. Click anywhere on the Velocity Ch1&2 graph, and then press the Scale-to-Fit button on the graph toolbar (The Scale-to-Fit button is the leftmost button of the graph toolbar.) This will make the data scale to the length of the graph on the screen. Repeat for all the other three graphs.
10. If any of the graphs of velocity is reading negative values, switch the yellow and black cables of the corresponding rotary motion sensor in the interface so that the yellow cord connects to where the black cord was, and vice versa. Repeat the data collection process and use the new data in the rest of the analysis.
11. Print the graph. If no printer is available, make a careful drawing of the graph, paying special attention to dips and peaks in the graphs. Attach the graph to the laboratory report.
12. Click anywhere on the Velocity Ch1&2 graph, and then press the Smart-Tool button on the graph toolbar.

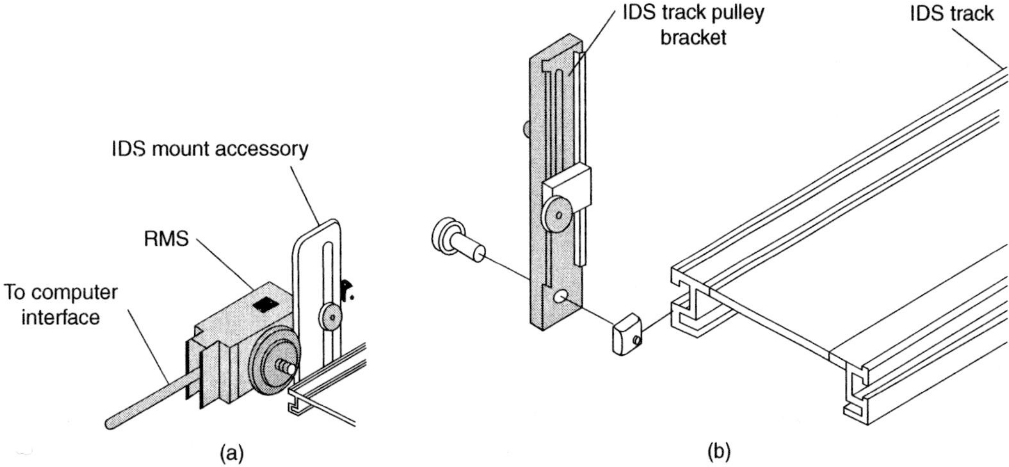

CI Figure 6 Mounting the RMS and the IDS track pulley to the track. (a) This figure shows how to mount the rotary motion sensor to one end of the track, using the mount accesory. (b) This figure shows how the IDS/RMS adapter (the track pulley bracket) should be mounted to the track.

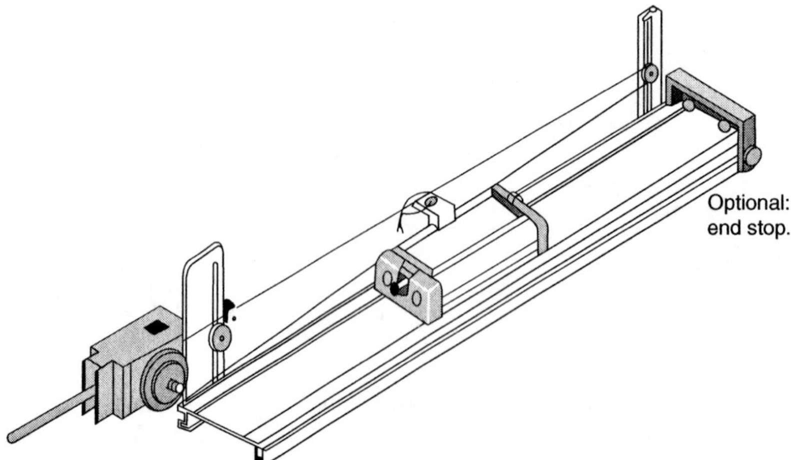

CI Figure 7 Example of one side of the experimental setup This diagram illustrates one of the carts completely set up. Notice the string connecting the pulleys to the cart-bracket is to have tension, but not be so tight that the cart cannot move freely.

(The Smart-Tool is a button of the graph toolbar labeled XY.) A set of crosshairs will appear on the graph. Repeat for each of the other graphs to get a set of crosshairs on each graph. The crosshairs can be dragged around to determine the exact (x,y) value of any point in the graphs.

13. Use the smart-tools to find the time t_o that corresponds to the moment just before the collision. Report the value of t_o in the laboratory report. (*Hint:* Use the velocity graphs and think of what the cars were doing just before the collision.)
14. In the graph printout, mark the time t_o in all graphs by drawing a single, vertical line from top to bottom of the page crossing time t_o.
15. Use the smart-tools to find the time t_f that corresponds to the moment just after the collision ended. Report the value of t_f in the laboratory report (*Hint:* The collision does not end at the same time as when it started, look carefully! Again, think of what the cars were doing right after the collision.)
16. In the graph printout, mark the time t_f in all graphs by drawing a single, vertical line from top to bottom of the page crossing time t_f. The two vertical lines now separate the before-collision from the after-collision moments.
17. Determine how long (in time) the collision lasted.
18. Use the smart-tools to determine, at time t_o:
    - the velocity of Car 1
    - the velocity of Car 2
    - the total momentum of the system
    - the total kinetic energy of the system

    Enter the results in CI Data Table 1.
19. Use the smart-tools to determine, at time t_f:
    - the velocity of Car1
    - the velocity of Car 2
    - the total momentum of the system
    - the total kinetic energy of the system

    Enter the results in CI Data Table 1.
20. Calculate the change in velocity of each car, the change in momentum of each car, the change in the total momentum of the system, and the change in the total kinetic energy of the system. Enter the results in CI Data Table 1.

CASE 2: INELASTIC COLLISION BETWEEN TWO CARS OF (NEARLY) EQUAL MASS, WITH ONE INITIALLY AT REST

21. Switch the cars on the track so that their magnetic ends are facing away from each other. The easiest way to do this without altering the strings is to unscrew the cart-string brackets from the carts but not from the strings. The cars can then be switched under the brackets and the brackets installed back.*
22. Place a small piece of clay on the colliding end of both cars. (*Note:* Velcro strips and sticky masking tape also work well for this. Some PASCO carts already come with Velcro strips attached.)
23. Set Car 2 somewhere on the middle of the track, at rest.
24. Set Car1 all the way to the end of the track.
25. Press the START button, and then give Car 1 a good push toward Car 2.
26. Press the STOP button after the collision, before the cars reach the end of the track and bounce. (The cars must stick together after the collision. Several practice runs, and the help of a partner, may be needed to get the hang of it.)
27. Repeat Steps 10 to 20, for this set of data, but enter the results in CI Data Table 2.

* Some PASCO carts have magnets on both ends. These won't work. A new set of carts with no magnets (plunger carts) will be needed, which means new masses must be measured and entered in the Calculator, if this is the case.

Name ______________________ Section ______________ Date ______________

Lab Partner(s) ____

C I EXPERIMENT 6

Conservation of Linear Momentum

CI Laboratory Report

CASE 1: ELASTIC COLLISION BETWEEN TWO CARS OF (NEARLY) EQUAL MASS, WITH ONE INITIALLY AT REST

Car 1: m_1 = ______________

Car 2: m_2 = ______________

Collision started at t_o = ______________

Total collision time $\Delta t = t_f - t_o$ = ______________

Collision ended at t_f = ______________

CI DATA TABLE 1

Purpose: To analyze an elastic collision between two objects of nearly identical mass.

	Just before the collision	Just after the collision	Changes	
Velocity of Car 1, v_1			Δv_1	
Velocity of Car 2, v_2			Δv_2	
Total momentum, $\mathbf{P}_{\text{Total}}$			$\Delta\mathbf{P}$	
Total kinetic energy, K_{Total}			ΔK	

Don't forget units

(continued)

CASE 2: INELASTIC COLLISION BETWEEN TWO CARS OF (NEARLY) EQUAL MASS, WITH ONE INITIALLY AT REST

Car 1: m_1 = ______________

Car 2: m_2 = ______________

Collision started at t_o = ______________ Total collision time $\Delta t = t_f - t_o$ = ______________

Collision ended at t_f = ______________

CI DATA TABLE 2

Purpose: To analyze an inelastic collision between two objects of nearly identical mass.

	Just before the collision	Just after the collision	Changes	
Velocity of Car 1, v_1			Δv_1	
Velocity of Car 2, v_2			Δv_2	
Total momentum, $\mathbf{P}_{\text{Total}}$			$\Delta \mathbf{P}$	
Total kinetic energy, K_{Total}			ΔK	

Name ______________________ Section ______________ Date ______________

Lab Partner(s) ____

CI QUESTIONS

1. How well do the results support the law of conservation of momentum, considering the possible sources of uncertainty?

2. Which collision took a longer time, the elastic or the inelastic collision? Discuss the possible reasons.

3. Was the kinetic energy of the system conserved? Discuss by comparing the results for the elastic collision and the inelastic collision.

4. During the inelastic collision, the kinetic energy was obviously not conserved. What do you think happened to the "lost" energy?

(continued)

5. During the collision, both cars changed their momentum. How does the change in momentum of each car compare to that of the other? Does one car change more than the other? What do you think would happen if the cars had different mass? (If time is available, try it.)

6. For an object to undergo a change in its momentum, a net force needs to be applied. The amount of change in momentum produced by the force depends on the length of the time during which the force acts and is called the *impulse*. That is,

$$\text{Impulse} = \Delta p = \text{F}\Delta\text{t}$$

where the force F is assumed to be constant, or to be an "average force." For each of the collisions, calculate the average force acting on the cars during the collision, and compare them.

7. Suppose a ball falls on your head. What is better for you (less damage), for the ball to bounce straight back off your head, or for it to stop and stick to you? Justify your answer.

Name ______________________ Section ______________ Date ______________

Lab Partner(s) ____

EXPERIMENT 7

Projectile Motion: The Ballistic Pendulum

TI Advance Study Assignment

Read the experiment and answer the following questions.

A. *The Ballistic Pendulum*

1. In determining the magnitude of the initial velocity of the ballistic pendulum projectile, what conservation laws are involved and in which parts of the procedure?

2. Why is it justified to say that the momentum in the horizontal direction is conserved over the collision interval? Is momentum conserved before and after the collision? Explain.

3. Is the center of mass of the pendulum-ball system at the center of the ball? If not, where and how is the center of mass located?

(continued)

B. Determination of the Initial Velocity of a Projectile from Range-Fall Measurements

4. After the horizontal projectile leaves the gun, what are the accelerations in the x and y directions?

5. How is the location where the ball strikes the floor determined?

6. Besides the range, what else is needed to determine the magnitude of the initial velocity of the ball?

C. Projectile Range Dependence on the Angle of Projection

7. For a given initial velocity, how does the range of a projectile vary with the angle of projection θ?

8. Theoretically, the angle of projection for maximum range is 45°. Does this set a limit on the range? Explain.

Projectile Motion: The Ballistic Pendulum

INTRODUCTION AND OBJECTIVES

Projectile motion is the motion of an object in a plane (two dimensions) under the influence only of gravity. The kinematic equations of motion describe the components of such motion and may be used to analyze projectile motion. In most textbook cases, the initial velocity of a projectile (speed and angle of projection) is given and the motion is described through the equations of motion.

However, in this laboratory experiment, the unknown initial velocity will be determined from experimental measurements. This will be done (1) through the use of the ballistic pendulum and (2) from range-fall distance measurements. The dependence of the projectile range on the angle of projection will also be investigated so as to obtain an experimental indication of the angle of projection that gives the maximum range.

These procedures will greatly assist you in understanding some of the most basic physical principles. After performing the experiment and analyzing the data, you should be able to do the following:

1. Explain the use of conservation laws (linear momentum and energy) in determining the initial velocity of a projectile using the ballistic pendulum.
2. Describe the components of motion and how they are used in determining the velocity of a projectile with range-fall measurements.
3. Tell how the range of a projectile varies with the angle of projection.

EQUIPMENT NEEDED

- Ballistic pendulum
- Sheets of plain paper (and carbon paper)*
- Meterstick

* May or may not be needed.

- Protractor
- Laboratory balance
- Masking tape
- Wooden blocks
- 1 sheet of Cartesian graph paper
- Safety glasses

THEORY

A. The Ballistic Pendulum

Types of ballistic pendula apparatus are shown in ● Fig. 1. The ballistic pendulum is used to measure the initial velocity of a horizontally projected object (a metal ball) fired from a spring gun. The projectile is fired into a stationary, hollow pendulum bob suspended by a rod, and the pendulum and the embedded projectile swing upward.

A catch mechanism stops the pendulum at its highest position of swing. By measuring the vertical distance that the center of mass of the pendulum-ball system rises, one can compute the initial velocity of the projectile through the use of the conservation of linear momentum and the conservation of mechanical energy (neglecting rotational considerations).

Consider the schematic diagram of a ballistic pendulum shown in ● Fig. 2. A projectile of mass m with an initial horizontal velocity of v_{x_o} is fired into and becomes embedded in a stationary pendulum of mass M.

The horizontal momentum is conserved during collision (if the external forces are vertical). To a good approximation, this applies over the time interval of the collision. Therefore, the horizontal component of total momentum is taken to be the same immediately before and after collision. The velocity of the pendulum bob is initially zero, and the combined system $(m + M)$ has a velocity of magnitude V just after collision. Hence, we may write for the horizontal direction

$$\underset{\text{(before)}}{mv_{x_o}} = \underset{\text{(after)}}{(m + M)V} \tag{1}$$

After the collision, the pendulum with the embedded projectile swings upward (momentum of the system no longer conserved) and stops. The center of mass of the system is raised a maximum vertical distance $h = h_2 - h_1$. By the conservation of mechanical energy, the increase in potential energy is equal to the kinetic energy of the system

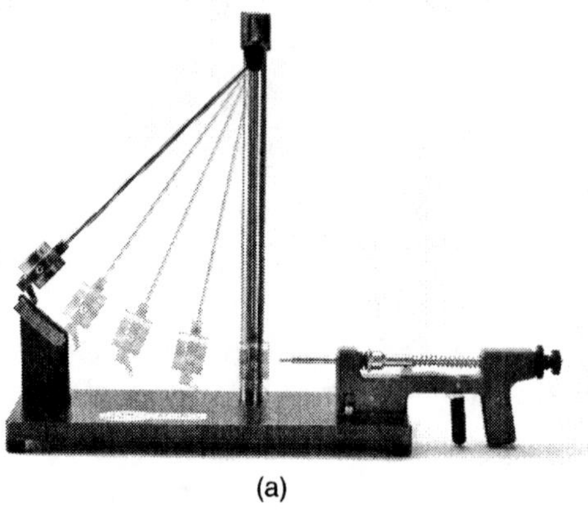

(a)

(c)

(b)

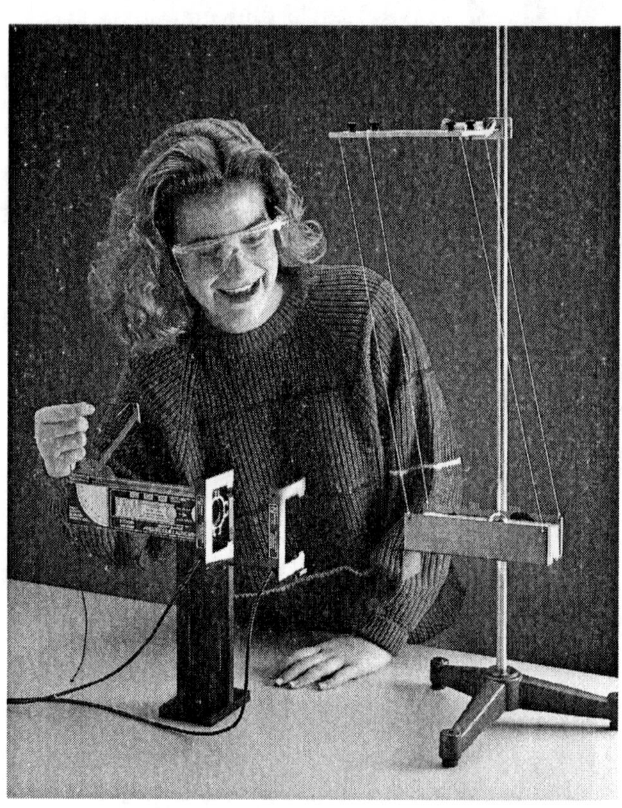

(d)

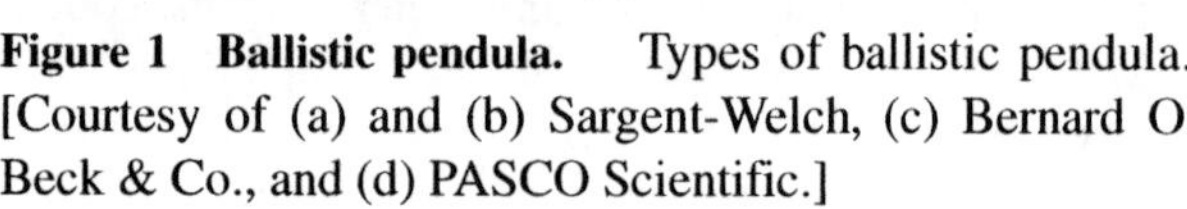

Figure 1 Ballistic pendula. Types of ballistic pendula. [Courtesy of (a) and (b) Sargent-Welch, (c) Bernard O. Beck & Co., and (d) PASCO Scientific.]

just after collision (the friction of the support is considered negligible). Hence,

$$\underset{\substack{\text{kinetic energy}\\ \text{just after collision}}}{\tfrac{1}{2}(m + M)V^2} = \underset{\substack{\text{change in}\\ \text{potential energy}}}{(m + M)gh} \tag{2}$$

Solving Eq. 7.2 for V, we obtain

$$V = \sqrt{2gh} \tag{3}$$

Substituting this expression into Eq. 7.1 and solving for v_{x_o} yields

$$\boxed{v_{x_o} = \frac{m + M}{m}\sqrt{2gh}} \tag{4}$$

(initial speed)

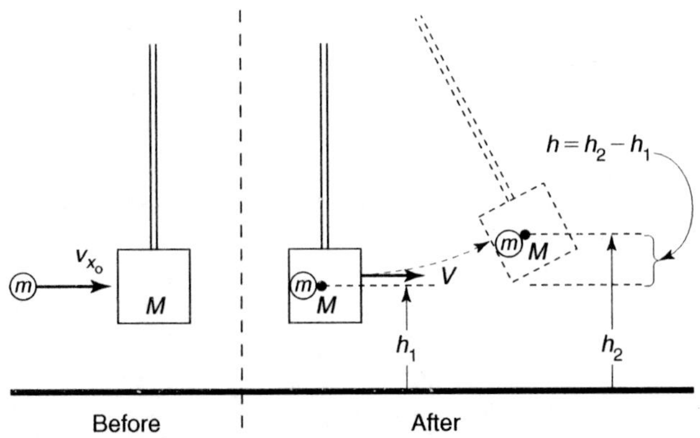

Figure 2 Ballistic pendulum action. Ideally, the horizontal linear momentum is conserved during collision. After collision, work is done against gravity, and kinetic energy is converted into potential energy. (Rotational considerations neglected.)

Hence, by measuring *m*, *M*, and *h*, we can compute the initial velocity of the projectile.

B. *Determination of the Initial Speed of a Horizontal Projectile from Range-Fall Measurements*

If a projectile is projected horizontally with an initial velocity of magnitude v_{x_o} from a height of *y*, it will describe an arc as illustrated in ● Fig. 3. The projectile will travel a horizontal distance *x* (called the *range* of the projectile) while falling a vertical distance *y*.

The initial vertical velocity is zero, $v_{y_o} = 0$, and the acceleration in the *y* direction has a magnitude of $a_y = g$ (acceleration due to gravity). There is no horizontal acceleration, $a_x = 0$; hence the components of the motion are described by

$$x = v_{x_o} t \tag{5}$$

and

$$-y = -\tfrac{1}{2}gt^2 \tag{6}$$

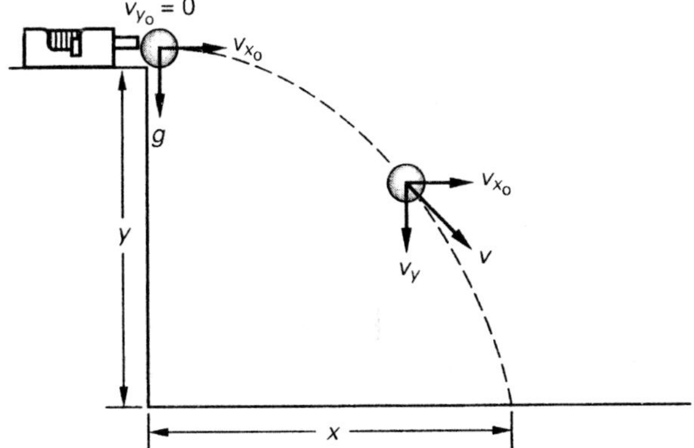

Figure 3 Range-fall. The configuration for range-fall measurements. See text for description.

Eliminating *t* from these equations and solving for v_{x_o}, we have (neglecting air resistance)

$$v_{x_o} = \sqrt{\frac{gx^2}{2y}} = \left(\frac{g}{2y}\right)^{\frac{1}{2}} x \tag{7}$$

Hence, by measuring the range *x* and the distance of fall *y*, one can compute the initial speed of the projectile.

C. *Projectile Range Dependence on the Angle of Projection*

The projectile path for a general angle of projection θ is shown in ● Fig. 4. The components of the initial velocity have magnitudes of

$$v_{x_o} = v_o \cos\theta$$
$$v_{y_o} = v_o \sin\theta \tag{8}$$

At the top of the arc path, $v_y = 0$, and since

$$v_y = v_{y_o} - gt$$
$$= v_o \sin\theta - gt$$

(downward taken as negative), we have

$$v_o \sin\theta - gt_m = 0$$

or

$$t_m = \frac{v_o \sin\theta}{g} \tag{9}$$

where t_m is the time for the projectile to reach the maximum height of y_m.

If the projectile returns to the same elevation as that from which it was fired, then the total time of flight *t* is

$$t = 2t_m = \frac{2v_o \sin\theta}{g} \tag{10}$$

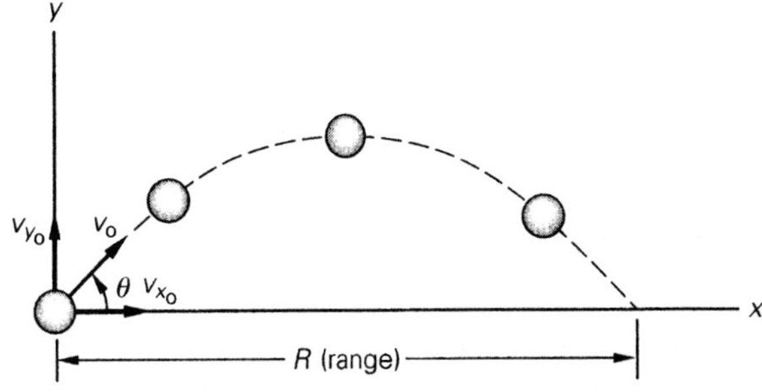

Figure 4 Projectile motion. For an arbitrary projection angle above the horizontal, the range *R* of a projectile depends on the initial velocity—that is, on the speed and angle of projection.

During the time t, the projectile travels a distance R (range) in the x direction:

$$R = v_{x_o} t = \frac{2v_o^2 \sin\theta \cos\theta}{g}$$

But using the trigonometric identity $2 \sin\theta \cos\theta = \sin 2\theta$, we find that the **range** or maximum distance in the x direction is

$$R = \frac{v_o^2 \sin 2\theta}{g} \quad \textbf{(11)}$$

(range)

From Eq. 11, we see that the range of the projectile depends on the angle of projection θ. The maximum range R_{max} occurs when $\sin 2\theta = 1$. Since $\sin 90° = 1$, by comparison

$$2\theta = 90° \quad \text{or} \quad \theta = 45°$$

Hence, a projectile has a maximum range for $\theta = 45°$, and

$$R_{max} = \frac{v_o^2}{g} \quad \textbf{(12)}$$

(maximum range, $\theta = 45°$)

which provides another convenient method to determine experimentally the initial speed of a projectile.

(*Note:* This development neglects air resistance, but the equations give the range to a good approximation for relatively small initial speeds and short projectile paths. Why?)

Experimental Procedure

***Caution:** With projectiles involved, it is recommended that safety glasses be worn during all procedures.*

A. *The Ballistic Pendulum*

1. Obtain the projectile ball, which may be in the pendulum bob. (*Note:* When removing the ball from the pendulum bob of some types of ballistic pendula, be sure to push up on the spring catch that holds the ball in the pendulum so as not to damage it.)

   Place the projectile ball on the ball rod of the spring gun, and cock the gun by pushing on the ball. Both ball and rod may move backward, or the ball may slip over the rod, depending on the type of ballistic pendulum. ***Caution:** In either case, be careful not to bruise or hurt your hand when cocking the gun. Also, keep your fingers away from the projectile end of the gun.*

   Fire the projectile into the pendulum to see how the apparatus operates. If the catch mechanism does not catch on the notched track, you should adjust the pendulum suspension to obtain the proper alignment.

2. A preset pointer or a dot on the side of the pendulum bob indicates the position of the center of mass of the pendulum-ball system. With the pendulum hanging freely, measure the height h_1 of the pointer above the base surface (Fig. 2) and record it in Data Table 1.

3. Fire the ball into the freely hanging stationary pendulum and note the notch at which the catch mechanism stops on the curved track. Counting upward on the curved track, record the notch number in Data Table 1. Repeat this procedure four times, and for each trial record the notch number in the data table. (Alternatively, the height may be measured each time. See procedure 4.)

4. Determine the average of these observations, which is the average highest position of the pendulum. Place the catch mechanism in the notch corresponding most closely to the average, and measure the height h_2 of the pointer or dot above the base surface used for the h_1 measurement (Fig. 2).

   Note: To minimize frictional losses, the catch mechanism may be disabled by tying it up with thread or using a rubber band. The mechanism then acts as a pointer to indicate the highest notch, which is observed by a lab partner. Holding some reference object, such as a pencil, by the notched track helps to determine the proper notch number.

5. Loosen the screw of the pendulum support and carefully remove the pendulum. Weigh and record the masses of the ball (m) and the pendulum (M). *Note:* The mass of the pendulum is that of the bob and the support rod. Do not attempt to remove the support rod from the bob. Consult your instructor for an explanation if a different model is used.

6. From the data, compute the magnitude of the initial velocity using Eq. 4 ($g = 9.80 \text{ m/s}^2 = 980 \text{ cm/s}^2$).

B. *Determination of the Initial Velocity of a Projectile from Range-Fall Measurements*

7. With the pendulum removed or in the upper catch mechanism notch so as not to interfere with the projectile, position the apparatus near one edge of the laboratory table as shown in Fig. 3.

   Fire the ball from the gun, and note where the ball strikes the floor. (The range of the ball is appreciable, so you will probably have to shoot the ball down an aisle. Be careful not to hit anyone with the ball, particularly the instructor.)

8. Place a sheet of paper where the ball hits the floor. Tape the paper to the floor (or weight it down) so that it will not move. When the ball strikes the paper, the indentation mark will enable you to determine the range of the projectile.* Also mark the position of the apparatus on the table (e.g., using a piece of tape as a reference). It is important that the gun be fired from the same position each time.

9. Fire the ball five times and measure the horizontal distance or range x the ball travels for each trial (see Fig. 3). [If the faint indentation marks cannot be found, cover the paper on the floor with a sheet of carbon paper (carbon side down). The ball will then make a carbon mark on the paper on impact.]

   Record the measurements in Data Table 2 and find the average range. Also measure the height y of the ball rod from the floor and record it in the data table. The height y is measured from the bottom of the ball (as it rests on the gun) to the floor.

10. Using Eq. 7, compute the magnitude of the initial velocity of the ball ($g = 9.80\ \text{m/s}^2 = 980\ \text{cm/s}^2$). Compare this to the velocity determined in part A, and compute the percent difference.

C. Dependence of Projectile Range on the Angle of Projection

11. With the ballistic pendulum apparatus on the floor (with pendulum removed), elevate the front end so that it can be fired at an angle θ relative to the horizontal. Your instructor will tell you how to do this. Aim the projectile down an aisle or hallway, *being careful not to aim at anything or anybody.*

12. Using a protractor to set the angles of projection, fire the projectile at angles of 20°, 30°, 40°, 45°, 50°, 60°, and 70° with two or three trials for each angle. The projectile should be aimed so that it lands as close as possible to the same spot for the trials of a particular angle.

   Station one or more lab partners near where the projectile strikes the floor. They are to judge the average range of the two or three trials. Measure the average range for each angle of projection, and record the data in Data Table 3.

   Suggestion: It is convenient to measure the distance from the gun to a position near where the ball lands and to mark this position. The range measurement then can be made relative to the measured mark, instead of from the starting point each time. Also, it is convenient to shoot toward a wall at the end of the hall or aisle or to lay a meterstick on the floor perpendicularly to the line of flight, in order to stop the ball from rolling.

13. Plot the range versus the angle of projection, and draw a smooth curve that fits the data best. As you might expect, the points may be scattered widely because of the rather crude experimental procedure. Even so, you should be able to obtain a good idea of the angle for the maximum range. Determine this angle from the graph, and record it in Data Table 3.

* The range will be measured from the position below the center of the ball just as it leaves the gun to the marks that are on the paper on the floor. This will be determined by putting the ball on the gun without loading the spring.

Name ______________________ Section ______________ Date ______________

Lab Partner(s) ____

EXPERIMENT 7

Projectile Motion: The Ballistic Pendulum

TI Laboratory Report

A. The Ballistic Pendulum

DATA TABLE 1

(Modify Data Table if it does not apply to your ballistic pendulum.)

Purpose: To determine the magnitude of initial projectile velocity.

Trials	Notch number of pendulum catch	
		Height h_2 of pointer with pendulum catch in closest-to-average notch number ______
1		Height h_1 of pointer with pendulum freely suspended ______
2		
3		$h = h_2 - h_1$ ______
4		Mass of ball m ______
5		
		Mass of pendulum M (bob and support) ______
Average		

Calculations (show work)

Computed v_{x_o} ______ (units)

Don't forget units

(continued)

B. Determination of the Initial Velocity of a Projectile from Range-Fall Measurements

DATA TABLE 2

Purpose: To determine the magnitude of initial projectile velocity.

Trial	Range
1	
2	
3	
4	
5	
Average	

Vertical distance of fall, y ______________

Computed v_{x_o} ______________
(units)

Percent difference between results of parts A and B ______________

Calculations
(show work)

C. Dependence of Projectile Range on the Angle of Projection

DATA TABLE 3

Purpose: To investigate projection angle from maximum range.

Angle of projection	Average range
20°	
30°	
40°	
45°	
50°	
60°	
70°	

Angle of projection for maximum range from graph ______________

Name ______________________ Section ______________ Date ______________

Lab Partner(s) ____

EXPERIMENT 7 *Laboratory Report*

TI QUESTIONS

A. *The Ballistic Pendulum*

1. Is the collision between the ball and the pendulum elastic or inelastic? Justify your answer by calculating the kinetic energy of the system before collision using the value of v_{x_o} found in the experiment and the kinetic energy just after collision using the experimental value of h in Eq. 2.

2. Using the results of Question 1 that would apply if the collision were inelastic, find the fractional kinetic energy loss during the collision. Express the "loss" as a percent. What became of the "lost energy"?

3. Expressing the kinetic energy in terms of momentum ($K = \frac{1}{2}mv^2 = p^2/2m$), prove using symbols, not numbers, that the fractional loss during the collision is equal to $M/(m + M)$.

4. Compute the fractional energy loss from the experimental mass values using the equation developed in Question 3, and compare this to the result in Question 2. Explain the difference, if any.

(continued)

5. Is the friction of the pendulum (pointer, support axis, etc.) a random or systematic error? Will this source of error cause your calculated velocity to be less than or greater than the actual velocity?

B. *Determination of the Initial Velocity of a Projectile from Range-Fall Measurements*

6. What effect does the force of gravity have on the horizontal velocity of the projectile? Explain.

7. What affect does air resistance have on the range of the projectile?

C. *Dependence of Projectile Range on the Angle of Projection*

8. Using experimental data, compute the magnitude of the initial velocity v_0 of the projectile from Eq. 12, and compare this to the results of parts A and B of the procedure.

9. If, for a given initial velocity, the maximum range is at a projection angle of 45°, then there must be equal ranges for angles above and below this. Show this explicitly.

Name ______________________ Section ______________ Date ______________

Lab Partner(s) ____

EXPERIMENT 8

Archimedes' Principle: Buoyancy and Density

TI Advance Study Assignment

Read the experiment and answer the following questions.

1. Describe the physical reason for the buoyant force in terms of pressure.

2. Show that the buoyant force is given by $F_b = \rho_f g V_f$ using the development in the Theory section.

3. Give the conditions on densities that determine whether an object will sink or float in a fluid.

4. Distinguish between density and specific gravity, and explain why is it convenient to express these quantities in cgs units?

(continued)

5. Describe how the density of an object less dense than water can be determined using Archimedes' principle. How about the density of a liquid?

6. Why is it important to make certain that no air bubbles adhere to objects during the submerged weighing procedures? How would the experimental results be affected if bubbles were present?

Archimedes' Principle: Buoyancy and Density

Introduction and Objectives

Some objects float and others sink in a given fluid—a liquid or a gas. The fact that an object floats means it is "buoyed up" by a force greater than or equal to its weight. Archimedes (287–212 B.C.), a Greek scientist, deduced that the upward buoyant force acting on a floating object is equal to the weight of the fluid it displaces. Thus, an object sinks if its weight exceeds that of the fluid it displaces.

In this experiment, Archimedes' principle will be studied in an application: determining the densities and specific gravities of solid and liquid samples.

After performing this experiment and analyzing the data, you should be able to:

1. Tell whether an object will sink or float in a fluid, knowing the density of each.
2. Distinguish between density and specific gravity.
3. Describe how the densities of objects that sink or float may be determined experimentally.

Equipment Needed

- Triple-beam pan balance with swing platform (or single-beam double-pan balance with swing platform and set of weights); see Fig. 2.
- Overflow can (or graduated cylinder and eye dropper)
- Two beakers
- Metal cylinder, irregularly shaped metal object, or metal sinker
- Waxed block of wood
- Saltwater solution or alcohol
- String
- Hydrometer and cylinder

Theory

When placed in a fluid, an object either floats or sinks. This is most commonly observed in liquids, particularly water, in which "light" objects float and "heavy" objects sink. But the same effect occurs for gases. A falling object is sinking in the atmosphere, whereas other objects float (● Fig. 1).

Things float because they are buoyant, or are buoyed up. That is, there must be an upward force that is greater

Figure 1 Gas buoyancy. Archimedes' principle applies to fluids—a liquid *or* a gas. Here, a helium-filled blimp floats in air. (Courtesy of Bill Aron/PhotoEdit.)

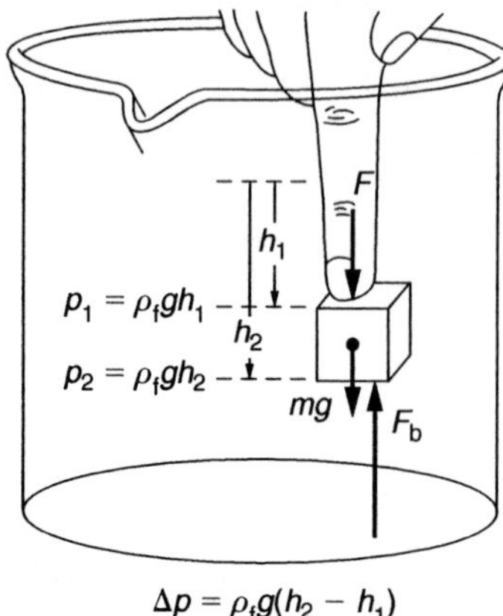

Figure 2 Buoyancy. A buoyant force arises from the difference in pressure at different depths. The pressure at the bottom of the submerged block (p_2) is greater than that at the top (p_1), so there is a (buoyant) force directed upward (the arrow is shifted for clarity).

than (or equal to) the downward force of the object's weight. The upward force resulting from an object being wholly or partially immersed in a fluid is called the **buoyant force.** How the buoyant force arises can be understood by considering a buoyant object being held under the surface of a liquid (● Fig. 2). The pressures on the upper and lower surfaces of the block are given by the pressure-depth equations $p_1 = \rho_f g h_1$ and $p_2 = \rho_f g h_2$, respectively, where ρ_f is the density of the fluid. Thus there is a pressure difference $\Delta p = p_2 - p_1 = \rho_f g(h_2 - h_1)$, which gives an upward force (the buoyant force). In this case, the buoyant force is balanced by the applied force and the weight of the block.

It is not difficult to derive an expression for the magnitude of the buoyant force. If both the top and bottom areas of the block are A, the buoyant force (F_b) is given by $F_b = \Delta pA = \rho_f g V_f$, where V_f is the volume of the fluid displaced. But $\rho_f V_f$ is simply the mass of the fluid displaced by the block, m_f (recall that $\rho = m/V$). Hence the magnitude of the buoyant force is equal to the weight of the fluid displaced by the block. This general result is known as **Archimedes' principle:**

An object immersed wholly or partially in a fluid experiences a buoyant force equal in magnitude to the weight of the volume of fluid that it displaces.

Thus the magnitude of the buoyant force depends only on the weight of the fluid displaced by the object, *not* on the weight of the object.

Archimedes' principle shows that an object

1. **will float** in a fluid if the density of the object ρ_o is less than the density of the fluid ρ_f that is, ($\rho_o < \rho_f$);
2. **will sink** if the object's density is greater than that of the fluid, ($\rho_o > \rho_f$) and
3. **will float in equilibrium** at any submerged depth where it is placed if its density is equal to that of the fluid, ($\rho_o = \rho_f$).

This can be shown mathematically as follows. The weight of an object is $w_o = m_o g = \rho_o g V_o$, where V_o is the volume of the object and $\rho_o = m_o/V_o$. Similarly, the weight of the fluid displaced by the object, or the buoyant force, is $F_b = w_f = m_f g = \rho_f g V_f$. If the object is completely submersed in the fluid, then $V_o = V_f$, and dividing one equation by the other yields

$$\boxed{\frac{F_b}{w_o} = \frac{\rho_f}{\rho_o} \quad \text{or} \quad F_b = \left(\frac{\rho_f}{\rho_o}\right) w_o} \tag{1}$$

Hence

1. If $\rho_o < \rho_f$, then $F_b > w_o$, and the object will be buoyed up to the surface and float.
2. If $\rho_o > \rho_f$, then $F_b < w_o$, and the object will sink.
3. If $\rho_o = \rho_f$, then $F_b = w_o$, and the object is in equilibrium.

Specific Gravity and Density

Specific gravity will be used in the study and determination of density. The **specific gravity** of a solid or liquid is defined as the ratio of the weight of a given volume of the substance to an equal volume of water:

$$\text{specific gravity (sp. gr.)} = \frac{w_s}{w_w}$$

$$= \frac{\text{weight of a substance (of given volume)}}{\text{weight of an equal volume of water}} \tag{2}$$

where the subscripts s and w refer to the substance and water, respectively.

Specific gravity is a density-type designation that uses water as a comparison standard. Since it is a weight ratio, specific gravity has no units. Conveniently, the numerical value of a substance's specific gravity is the same as the magnitude of its density *in cgs units.* This can be seen as follows:

$$\text{sp. gr.} = \frac{w_s}{w_w} = \frac{w_s/V_s}{w_w/V_w} = \frac{m_s g/V_s}{m_w g/V_w}$$

$$= \frac{m_s/V_s}{m_w/V_w} = \frac{\rho_s}{\rho_w}$$

$$\boxed{\text{sp. gr.} = \frac{\rho_s}{\rho_w}} \tag{3}$$

Since, for practical purposes, the density of water is 1 g/cm^3 over the temperature range in which water is liquid,

$$\text{sp. gr.} = \frac{\rho_s}{\rho_w} = \frac{\rho_s(\text{g/cm}^3)}{1\ (\text{g/cm}^3)} = \rho_s \tag{4}$$

where ρ_s is the numerical value of the density of a substance in g/cm^3.

For example, the density of mercury is 13.6 g/cm^3, and mercury has a specific gravity of 13.6. A specific gravity of 13.6 indicates that mercury is 13.6 times more dense than water, $\rho_s = (\text{sp. gr.})\rho_w$, or that a sample of mercury will weigh 13.6 times as much as an equal volume of water.

Archimedes' principle can be used to determine the specific gravity and density of a *submerged* object:

$$\text{sp. gr.} = \frac{w_o}{w_w} = \frac{w_o}{F_b} \tag{5}$$

where w_o is the weight of the object, w_w is the weight of the water it displaces, and, by Archimedes' principle, $w_w = F_b$.

For a heavy object that sinks, the net force as it does so is equal to $w_o - F_b$. (Why?) If attached to a scale while submerged, it would have a measured *apparent* weight w_o' and $w_o' = w_o - F_b$. Thus $F_b = w_o - w_o'$, and Eq. 5 may be written

$$\text{sp. gr.} = \frac{w_o}{w_w} = \frac{w_o}{w_o - w_o'}$$

or, in terms of mass measured on a balance ($w = mg$),

$$\text{sp. gr.} = \frac{m_o}{m_o - m_o'} = \rho_o \tag{6}$$

(of a heavy object that sinks)

where ρ_o is the magnitude of the density of the object in g/cm^3. This provides us with an experimental method to determine the specific gravity and density of an object that sinks.

To measure the specific gravity and density of an object that floats, or is less dense than water, using Archimedes' principle, it is necessary to use another object of sufficient weight and density to submerge the light object completely.

$w_1 = w_o + w_s'$ is the measured weight (mass) of the object and the sinker, with only the sinker submerged, and $w_2 = w_o' + w_s'$ is the measured weight when both are submerged. Then

$$w_1 - w_2 = (w_o + w_s') - (w_o' + w_s') = w_o - w_o'$$

or, in terms of mass,

$$m_1 - m_2 = m_o - m_o'$$

and the specific gravity and density can be found from Eq. 6. That is,

$$\text{sp. gr.} = \frac{m_o}{m_1 - m_2} = \rho_o \tag{7}$$

(of a light object that floats)

The specific gravity and density of a liquid can also be found using Archimedes' principle. A heavy object is weighed first in air (w_o) and then when submerged in liquid (w_o'). Then $(w_o - w_o')_l$ is the weight of the volume of liquid the object displaces, by Archimedes' principle. When we carry out a similar procedure for the object in water, $(w_o - w_o')_w$ is the volume of water the object displaces.

Then, by the definition of specific gravity (Eq. 2),

$$\text{sp. gr.} = \frac{(w_o - w_o')_l}{(w_o - w_o')_w} = \rho_\ell \tag{8}$$

(of a liquid)

where ρ_ℓ is the density of the liquid in g/cm^3.

You may have been thinking that there are easier ways to determine the density or specific gravity of a solid or liquid. This is true, but the purpose of the experiment is to familiarize you with Archimedes' principle. You may wish to check your experimental results by determining the densities and specific gravities of the solid samples by some other method. The specific gravity of the liquid sample will also be determined using a hydrometer.

EXPERIMENTAL PROCEDURE

A. *Direct Proof of Archimedes' Principle*

1. Weigh the metal sample and record its mass m_o and the type of metal in the Laboratory Report. Also, determine the mass of an empty beaker m_b and record. Fill the overflow can with water, and place it on the balance platform. Attach a string to the sample and suspend it from the balance arm as illustrated in ● Fig. 3.*

2. The overflow from the can when the sample is immersed is caught in the beaker. Take a mass reading m_o' of the submerged object. Make certain that no bubbles adhere to the object. (It is instructive to place the overflow can on a second balance, if available, and note that the "weight" of the overflow can does not change as the sample is submerged.)

* You may use an alternative method if no overflow can is available. Attach a string to the sample and place it in a graduated cylinder. Fill the cylinder with water until the sample is completely submerged. Add water (with an eyedropper) until the water level is at a specific reference mark on the cylinder (e.g., 35 mL). Remove the sample, shaking any drops of water back into the cylinder, and weigh the cylinder and water (m_b). Refill the cylinder to the reference mark and weigh it again ($m_w + m_b$). The mass of the "overflow" water is then the difference between these measurements.

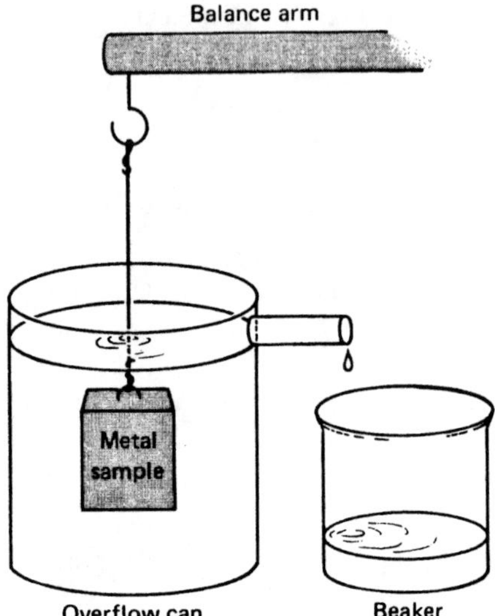

Figure 3 Archimedes' principle. The arrangement for proving Archimedes' principle. The weight of the displaced liquid that overflows into the beaker is equal to the reduction in weight of the metal sample when it is submerged, which is equal to the buoyant force.

Next weigh the beaker and water so as to determine the mass of the displaced water m_w (If the can does not fit on the balance platform, first suspend and immerse the object in the full overflow can, and catch the overflow in the beaker and find m_w. Then attach the sample to the balance arm and suspend it in a beaker of water that will fit on the balance platform to find m_o'.)

3. The buoyant force is then the difference between the object's true weight and its submerged weight, $F_b = m_o g - m_o' g$. According to Archimedes' principle, the magnitude of the buoyant force F_b should equal the weight of the displaced water:

$$F_b + w_w + m_w g$$

or

$$F_b = (m_o - m_o')g = m_w g$$

Compute the buoyant force, and compare it with the weight of the displaced water by finding the percent difference.

B. *Density of a Heavy Solid Object ($\rho_o > \rho_w$)*

4. Determine the specific gravity and density of the metal sample. This can be computed using the data from part A.

C. *Density of a Light Solid Object ($\rho_o < \rho_w$)*

5. Determine the specific gravity and density of the wooden block by the procedure described in the Theory section. First, measure the mass of the wooden block alone (in air). Then set up as in Fig. 3.

Tie the sinker to the wood block, and tie the block to the lower hook of the balance. With the beaker empty, check that the sinker does not touch the bottom of the beaker and that the top of the wooden block is below the top of the beaker. Pour enough water into the beaker to cover the sinker, weigh, add more water until the wooden block is submerged, and then weigh again. Make certain that no air bubbles adhere to the objects during the submerged weighing procedures. The block is waxed so that it does not become waterlogged.

D. *Density of a Liquid (ρ_ℓ)*

6. Determine the specific gravity and density of the liquid provided, by the procedure described in the Theory section. Again, make certain that no air bubbles adhere to the object during the submerged weighing procedures.

7. Determine the specific gravity of the liquid using the hydrometer and cylinder. Compare this value with that found in procedure 6 by computing the percent difference.

Name ______________________ Section ______________ Date ______________

Lab Partner(s) ______________________

EXPERIMENT 8

Archimedes' Principle: Buoyancy and Density

TI Laboratory Report

A. *Direct Proof of Archimedes' Principle*

Type of metal ______________

Mass of metal m_o in air ______________

Mass of beaker m_b ______________

Mass of metal m_o' submerged in water ______________

Mass of beaker and displaced water $m_w + m_b$ ______________

Mass of displaced water m_w ______________

Buoyant force (in newtons) ______________

Weight of displaced water (in newtons) ______________

Percent difference ______________

Calculations
(show work)

Don't forget units

(continued)

B. Density of a Heavy Solid ($\rho_o > \rho_w$)

Calculations
(show work)

Specific gravity ____________________

Density ____________________

C. Density of a Light Solid ($\rho_o < \rho_w$)

Mass of block in air ____________________

Mass of block and sinker with only sinker submerged ____________________

Mass of block and sinker with both submerged ____________________

Specific gravity ____________________

Density ____________________

Calculations
(show work)

Name ______________________ Section ______________ Date ______________

Lab Partner(s) ______________________

EXPERIMENT 8 *Laboratory Report*

D. Density of a Liquid (ρ_ℓ)

Mass of object in air ______________

Mass of object submerged in liquid ______________

Mass of object submerged in water ______________

Computed sp. gr. ______________

Sp. gr. from hydrometer measurement ______________

Percent difference ______________

Calculations (show work)

TI QUESTIONS

1. Look up the density of the metal of the object used in parts A and B of the procedure, and compare it with the experimental value. Comment on the purity of the metal of the object. (Archimedes developed his principle while working on a similar inquiry. His problem was to determine whether a crown alleged to be made of pure gold had actually been made with some content of cheaper metal.)

(continued)

2. In part B, the string will cause error. When does it lead to an experimental density that is too high? Too low?

3. Discuss the situation that occurs when an object is immersed in a fluid that has the same density as the object.

4. (a) Explain how a submarine is caused to submerge and surface without the use of its propulsion propeller and fins.

   (b) Which is heavier, a given volume of ice or the same volume of water? Justify your answer.

5. A block of wood floats in a beaker of water. According to Archimedes' principle, the block experiences an upward buoyant force. If the beaker with the water and floating block were weighed, would the measured weight be less than the sum of the weights of the individual components? Explain.

Name ______________________ Section ______________ Date ______________

Lab Partner(s) ____

6. A person can lift 45 kg ($\approx$ 100 lb). Using the experimental value of the specific gravity for the metal object in part B, how many cubic meters of the metal could the person lift (a) in air, (b) in water? How many actual kilograms of metal is this in air, and in water?

7. Explain the principle and construction of a hydrometer. What is the purpose of the common measurements of the specific gravities of an automobile's radiator coolant and battery electrolyte?

Name ______________________ Section ______________ Date ______________

Lab Partner(s) ____

EXPERIMENT 9

Work and Energy

TI Advance Study Assignment

Read the experiment and answer the following questions.

1. Distinguish between the conservation of mechanical energy and the conservation of total energy.

2. Is mechanical energy conserved in real situations? Is the total energy conserved? Explain.

3. Discuss the relationship between work and energy for a car moving with a constant speed (a) up an incline and (b) down an incline.

4. Under what conditions would the frictional forces be expected to be equal in magnitude for a car moving up an incline and a car moving down an incline?

(continued)

5. Is the force of friction the same for different angles of incline if all other parameters are equal? Explain by specifically considering the angles used in the experiment.

6. What are possible sources of error in this experiment?

Work and Energy

Introduction and Objectives

Work and **energy** are intimately related, as emphasized in a common definition of energy as the ability to do work. That is, an object or system possessing energy has the *capability* of doing work. When work is done by a system, energy is expended—the system loses energy. Conversely, when there is work input to a system, the system gains energy.

In an ideal conservative system, energy is transferred back and forth between kinetic energy and potential energy. In such a system, the sum of the kinetic and potential energies is constant, as expressed by the *law of conservation of mechanical energy.* However, in actual systems, friction is always present, and these systems are nonconservative. That is, some energy is lost as a result of the work done against frictional forces. Even so, the *total* energy is conserved (*conservation of total energy*).

In this experiment you will make use of the conservation of energy to study the relationship between work and energy in the cases of a car rolling up and down an inclined plane. The ever-present frictional forces and the work done against friction will be investigated and taken into account so as to provide a better understanding of the concept of work-energy. To simplify matters, experimental conditions with constant speeds will be used so that only the relationship between work and changes in gravitational potential energy will have to be considered.

After performing this experiment and analyzing the data, you should be able to:

1. Explain how work and energy are related.
2. Describe how frictional work can be determined experimentally using either force-distance or energy considerations.
3. Better appreciate the nonconservative aspects of real situations and the difference between the conservation of mechanical energy and the conservation of total energy.

Equipment Needed

- Inclined plane with pulley and Hall's carriage (car)
- Weight hanger and slotted weights
- String
- Meterstick
- Protractor (if plane not so equipped)
- Laboratory balance

Theory

A. Work of Friction: Force-Distance Method

Car Moving Up the Plane

The situation for a car moving up an inclined plane with a constant velocity is illustrated in ● Fig. 1. Since the car is not accelerating, the force up the plane (F) must be equal in magnitude to the sum of the forces down (parallel to) the plane:

$$F = F_{\parallel} + f$$

where f is the force of friction and $F_{\parallel} = m_c g \sin\theta$ is the component of the car's weight parallel to the plane. (See Fig. 1.)

Since the magnitude of F is equal to the weight w_1 of the suspended mass (m_1), we may write

$$w_1 = F_{\parallel} + f$$

Then, solving for f and expressing the other forces in terms of the experimental parameters,

$$f = w_1 - F_1$$

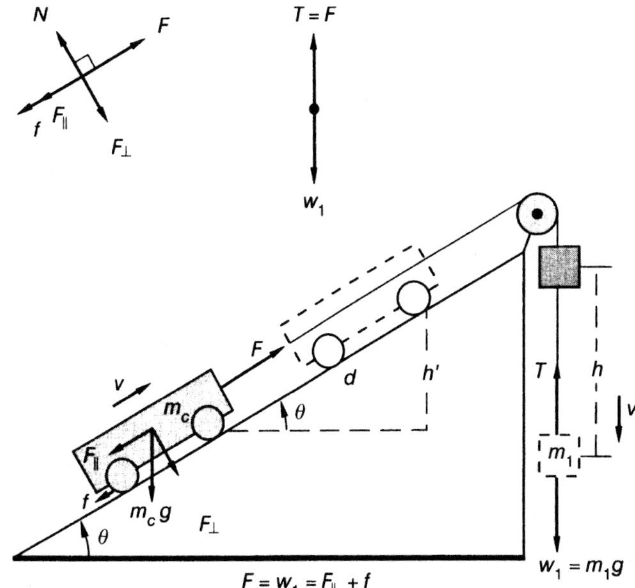

Figure 1 Car moving up the incline with a constant velocity. With no acceleration, the net force on the car is zero, and $F = F_{\parallel} + f = w_1$ (see free-body diagrams).

or

$$f = m_1 g - m_c g \sin\theta \quad (1)$$

(car moving up)

Car Moving Down the Plane

The situation for a car moving down an inclined plane with the same constant speed is illustrated in ● Fig. 2. Again, since the car is not accelerating, the sum of the forces up the plane must be equal in magnitude to the force down the plane, and

$$F = F_{\parallel} - f$$

where, in this case, the direction of f is up the plane. Since $F = w_2$,

$$F_{\parallel} = w_2 + f$$

and, expressing f as before,

$$f = m_c g \sin\theta - m_2 g \quad (2)$$

(car moving down)

Then, in either case, the frictional work is given by

$$W_f = fd \quad (3)$$

where d is the distance the car moves.

If the car moves approximately at the same constant speed in each case, it might be assumed that the magnitude of the frictional force f would be the same in each case

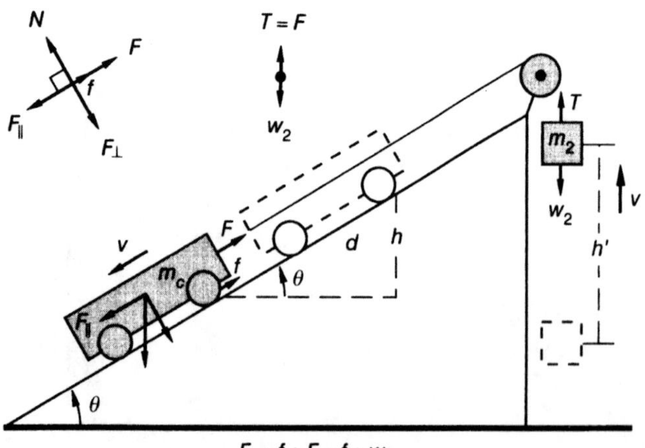

Figure 2 **Car m vingd wn the incline with the same constant speed as in Fig. 1.** With no acceleration, the force on the car is zero, and $F_{\parallel} = F + f = w_2 + f$ (see free-body diagrams).

(same angle of incline and load). This will be investigated experimentally.

B. *Work of Friction: Energy Method*

Another way of looking at the frictional work is in terms of energy.

Car Moving up the Plane

For the case of the car moving up the plane, by the conservation of energy, the *decrease* in the potential energy of the descending weight on the weight hanger $\Delta U_w = m_1 gh$ is equal to the *increase* in the potential energy of the car $\Delta U_c = m_c gh'$ *plus* the energy lost to friction, which is equal to the work done against the force of friction W_f. That is,

$$\Delta U_w = \Delta U_c + W_f$$

or

$$W_f = \Delta U_w - \Delta U_c$$

and

$$W_f = m_1 gh - m_c gh' \quad (4)$$

(car moving up)

Car Moving Down the Plane

Similarly, for the case of the car moving down the plane, by the conservation of energy, the *decrease* in the potential energy of the descending car is equal to the *increase* in the potential energy of the ascending weight *plus* the work done against the force of friction:

$$\Delta U_c = \Delta U_w + W_f$$

or

$$W_f = \Delta U_c - \Delta U_w$$

and

$$W_f = m_c gh' - m_2 gh \quad (5)$$

(car moving down)

In terms of the experimental parameters, the methods for determining W_f are equivalent.

Experimental Procedure

1. Using a laboratory balance, determine the mass of the car m_c and record it in the Laboratory Report.

2. Arrange the inclined plane and the car as shown in ● Fig. 3 with an angle of incline of $\theta = 30°$. Make certain that the pulley is adjusted so that the string at-

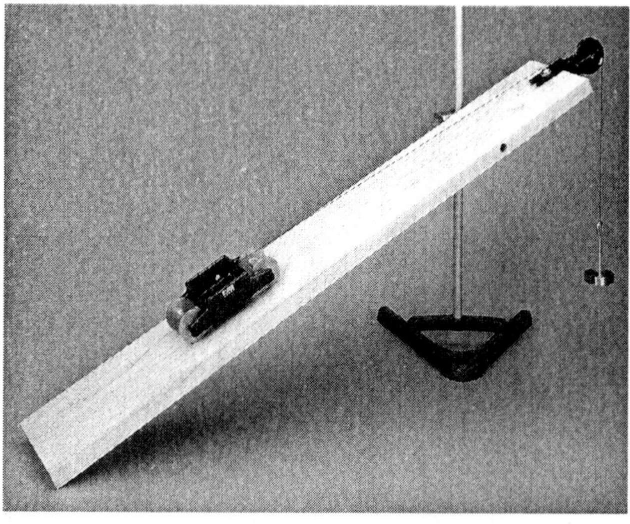

(a)

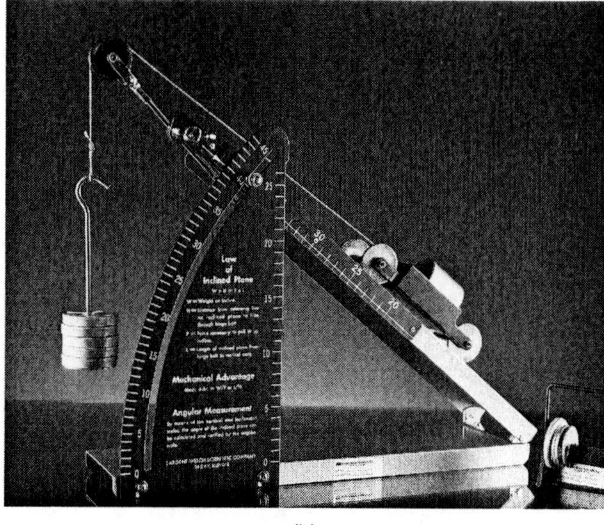

(b)

Figure 3 Types of inclined planes. (a) Inclined plane with board and stand. (b) Calibrated incline plane. (Courtesy of Sargent-Welch.)

tached to the car is parallel to the plane. (Should the car accelerate up the plane by the weight of the weight hanger alone, place some weights in the car so that the car is initially stationary. Add the additional mass to that of the car in Data Table 1.)

3. Add enough weights to the weight hanger so that the car moves up the incline with a slow uniform speed when the car is given a slight tap. Record the total suspended mass in Data Table 1.

4. With the car positioned near the bottom of the incline, mark the position of the car's front wheels and give the car a slight tap to set it into motion. Stop the car near the top of the plane after it moves up the plane (with a constant speed), and measure the distance of d it moved up the plane as determined by the stopped position of the car's front wheels. Or measure the height h the weight hanger descends. This corresponds to the situation in Fig. 1. The lengths d and h are the same. Record this length in Data Table 1 as d.

5. With the car near the top of the plane, remove enough weights from the weight hanger so that the car rolls down the inclined plane with a slow uniform speed on being given a slight tap. Use as close to the same speed as for the upward case as is possible. This corresponds to the situation in Fig. 2. Record the total suspended mass in Data Table 1. For convenience, use the same d (or h) as in procedure 4.

6. Compute the frictional force f (Eqs. 1 and 2) and work done against friction W_f (Eq. 3) for each case. Show your calculations and record the results in Data Table 1.

7. Compare the frictional work for the two cases by computing the percent difference.

8. Adjust the angle of the inclined plane to $\theta = 45°$ and repeat procedures 3 through 7, recording your measurements in Data Table 2.

Name ______________________ Section ______________ Date ______________

Lab Partner(s) ____

EXPERIMENT 9

Work and Energy

TI Laboratory Report

Angle of incline ______________

DATA TABLE 1

Purpose: To determine work done against friction.

Mass of car m_c ______________

		Suspended mass ( )	d ( )	f ( )	W_f ( )
Car moving up incline	m_1				
Car moving down incline	m_2				

Calculations
(show work)

Percent difference in W_f ______________

Don't forget units

(continued)

Angle of incline ________________

Mass of car m_c ________________

DATA TABLE 2

Purpose: To determine work done against friction.

		Suspended mass ( )	d ( )	f ( )	W_f ( )
Car moving up incline	m_1				
Car moving down incline	m_2				

Calculations
(show work)

Percent difference in W_f ________________

Name ______________________ Section ______________ Date ______________

Lab Partner(s) ____

EXPERIMENT 9 *Laboratory Report*

TI QUESTIONS

1. What was the work done by the suspended weight when the car (a) moved up the incline and (b) moved down the incline? (*Show your calculations.*)

	$\theta = 30°$	$\theta = 45°$
Car moving up incline	________	________
Car moving down incline	________	________

2. What was the work done by gravity acting on the car when it (a) moved up the incline and (b) moved down the incline? (*Show your calculations.*)

	$\theta = 30°$	$\theta = 45°$
Car moving up incline	________	________
Car moving down incline	________	________

3. (a) For the car going up the incline, what percentage of the work done by the suspended weight was lost to friction? (b) For the car moving down the incline, what percentage of the work done by gravity was lost to friction? (*Show your calculations.*)

	$\theta = 30°$	$\theta = 45°$
Car moving up incline	________	________
Car moving down incline	________	________

(*continued*)

4. Suppose the car accelerated up and down the incline. How would this affect the experimental determinations?

5. Is the assumption justified that f would be the same for both up and down cases for the same constant speed? If not, speculate as to why there is a difference.

6. Assuming that $f = \mu N$ (see Experiment 9), show that the coefficient of (rolling) friction for the car moving down the inclined plane with a constant speed is given by $\mu = \tan\theta - \dfrac{m_2}{m_c \cos\theta}$. (Use symbols, not numbers.)

Name ____________ Section ____________ Date ____________

Lab Partner(s) ____________

EXPERIMENT 10

Torques, Equilibrium, and Center of Gravity

TI Advance Study Assignment

Read the experiment and answer the following questions.

1. What conditions must be present for (a) translational equilibrium and (b) rotational equilibrium of a rigid body?

2. If these conditions for equilibrium are satisfied, is the rigid body necessarily in static equilibrium? Explain.

3. Write a definition and a mathematical expression for torque.

Don't forget units

(continued)

4. If torque is a vector, with specific direction in space, what is meant by clockwise and counterclockwise torques? If the sums of these torques on a rigid body are equal, what does this imply physically?

5. What defines the center of gravity of a rigid body, and how is it related to the center of mass?

6. Define the term *linear mass density*. Also, what is implied if it is assumed that the linear mass density of an object is constant?

Torques, Equilibrium, and Center of Gravity

Introduction and Objectives

In introductory physics, forces act on "objects." That is, we consider an object as a particle, which generally responds linearly to a force. In reality, an object is an extended collection of particles, and where a force is applied makes a difference. Rotational motion becomes relevant when we analyze the motion of a solid extended object or a rigid body. A **rigid body** is an object or system of particles in which the distances between particles are fixed and remain constant. A quantity of liquid water is *not* a rigid body, but the ice that would form if the water were frozen is.

Actually, the concept of a rigid body is an idealization. In reality, the particles (atoms and molecules) of a solid vibrate constantly. Also, solids can undergo deformations. Even so, most solids can be considered to be rigid bodies for the purposes of analyzing rotational motion.

An important condition of rigid bodies in many practical applications is **static equilibrium.** Examples include beams in bridges and beam balances. When a rigid body such as a beam or a rod is "in balance," it is at rest, or in static equilibrium. In particular, the beam is in rotational static equilibrium; it does not rotate about some point or axis of rotation.

The criterion for rotational static equilibrium is that the sum of the torques, or moments of force acting on a rigid body, be equal to zero. To study torques and rotational equilibrium, we will use a "beam" balance in the form of a meterstick and suspended weights. The mass of an object will be determined experimentally by the "moment-of-force" method, and the experimental value will be compared to the mass of the object as measured on a laboratory balance. Also, the concepts of center of gravity and center of mass will be investigated.

After performing this experiment and analyzing the data, you should be able to:

1. Explain mechanical equilibrium and how it is applied to rigid bodies.
2. Distinguish between center of mass and center of gravity.
3. Describe how a laboratory beam balance measures mass.

Equipment Needed

- Meterstick
- Support stand
- Laboratory balance
- String and one knife-edge clamp *or* four knife-edge clamps (three with wire hangers)
- Four hooked weights (50 g, two 100 g, and 200 g)
- Unknown mass with hook

Theory

A. *Equilibrium*

The conditions for the mechanical equilibrium of a rigid body are

$$\Sigma \mathbf{F} = 0 \quad \textbf{(1a)}$$

$$\Sigma \boldsymbol{\tau} = 0 \quad \textbf{(1b)}$$

That is, the (vector) sums of the forces **F** and torques $\boldsymbol{\tau}$ acting on the body are zero.

The first condition, $\Sigma \mathbf{F} = 0$, is concerned with **translational equilibrium** and ensures that the object is at a particular location (not moving linearly) or that it is moving with a uniform linear velocity (Newton's first law of motion). In this experiment, the rigid body (the meterstick) is restricted from linear motion, so this is not a consideration.

To be in static equilibrium, a rigid body must also be in rotational static equilibrium. Although the sum of the forces on the object may be zero and it is not moving linearly, it is possible that it may be rotating about some fixed axis of rotation. However, if the sum of the torques is zero, $\Sigma \boldsymbol{\tau} = 0$, the object is in **rotational equilibrium,** and either it does not rotate (static case) or it rotates with a uniform angular velocity. (Forces produce linear motion, and torques produce rotational motion.)

A **torque** (or moment of force) results from the application of a force acting at a distance from an axis of rotation (● Fig. 1). The magnitude of the torque is equal to the product of the force's magnitude F and the perpendicular

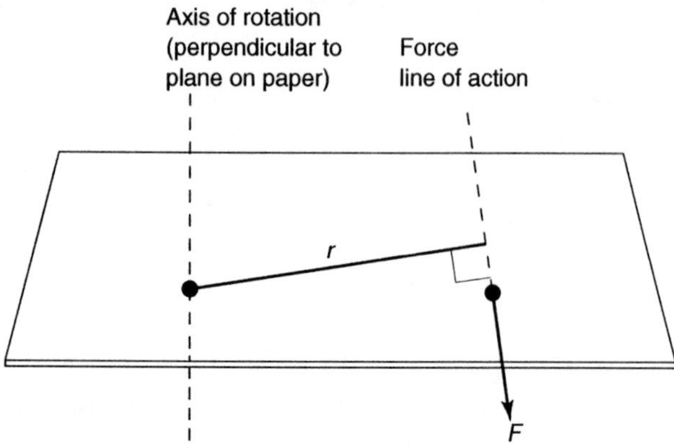

Figure 1 **Torque.** The magnitude of a torque is equal to the product of the magnitude of the force F and the perpendicular distance (lever arm) r from the axis of rotation to the force's line of action; that is, $\tau = rF$.

distance r from the axis of rotation to the force's line of action (a straight line through the force vector arrow). That is,

$$\tau = rF \tag{2}$$

The perpendicular distance r is called the **lever arm** or **moment arm.** The unit of torque can be seen to be the meter-newton (m-N). Notice that these units are the same as those of work, newton-meter (N-m) = joule (J). The unit of torque is usually written meter-newton (m-N) to emphasize the distinction.

Torque is a vector quantity that points along the axis of rotation that is perpendicular to the plane of the **r** and **F** vectors. By convention, if the torque tends to rotate the body in a counterclockwise direction (as viewed from above), then the torque is positive and the torque vector points toward you along the axis of rotation. If the torque tends to rotate the body in a clockwise direction, then the torque is negative and the vector points away from you.

For example, in ● Fig. 2, taking the axis of rotation at the 50-cm position, F_1 and F_2 produce counterclockwise torques and F_3 and F_4 produce clockwise torques, but no

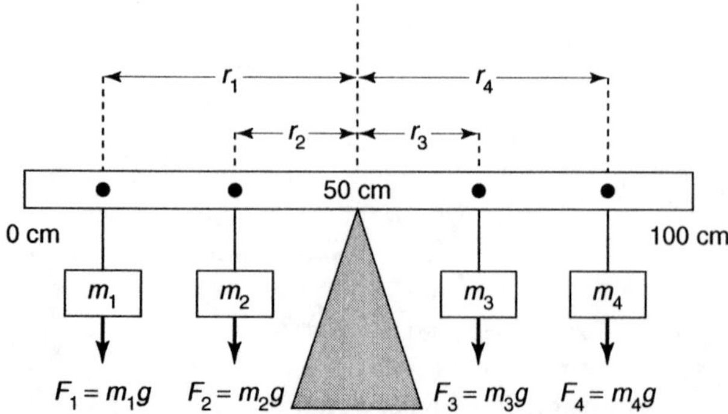

Figure 2 **Torques in different directions.** The forces F_1 and F_2 give rise to counterclockwise torques, and F_3 and F_4 give rise to clockwise torques, as applied to the meterstick.

rotation takes place if the torques are balanced and the system is in rotational static equilibrium.

It is convenient to sum the torques using magnitudes and directional signs, as determined by the counterclockwise (cc) and clockwise (cw) convention. In this case, the condition for rotational equilibrium (Eq. 1b) becomes

$$\Sigma\tau_{cw} - \Sigma\tau_{cc} = 0$$

or

$$\Sigma\tau_{cc} = \Sigma\tau_{cw} \tag{3}$$

(sum of counterclockwise torques = sum of clockwise torques.)

Hence, we may simply equate the magnitudes of the cc and cw torques. For example, for the meterstick in Fig. 2, we have

$$\underset{\text{Counterclockwise}}{\tau_1 + \tau_2} = \underset{\text{Clockwise}}{\tau_3 + \tau_4}$$

or

$$F_1r_1 + F_2r_2 = F_3r_3 + F_4r_4$$

The forces are due to weights suspended from the rod, and with $F = mg$,

$$m_1gr_1 + m_2gr_2 = m_3gr_3 + m_4gr_4 \tag{4}$$

and, canceling g,

$$m_1r_1 + m_2r_2 = m_3r_3 + m_4r_4$$

Example 1 Let $m_1 = m_3 = 50$ g, $m_2 = m_4 = 100$ g in Fig. 2, where m_1, m_2, and m_3 are at the 10-, 40-, and 60-cm marks or positions, respectively, on the meterstick*. Where would m_4 have to be suspended for the stick to be in static equilibrium?

Solution In static equilibrium, the sum of the torques is zero, or the sum of the counterclockwise torques is equal to the sum of the clockwise torques (Eq. 3),

$$\Sigma\tau_{cc} = \Sigma\tau_{cw}$$

In terms of forces and lever arms, we have (writing the forces first)

$$F_1r_1 + F_2r_2 = F_3r_3 + F_4r_4$$

where the forces are $F_i = m_ig$. The lever arms are measured from the 50-cm position of the meterstick, which is the pivot point, or the location of the axis of rotation. In gen-

* The official abbreviation for gram is g, and the commonly used symbol for acceleration due to gravity is g. The gravity g is written in italics, and the gram g is not. Look closely to avoid confusion.

eral, $r_i = (50 \text{ cm} - x_i)$, where x_i is the centimeter location of a mass. Hence,

$$m_1g(50 \text{ cm} - 10 \text{ cm}) + m_2g(50 \text{ cm} - 40 \text{ cm}) = m_3g(60 \text{ cm} - 50 \text{ cm}) + m_4gr_4$$

and, canceling the gs,

$$m_1(40 \text{ cm}) + m_2(10 \text{ cm}) = m_3(10 \text{ cm}) + m_4r_4$$

Then, putting in the mass values,

$$(50 \text{ g})(40 \text{ cm}) + (100 \text{ g})(10 \text{ cm}) = (50 \text{ g})(10 \text{ cm}) + (100 \text{ g})r_4$$

and solving for r_4,

$$r_4 = \frac{2500 \text{ g-cm}}{100 \text{ g}} = 25 \text{ cm}$$

Hence, for rotational equilibrium m_4 is 25 cm from the support position (axis of rotation), or at the 75-cm position on the meterstick (measured from the zero end).

Here it is assumed that the meterstick is uniform (uniform mass distribution) so that the torques caused by the masses of the portions of the meterstick are the same on both sides of the support and therefore cancel.

B. *Center of Gravity and Center of Mass*

The gravitational torques due to "individual" mass particles of a rigid body define what is known as the body's center of gravity. The **center of gravity** is the "balance" point, the point of the body about which the sum of the gravitational torques about an axis through this point is zero. For example, consider the meterstick shown in ● Fig. 3. If the uniform meterstick is visualized as being made up of individual mass particles and the point of support is selected such that $\Sigma\tau = 0$, then

$$\Sigma\tau_{cc} = \Sigma\tau_{cw}$$

or

$$\sum_{cc}(m_ig)r_i = \sum_{cw}(m_ig)r_i$$

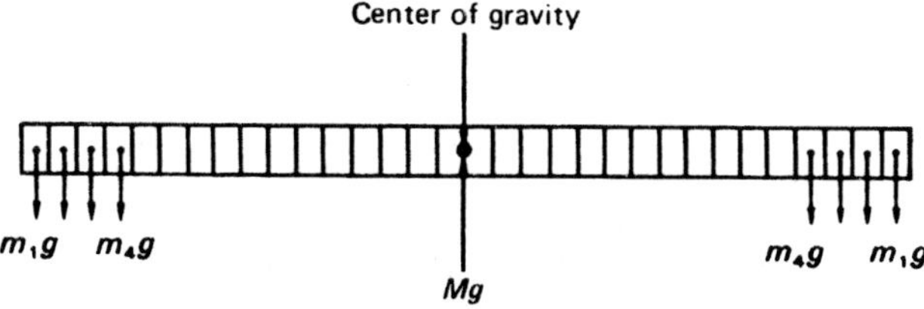

Figure 3 Center of gravity. A rod may be considered to be made up of individual masses in rotational equilibrium when the vertical support is directly through the center of gravity.

and

$$(m_1r_1 + m_2r_2 + m_3r_3 + \cdots)_{cc} = (m_1r_1 + m_2r_2 + m_3r_3 + \cdots)_{cw}$$

where g cancels. When the meterstick is in equilibrium, it is supported by a force equal to its weight, and the support force is directed through the center of gravity. Hence, it is as though all of the object's weight (Mg) is concentrated at the center of gravity. That is, if you were blindfolded and supported an object at its center of gravity on your finger, weightwise you would not be able to tell, from its weight alone, whether it was a rod or a block or an irregularly shaped object of equal mass. For a uniform meterstick, the center of gravity would be at the 50-cm position. (Why?)

If an object's weight is concentrated at its center of gravity, so should its mass be concentrated there, and we often refer to an object's **center of mass** instead of its center of gravity. *These points are the same as long as the acceleration due to gravity g is constant* (uniform gravitational field). Notice how g can be factored and divided out of the previous *weight* equations, leaving *mass* equations.

Also, it should be evident that for a symmetric object with a uniform mass distribution, the center of gravity and center of mass are located at the center of symmetry. For example, if a rod has a uniform mass distribution, its center of gravity is located at the center of the rod's length. For a uniform sphere, the centers are at the center of the sphere.

Linear Mass Density

In part of the experiment, the masses of certain lengths of the meterstick will need to be known. These may be obtained from the **linear mass density** μ of the stick—that is, the mass per unit length

$$\boxed{\mu = \frac{m}{L}} \qquad \textbf{(5)}$$

with units of grams/centimeter or kilograms/meter. For example, suppose a meterstick is measured to have a mass of 50 g on a balance. Then, since the stick is 100 cm long (L = 100 cm), the linear mass density of the stick is $\mu = m/L$ = 50 g/100 cm = 0.50 g/cm. If the mass distribution of the stick were uniform, then every centimeter would have a mass of 0.50 g. However, metersticks are not uniform, so this is an average value.

Example 2 If a meterstick has a linear mass density of 0.50 g/cm, what is the mass of a 16-cm length of the stick?

Solution Since $\mu = m/L$, we have $m = \mu L$, and for μ = 0.50 g/cm and L = 16 cm,

$$m = \mu L = (0.50 \text{ g/cm})(16 \text{ cm}) = 8.0 \text{ g}$$

Experimental Procedure

A. *Apparatus with Support Point at Center of Gravity*

1. A general experimental setup is illustrated in ● Fig. 4, where the masses or weights are suspended by clamp weight hangers. The hooked masses may also be suspended from small loops of string, which can be slid easily along the meterstick. The string allows the position of a mass to be read easily and may be held in place by a small piece of masking tape.
   (a) Determine the mass of the meterstick (without any clamps) and record it in the Laboratory Report.
   (b) Weights may be suspended by loops of string or clamps with weight hangers. The string method is simpler; however, if you choose or are instructed to use weight hangers, weigh the three clamps together on a laboratory balance and compute the average mass of a clamp. Record it in the Laboratory Report.

2. With a knife-edge clamp on the meterstick near its center, place the meterstick (without any suspended weights) on the support stand. Make certain that the knife edges are on the support stand. (The tightening screw head on the clamp will be down.)

   Adjust the meterstick through the clamp until the stick is balanced on the stand. Tighten the clamp screw, and record in Data Table 1 the meterstick reading or the distance of the balancing point x_o from the zero end of the meterstick.

3. *Case 1: Two known masses.*
   (a) With the meterstick on the support stand at x_o, suspend a mass $m_1 = 100$ g at the 15-cm position on the meterstick—that is, 15 cm from the zero end of the meterstick.
   (b) Set up the conditions for static equilibrium by adjusting the moment arm of a mass $m_2 = 200$ g suspended on the side of the meterstick opposite m_1. Record the masses and moment arms in Data Table 1. If clamps are used instead of string, do not forget to add the masses of the clamps. Remember the moment arms are the distances from the pivot point to the masses (i.e., $r_i = |x_i - x_o|$).
   (c) Compute the torques and find the percent difference in the computed values (i.e., compare the clockwise torque with the counterclockwise torque).

4. *Case 2: Three known masses.*
   Case (a)
   (i) With the meterstick on the support stand at x_o, suspend $m_1 = 100$ g at the 30-cm position and $m_2 = 200$ g at the 70-cm position. Suspend $m_3 = 50$ g and adjust the moment arm of this mass so that the meterstick is in static equilibrium. Record the data in Data Table 1.
   (ii) Compute the torques and compare as in procedure 3.
   Case (b)
   (i) Calculate theoretically the lever arm (r_3) for the mass $m_3 = 50$ g for the system to be in equilibrium if $m_1 = 100$ g is at the 20-cm position and $m_2 = 200$ g is at the 60-cm position. (Remember to add the masses of the hanger clamps if used.) Record this value in the data table.
   (ii) Check your results experimentally, and compute the percent error of the experimental value of r_3, taking the previously calculated value as the accepted value.

5. *Case 3: Unknown mass—The balance principle.* A balance (scale) essentially uses the method of moments to compare an unknown mass with a known mass. Some balances have constant and equal lever arms, and others do not (see Experiment 2, Fig. 2.1). This procedure will illustrate the balance principle.
   (a) With the meterstick on the support stand at x_o, suspend the unknown mass (m_1) near one end of the meterstick (for example, at the 10-cm position).

Figure 4 **Torque apparatus.** Example of experimental setup and equilibrium conditions. (Courtesy of Sargent-Welch.)

Suspend from the other side of the meterstick an appropriate known countermass m_2 (for example, 200 g) and adjust its position until the meterstick is "in balance" or equilibrium. Record the value of the known mass and the moment arms in Data Table 1.

(b) Remove the unknown mass and determine its mass on a laboratory balance.

(c) Compute the value of the unknown mass by the method of moments and compare it with the measured value by calculating the percent error.

6. *Case 4: Instructor's choice (optional).* Your instructor may have a particular case he or she would like you to investigate. If so, the conditions will be given. Space has been provided in the data table for reporting your findings.

B. Apparatus Supported at Different Pivot Points

In the previous cases, the mass of the meterstick was not explicitly taken into account since the fulcrum or the position of the support was at the meterstick's center of gravity or center of mass. In effect, the torques due to the mass of the meterstick on either side of the support position canceled each other. The centers of gravity of the lengths of the stick on either side of the support are equidistant from the support (for example, at the 25-cm and 75-cm positions for a uniform stick) and have equal masses and moment arms.

For the following cases, the meterstick will not be supported at its center-of-gravity position (x_o) but at some other pivot points (designated in general by x'_o; for example, see ● Fig. 5). In these cases, the mass of the meterstick needs to be taken into account. To illustrate this very vividly, let's start off with a case with only one suspended mass.

7. *Case 5: Meterstick with one mass.* Suspend a mass $m_1 = 100$ g at or near the zero end of the meterstick (Fig. 5). Record the mass position x_1 in Data Table 2. If a string loop is used, a piece of tape to hold the string in position helps. Move the meterstick in the support clamp until the system is in equilibrium. (This case is analogous to the solitary seesaw—sitting on one side of a balanced seesaw with no one on the other side.) Record the support position x'_o in Data Table 2.

Since the meterstick is in balance (static equilibrium), the point of support must be at the center of gravity of the system; that is, the torques (clockwise and counterclockwise) on either side of the meterstick must be equal. But where is the mass or force on the side of the meterstick opposite the suspended mass? The balancing torque must be due to the mass of length L_2 of the meterstick (Fig. 5). To investigate this:

(a) Using the total mass m of the meterstick (measured previously) as m_2, with a moment arm r_2 (see the diagram in Data Table 2), compute the counterclockwise and clockwise torques, and compare them by computing the percent difference. Record it in Data Table 2.

(b) Now the masses of the lengths of meterstick will be taken into account. Compute the average linear mass density of the meterstick (see Theory, Section B) and record it in the data table.

If we assume that the mass of the meterstick is uniformly distributed, the center of mass (or center of gravity) of the length of meterstick L_2 on the *opposite* side of the support from m_1 is at its center position (see Fig. 5). Compute the mass m_2 of this length of stick (see Example 2) and record. Also, record the center position of L_2, where this mass is considered concentrated (x_2), and find the length of the lever arm r_2. It should be evident that $r_2 = L_2/2$.

Compute the torque due to m_2 and record it as τ_{cw}. From the linear mass density compute the m_3 of the portion of the meterstick remaining to the left of the pivot. Calculate the torque due to this portion of the meterstick, add it to the torque due to mass m_1 to find the total counterclockwise torque, and record it as τ_{cc}. Compare the torque *differences* with those found in Case 5(a).

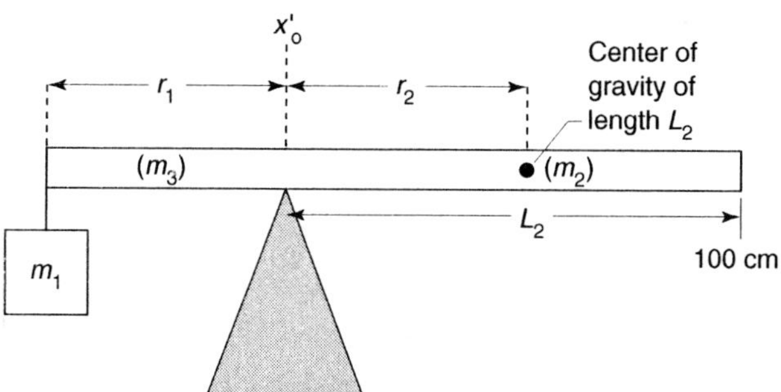

Figure 5 Equilibrium. A meterstick in equilibrium with one suspended mass. See text for description.

8. *Case 6: Center of gravity.*

(a) With a mass $m_1 = 100$ g positioned at or near one end of the meterstick as in Case 5, suspend a mass $m_2 = 100$ g on the opposite side of the support stand at the 60-cm position. Adjust the meterstick in the support-stand clamp until the stick is in balance. This locates the center of gravity x'_o of the system. Record in Data Table 2 and find r_1 and r_2.

(b) Repeat the procedure with m_2 positioned at 70 cm.

(c) Repeat the procedure with m_2 positioned at 80 cm. Notice how the position of the center of gravity moves as the mass distribution is varied.

(d) Based on the experimental data, what would you predict the position of the center of gravity x'_0 of the system would be if m_2 were moved to the 90-cm position? Record your prediction in the data table.

Using your prediction, compute the counterclockwise and clockwise torques, taking into account the mass of the meterstick as in procedure 7(c). Compare the torques by computing the percent difference.

Experimentally determine the position of the center of gravity of the system, and compute the percent difference between the experimental and predicted values.

Name ______________________ Section ______________ Date ______________

Lab Partner(s) ____

EXPERIMENT 10

Torques, Equilibrium, and Center of Gravity

TI Laboratory Report

A. Apparatus with Point of Support at Center of Gravity

Mass of meterstick ______________

Total mass of clamps ______________

Average mass of one clamp m_c ______________

Balancing position (center of gravity) of meterstick x_o ______________

DATA TABLE 1

Diagram*	Values (add m_c to masses if clamps used)	Moment (lever) arms	Results†
Case 1 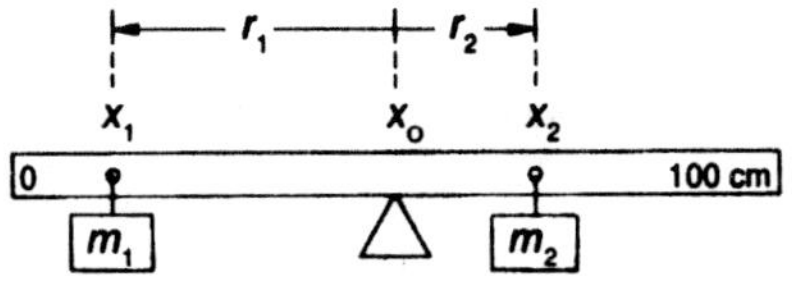 	m_1 ________ $x_1 = 15$ cm m_2 ________ x_2 ________	r_1 ________ r_2 ________	τ_{cc} ________ τ_{cw} ________ Percent diff. ________
Case 2(a)	m_1 ________ $x_1 = 30$ cm m_2 ________ $x_2 = 70$ cm m_3 ________ x_3 ________	r_1 ________ r_2 ________ r_3 ________	τ_{cc} ________ τ_{cw} ________ Percent diff. ________
Case 2(b)	m_1 ________ $x_1 = 20$ cm m_2 ________ $x_2 = 60$ cm m_3 ________ x_3 ________	r_1 ________ r_2 ________	r_3 ________ (calculated) r_3 ________ (measured) Percent error ________

* Draw a diagram to illustrate each case, using the Case 1 diagram as an example.

† Attach a sheet to the Laboratory Report showing calculations for each use.

Don't forget units

(continued)

Diagram*	Values (add m_c to masses if clamps are used)	Moment (lever) arms	Results†
Case 3	x_1 ______ (known) m_2 ______ (known) x_2 ______ (from expt.)	r_1 ______ r_2 ______	m_1 ______ (measured) m_1 ______ (calculated) Percent error ______
Case 4 (instructor's option)			

* Draw a diagram to illustrate each case, using the Case 1 diagram as an example.
† Attach a sheet to the Laboratory Report showing calculations for each use.

B. Apparatus Supported at Different Pivot Points

DATA TABLE 2 Linear mass density of meterstick, $\mu = m/L$ ______

Diagram*	Values (add m_c if applicable)	Moment (lever) arms	Results†
Case 5(a) r_1 r_2 x_1 x'_o x_2 0 100 cm m_1 (m_2)	m_1 ______ x_1 ______ m_2 ______ x_2 ______ x'_o ______	r_1 ______ r_2 ______	τ_{cc} ______ τ_{cw} ______ Torque differences (show below table)
Case 5(b)	m_1 ______ x_1 ______ m_2 ______ x_2 ______ m_3 ______ x_3 ______ x'_o ______	r_1 ______ r_2 ______ r_3 ______	τ_{cc} ______ τ_{cw} ______ Torque differences (show below table)

* Draw a diagram to illustrate each case, using the Case 5(a) diagram as an example. Put the mass of a length of stick in parentheses as in that diagram.
† Attach a sheet to the Laboratory Report showing calculations for each use.

Name ______________________ Section ______________ Date ______________

Lab Partner(s) ____

EXPERIMENT 10 *Laboratory Report*

Diagram*	Values (add m_c if applicable)	Moment (lever) arms	Results†
Case 6(a)	m_1 ________ $x_1 = 0$ cm m_2 ________ $x_2 = 60$ cm x'_o ________	r_1 ________ r_2 ________	
Case 6(b)	same except $x_2 = 70$ cm x'_o ________	r_1 ________ r_2 ________	
Case 6(c)	same except $x_2 = 80$ cm x'_o ________	r_1 ________ r_2 ________	
Case 6(d)	same except $x_2 = 90$ cm x'_o ________ (predicted)	τ_{cc} ________ τ_{cw} ________ Percent diff. ________	x'_o ________ (measured) Percent diff. ________

* Draw a diagram to illustrate each case, using the Case 5(a) diagram as an example. Put the mass of a length of stick in parentheses as in that diagram.
† Attach a sheet to the Laboratory Report showing calculations for each use.

TI QUESTIONS (Answer those that are applicable.)

1. Explain how the condition $\Sigma \mathbf{F} = 0$ is satisfied for the meterstick in part A of the experiment.

(continued)

2. Why are clockwise and counterclockwise referred to as "senses," rather than directions?

3. Suppose in a situation like Case 2(a) in the experiment, $m_1 = 200$ g were at the 20-cm position and $m_2 = 100$ g at the 65-cm position. Would there be a problem in experimentally balancing the system with $m_3 = 50$ g? Explain. If so, how might the problem be resolved?

4. Describe the effects of taking the mass of the meterstick into account when the balancing position is not near the 50-cm position.

5. *(Optional)* A uniform meterstick is in static rotational equilibrium when a mass of 220 g is suspended from the 5.0-cm mark, a mass of 120 g is suspended from the 90-cm mark, and the support stand is placed at the 40-cm mark. What is the mass of the meterstick?

Name ______________________ Section ______________ Date ______________

Lab Partner(s) ____

EXPERIMENT 11

Specific Heats of Metals

TI Advance Study Assignment

Read the experiment and answer the following questions.

1. Distinguish between heat capacity and specific heat.

2. Why is the specific heat of water equal to unity, i.e., 1.0 cal/g-C° or 1.0 kcal/kg-C°?

3. Given that the specific heat of one material is twice that of another, compare the relative amounts of heat required to raise the temperature of equal masses of each material by 1C°.

4. Say the same amount of heat was added to samples of the materials in Question 3, and each sample had the same increase in temperature. Compare the relative masses of the samples.

(continued)

5. What is the method of mixtures, and how is it used to determine specific heat?

6. On what does the accuracy of the method of mixtures depend? That is, what are possible sources of error?

Specific Heats of Metals

Introduction and Objectives

Different substances require different amounts of heat to produce a given temperature change. For example, about three and one-half times as much heat is needed to raise the temperature of 1 kg of iron through a given temperature interval ΔT as is needed to raise the temperature of 1 kg of lead by the same amount.

This material behavior is characterized quantitatively by **specific heat,** which is the amount of heat necessary to raise the temperature of a unit mass of a substance by one unit temperature interval, e.g., to raise 1 gram or 1 kilogram of a substance 1 Celsius degree. Thus, in the previous example, iron has a greater specific heat than that of lead.

The specific heat of a material is *specific,* or characteristic, for that material. As can be seen from the definition, the specific heat of a given material can be determined by adding a known amount of heat to a known mass of material and noting the corresponding temperature change. It is the purpose of this experiment to determine the specific heats of some common metals by calorimetry methods.

After performing this experiment and analyzing the data, you should be able to:

1. Tell what is meant by the specific heat of a substance, and compare the effects of different specific heats.
2. Calculate the heat necessary to raise the temperature of a given mass of a substance a particular number of degrees.
3. Describe and explain calorimetry and the method of mixtures.

Equipment Needed

- Calorimeter
- Boiler and stand
- Hot plate or Bunsen burner and striker
- Two thermometers (0 to 110°C)
- Two kinds of metal (shot form or slugs with attached strings)
- Laboratory balance
- Ice
- Safety glasses
- Strainer

Theory

The change in temperature ΔT of a substance is proportional to the amount of heat ΔQ added (or removed) from it:

$$\Delta Q \propto \Delta T$$

In equation form, we may write

$$\Delta Q = C\,\Delta T \qquad (1)$$

where the constant of proportionality C is called the **heat capacity** of the substance.

However, the amount of heat required to change the temperature of an object is also proportional to the mass of the object. Hence, it is convenient to define a *specific heat capacity* (or simply **specific heat**) c:

$$c = \frac{C}{m} \qquad (2)$$

which is the heat capacity per unit mass of a substance. Thus, Eq. 1 becomes $\Delta Q = mc\,\Delta T$, or

$$\boxed{c = \frac{\Delta Q}{m\Delta T}} \qquad (3)$$

(specific heat)

The specific heat is then the amount of heat required to change the temperature of 1 g of a substance 1 C°.*

The calorie (cal) unit of heat is defined as the amount of heat required to raise the temperature of 1 g of water

* It is convenient to write the unit of a ΔT as C° (Celsius degree) so as to distinguish it from a particular temperature T (°C, degrees Celsius).

1C°. By definition, then, water has a specific heat of 1 cal/g-C°.

$$c = \frac{\Delta Q}{m\Delta T} = \frac{1 \text{ cal}}{(1\text{g})(1°\text{C})} = 1 \text{ cal/g-C°}$$

[A kilocalorie (kcal) is the unit of heat defined as the amount of heat required to raise the temperature of 1 kg of water by 1C°. In these units, water has a specific heat of 1 kcal/kg-C°, or, in SI units, 4.18×10^3 J/kg-C°. Your instructor may recommend that you use one of these units.]

The specific heat of a material can be determined experimentally by measuring the temperature change of a given mass of material produced by a quantity of heat. This is done indirectly by a calorimetry procedure known as the **method of mixtures.** If several substances at various temperatures are brought together, the hotter substances lose heat and the colder substances gain heat until all the substances reach a common equilibrium temperature. If the system is insulated so that no heat is lost to or gained from the surroundings, then, by the conservation of energy, the heat lost is equal to the heat gained.

In this experiment, hot metal is added to water in a calorimeter cup, and the mixture is stirred until the system is in thermal equilibrium. The calorimeter insulates the system from losing heat (● Fig. 1). Heat is lost by the metal and is gained by the water and cup and stirrer. In equation form, we may write

$$\text{heat lost} = \text{heat gained}$$

or

$$\Delta Q_{\text{metal}} = \Delta Q_{\text{water}} + \Delta Q_{\text{cup and stirrer}}$$

and

$$\begin{aligned} m_{\text{m}}c_{\text{m}}(T_{\text{m}} - T_{\text{f}}) &= m_{\text{w}}c_{\text{w}}(T_{\text{f}} - T_{\text{w}}) + m_{\text{cs}}c_{\text{cs}}(T_{\text{f}} - T_{\text{w}}) \\ &= (m_{\text{w}}c_{\text{w}} + m_{\text{cs}}c_{\text{cs}})(T_{\text{f}} - T_{\text{w}}) \end{aligned} \quad \textbf{(4)}$$

where T_{f} is the final intermediate equilibrium temperature of the system. The other subscripts indicate the masses, specific heats, and initial temperatures of the respective components. Hence, Eq. 4 may be used to determine the specific heat c_{m} of the metal if all the other quantities are known.

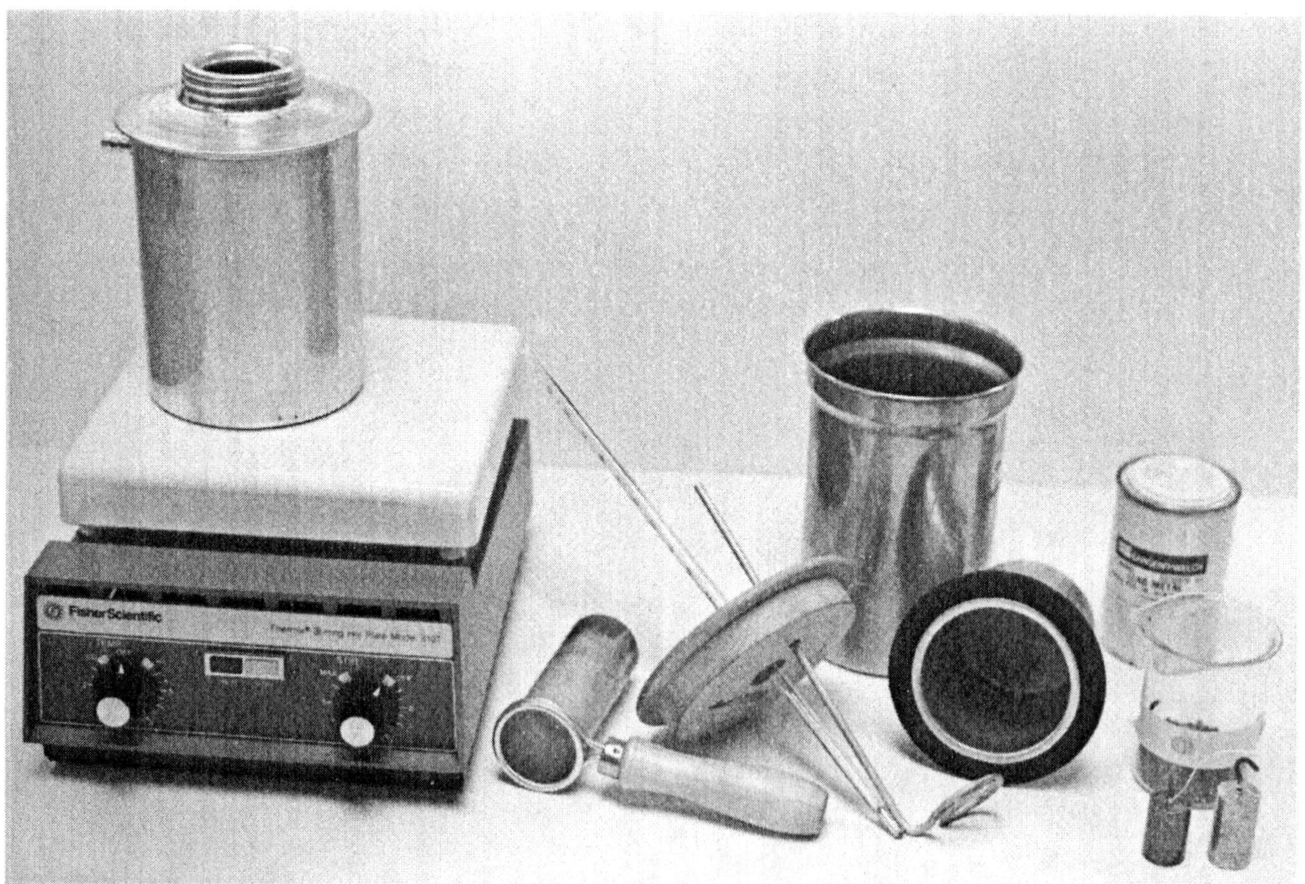

Figure 1 Apparatus for measurement of specific heats. Metal shot or a piece of metal (right) is heated with boiling water in the container on the hot plate. The metal is then placed in a known amount of water in the calorimeter, which insulates the system from losing heat. The inner calorimeter cup is shown with its dark, insulating ring laying in front of the outer cup. A thermometer and stirrer extend through the calorimeter cover.

Experimental Procedure

1. Weigh out 400 to 500 g (0.4 to 0.5 kg) of one kind of dry metal shot. [Do this by first determining the mass of the empty boiler cup (in which the metal shot is heated) and then adding an appropriate amount of metal shot to the cup and reweighing.]

   Record the mass of the metal m_m and the room temperature T_r in the data table. Your instructor may prefer to use a solid piece of metal with a string attached instead of metal shot. In this case it is necessary to weigh only the piece of metal.

2. Insert a thermometer well into the metal shot (or into the cup with a piece of metal, if used), place the cup and shot into the boiler, and start heating the boiler water.

   Caution: *If a mercury thermometer is used, special care must be taken. If the thermometer should break and mercury spill into the hot metal, immediately notify your instructor. The cup should be removed from the room (to an exhaust hood or outdoors). Mercury fumes are* ***highly*** *toxic.*

   The boiler should be about half full of water. Keep steam or water from dampening the dry metal by shielding the cup with a cardboard lid (with a hole for the thermometer).

3. While the boiler is heating, determine and record the mass of the inner calorimeter cup and the stirrer (without the ring). Record the total mass m_{cs}. Also, note and record the type of metal and specific heat of the cup and stirrer, which is usually stamped on the cup.* (The specific heat may be found in Appendix A, Table A4, if it is not stamped on the cup.)

4. Fill the calorimeter cup about one-half to two-thirds full of cold tap water, and weigh the cup, stirrer, and water to determine the mass of the water m_w.

   (If a solid piece of metal is used, which usually has less mass than the recommended amount of shot, less water should be used so as to obtain an appreciable ΔT temperature change. This may also be the case at high elevations, where the temperature of boiling water is substantially less than 100°C).

   Place the calorimeter cup with the water and stirrer in the calorimeter jacket, and put on the lid, with a thermometer extending into the water.

5. After the water in the boiler boils and the thermometer in the metal has stabilized (allow several minutes), read and record the temperature of the metal T_m.

   Start with the water and stirrer in the cup at a temperature T_w several degrees below room temperature T_r. Adjust the temperature of the inner calorimeter cup and its contents by placing it in a beaker of ice water. Measure and record the temperature T_w.

6. Remove the thermometer from the metal. Then remove the lid from the calorimeter and quickly, but carefully, lift the cup with the hot metal from the boiler and pour the metal shot into the calorimeter cup with as little splashing as possible so as not to splash out and lose any water. (If a solid piece of metal is used, carefully lower the metal piece into the calorimeter cup by means of the attached string.)

   Replace the lid with the thermometer, and stir the mixture gently. The thermometer should not touch the metal. While stirring, watch the thermometer and record the temperature when a maximum equilibrium temperature is reached (T_f).

   For best results, the final temperature T_f should be above room temperature T_r by about as many degrees as T_w was below it. If this is not approximately the case, repeat procedures 4 through 6, adjusting T_w until the relationship $T_f - T_r \approx T_r - T_w$ is satisfied.

7. Repeat procedures 1 through 6 for another kind of metal sample. Make certain that you use fresh water in the calorimeter cup. (Dump the previous metal shot and water into a strainer in a sink so that it may be dried and used by others doing the experiment later.)

8. Compute the specific heat of each metal, using Eq. 4. Look up the accepted values in Appendix A, Table A4, and compute the percent errors.

* If the cup and stirrer are not of the same material, they must be treated separately, and the last term in Eq. 4 becomes $(m_w c_w + m_c c_c + m_s c_s)(T_f - T_w)$.

Name ______________________ Section ______________ Date ______________

Lab Partner(s) ____

EXPERIMENT 11

Specific Heats of Metals

TI Laboratory Report

DATA TABLE

Purpose: To determine the specific heats of metal samples.

Room temperature T_r ______________

Type of metal	Mass of metal m_m ( )	Mass of calorimeter and stirrer m_{cs} ( )	Specific heat of calorimeter and stirrer c_{cs} ( )	Mass of water m_w ( )	T_m ( )	T_w ( )	T_f ( )

Calculations (show work)

Type of metal	c_m (experimental)	c_m (accepted)	Percent error

Don't forget units

(continued)

TI QUESTIONS

1. (a) The percent errors of your experimental values of the specific heats may be quite large. Identify several sources of experimental error.

   (b) Why does it improve the accuracy of the experiment if $T_f - T_r \approx T_r - T_w$?

2. The specific heat of aluminum is 0.22 cal/g-C°. What is the value of the specific heat in (a) kcal/kg-C°, (b) J/kg-C°? (Show your calculations.)

3. (a) If wet shot had been poured into the calorimeter cup, how would the experimental value of the specific heat have been affected?

(b) If some water had splashed out as you were pouring dry shot into the cup, how would the experimental value of the specific heat have been affected?

4. In solar heating applications, heat energy is stored in some medium until it is needed (e.g., to heat a home at night). Should this medium have a high or a low specific heat? Suggest a substance that would be appropriate for use as a heat-storage medium, and explain its advantages.

5. Explain why specific heat is *specific* and how it gives a relative indication of molecular configuration and bonding.

Name ______________________ Section ____________ Date ____________

Lab Partner(s) ____

EXPERIMENT 12

TI Latent Heats: Heats of Fusion and Vaporization of Water

CI Latent Heat of Fusion of Water

TI *Advance Study Assignment*

Read the experiment and answer the following questions.

1. What is latent heat?

2. The heat of vaporization of water is almost seven times its heat of fusion. What does this imply?

3. Why is the water used in the experimental procedures for the heat of fusion and heat of vaporization initially heated above room temperature and cooled below room temperature?

(continued)

4. Why are the pieces of ice in the heat-of-fusion procedure dried and handled with a paper towel? Explain the effect on the experimental result if this were not done.

5. What is the purpose of the water trap in the steam line in the heat-of-vaporization procedure? Explain the effect on the experimental result if it were not used.

6. Explain how latent heat is computed from the experimental data.

CI Advance Study Assignment

Read the experiment and answer the following questions.

1. What is the definition of the latent heat of fusion of water?

2. Describe the mixture that will be made in this experiment by listing all the ingredients.

Name ______________________ Section ______________ Date ______________

Lab Partner(s) ____

3. What ingredients of the mixture will lose heat?

4. What ingredients of the mixture will gain heat?

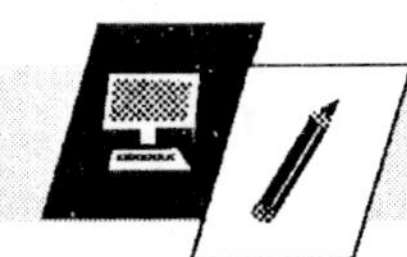

TI Latent Heats: Heats of Fusion and Vaporization of Water

CI Latent Heat of Fusion of Water

OVERVIEW

Experiment examines the latent heats of water. The TI procedure considers both the latent heat of fusion and the latent heat of vaporization. The CI procedure considers only the latent heat of fusion. Calorimeter methods are used in both procedures, and the temperature in the CI procedure is measured by a temperature sensor.

(An addendum at the end of this experiment gives a TI procedure for the calibration of a thermometer. It is a short but interesting procedure that enhances an understanding of calibration.)

INTRODUCTION AND OBJECTIVES

When heat is added to a substance, its temperature normally rises. However, when a substance undergoes a change of phase (for example, solid to liquid or liquid to gas), the heat energy goes into doing work against the intermolecular forces and is not reflected in a change in the temperature of the substance. This heat energy is called the **heat of fusion** and the **heat of vaporization** for the phase changes that occur at the melting- (or freezing-) point temperature and boiling- (or condensation-) point temperature, respectively.

The energy involved in a phase change is commonly referred to as **latent heat,** because the heat energy is seemingly hidden or concealed in that it is not evidenced by a temperature change. For the inverse processes, when a vapor or gas condenses or a liquid freezes, by the conservation of energy the (latent) heat of vaporization is given up or the (latent) heat of fusion must be extracted.

In this experiment, the heats of fusion and vaporization of water will be determined through the calorimetry method of mixtures.

TI OBJECTIVES

After performing this experiment and analyzing the data, you should be able to:

1. Clearly distinguish between latent heat and specific heat. (Consult your text book if necessary.)
2. Explain the role of latent heat in a phase change.
3. Describe how latent heat can be determined experimentally.

CI OBJECTIVES

After performing this experiment and analyzing the data, you should be able to:

1. Understand and use calorimetery methods.
2. Experimentally determine the latent heat of fusion of water.

TI EXPERIMENT 12

TI EQUIPMENT NEEDED

- Calorimeter
- Steam generator and stand
- Hot plate or Bunsen burner and striker
- Thermometer (0 to 110°C)
- Rubber hose
- Water trap
- Ice
- Paper towels
- Laboratory balance
- Beaker
- Safety glasses

TI THEORY

A general graph of temperature versus heat energy for a given mass m of water is shown in ● TI Fig. 1. The sloping phase lines follow the relationship

$$\Delta Q = mc\,\Delta T \qquad \textbf{(TI 1)}$$

The slopes of the lines are mc, where c is the specific heat of the particular phase:

$c_{water} = 1.0$ kcal/kg-C°, or 1.0 cal/g-C°

$c_{ice} \approx c_{steam} = 0.5$ kcal/kg-C°, or 0.5 cal/g-C°.

Actually,

$$c_{ice} = 0.50 \text{ kcal/kg-C°}$$

$$c_{steam} = 0.48 \text{ kcal/kg-C°}.$$

At the freezing and boiling points, the addition of certain amounts of heat has no effect on the temperature, as indicated by the vertical lines. At these points, the heat energy goes into the work of effecting the phase changes and not into increasing the molecular activity, which would be reflected as a temperature increase.

The **latent heat** L is defined as the amount of heat required to change the phase of a unit mass of a substance (without a change of temperature) and has the common units of kcal/kg (or cal/g) and J/kg in the SI system. Hence the amount of heat absorbed or given up by a quantity of a substance when it undergoes a change of phase is

$$\Delta Q = mL_i \qquad \textbf{(TI 2)}$$

where m is the mass of the substance and L_i is the latent heat for the particular phase change.

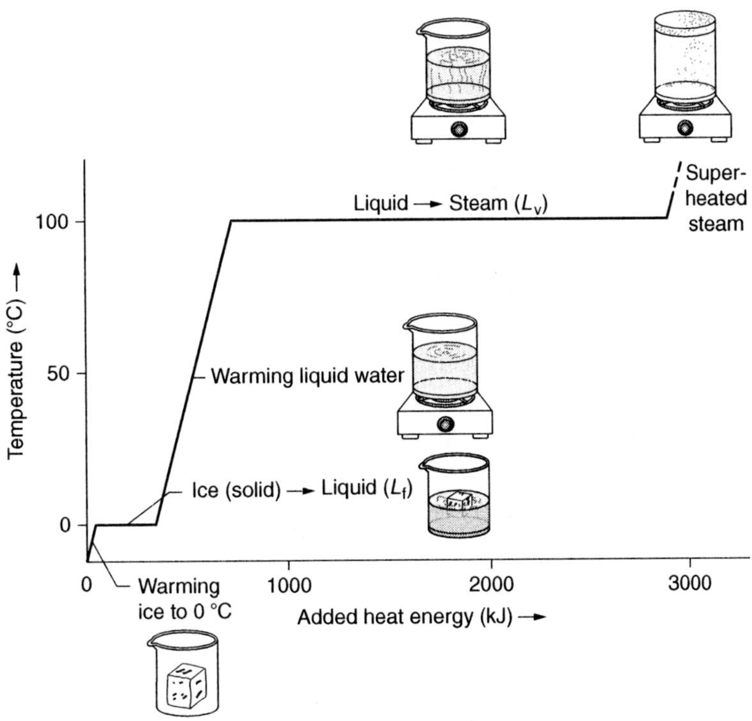

TI Figure 1 Graph of temperature versus heat for water. As heat is added to the various phases of water, the temperature increases. However, during a phase change (horizontal lines), the temperature remains constant.

The latent heats are, of course, characteristic of the substance. For example, the **(latent) heat of fusion** L_f of water is 80 kcal/kg (or 80 cal/g) or 3.33×10^5 J/kg, and its **(latent) heat of vaporization** L_v is 540 kcal/kg (or 540 cal/g) or 2.26×10^6 J/kg. This means that 80 kcal is required to melt 1 kg of ice at 0°C (or 80 kcal must be removed from 1 kg of water at 0°C to freeze it). Also, 540 kcal is required to convert 1 kg of water at 100°C to steam (or 540 kcal is released when 1 kg of steam at 100°C condenses to water). Other substances have different latent heats.

In this experiment, the heats of fusion and vaporization of water will be measured by a calorimetry procedure called the methods of mixtures (see Experiment 15). If several substances at various temperatures are brought together, the hotter substances lose heat and the colder substances gain heat until all the substances reach a common equilibrium temperature.

This is generally true even if one or more of the substances undergoes a phase change in the process. If the system is insulated and no heat is lost to the surroundings, then by the conservation of energy, the heat lost by the hot substances will equal the heat gained by the colder substances.

A. *Heat of Fusion*

If a quantity of ice of mass m_i at 0°C is added to a sufficient quantity of warm water in a calorimeter cup with a stirrer at an initial temperature T_h, the ice melts and the system comes to equilibrium at some intermediate or final temperature T_f. (The calorimeter insulates the system against heat loss. See TI Fig. 15.1.) Then, by the conservation of energy,

$$\text{Heat of fusion to melt the ice} + \text{heat gained by the ice water} = \text{heat lost by the warm water} + \text{heat lost by the calorimeter cup and stirrer}$$

or

$$\Delta Q_{\text{fusion}} + \Delta Q_{\text{ice water}} = \Delta Q_{\substack{\text{warm}\\ \text{water}}} + \Delta Q_{\substack{\text{calorimeter cup}\\ \text{and stirrer}}}$$

and

$$\begin{aligned} m_iL_f + m_ic_w(T_f - 0) &= m_wc_w(T_h - T_f) + m_{cs}c_{cs}(T_h - T_f) \\ &= (m_wc_w + m_{cs}c_{cs})(T_h - T_f) \end{aligned} \qquad \textbf{(TI 3)}$$

where the m's and c's are the masses and specific heats, respectively, of the various components as indicated by the subscripts i = ice, w = water, cs = calorimeter-stirrer. Hence, TI Eq. 3 may be used to determine the heat of fusion L_f of water if all the other quantities are known.

B. *Heat of Vaporization*

If a quantity of steam of mass m_s at 100°C is added to cool water in a calorimeter cup with a stirrer at an initial temperature T_c, the steam condenses and the system comes to equilibrium at some intermediate or final temperature T_f. Assuming no heat loss to the surroundings, by the conservation of energy,

$$\text{Heat of vaporization lost by steam in condensing} + \text{heat lost by hot condensed water} = \text{heat gained by the cool water} + \text{heat gained by the calorimeter cup and stirrer}$$

or

$$\Delta Q_{\text{vaporization}} + \Delta Q_{\substack{\text{hot}\\ \text{water}}} = \Delta Q_{\substack{\text{cool}\\ \text{water}}} + \Delta Q_{\substack{\text{calorimeter cup}\\ \text{and stirrer}}}$$

and

$$\begin{aligned} m_sL_v + m_sc_w(100 - T_f) &= m_wc_w(T_f - T_c) + m_{cs}c_{cs}(T_f - T_c) \\ &= (m_wc_w + m_{cs}c_{cs})(T_f - T_c) \end{aligned} \qquad \textbf{(TI 4)}$$

where the m's and c's are the masses and specific heats, respectively, of the various components, as indicated by the subscripts. Hence, CI Eq. 4 may be used to determine the heat of vaporization L_v of water if all the other quantities are known.

TI EXPERIMENTAL PROCEDURE

A. *Heat of Fusion*

1. Heat some water in the beaker (enough to fill the inner calorimeter cup about half full) to about 10 to 15°C above room temperature. While the water is heating, determine the mass of the inner calorimeter cup (without ring) and stirrer (total mass m_{cs}) on a laboratory balance. Also, note and record the type of metal and specific heat of the cup and stirrer, usually stamped on the cup.*

2. Fill the inner calorimeter cup about half full of the warm water and weigh it (with the stirrer) to determine the mass of the water m_w.

   Place the calorimeter cup with the water and stirrer in the calorimeter jacket and put on the lid with a thermometer extending into the water. Stir the water gently and record its temperature T_h.

3. Select several small pieces of ice about the size of the end of your thumb and dry them with a paper towel. (It is important that the ice be dry.) Without touching the ice with your bare fingers (use the paper towel), carefully add the pieces of ice to the calorimeter cup one at a time without splashing. (It is good procedure to stir

* If the cup and stirrer are not of the same material, they must be treated separately, and the mass term in TI Eqs. 3 and 4 becomes

$$(m_wc_w + m_cc_c + m_sc_s).$$

the water and check its temperature again just before adding the ice. If that temperature has changed, take the later reading as T_h.)

4. Gently stir the water-ice mixture while adding the ice. Add enough ice so that the temperature of the mixture is about 10 to 15°C below room temperature after the ice has melted. Add the ice more slowly toward the end so that you can better control the final temperature. Continue to stir gently, and read and record the equilibrium temperature T_f when the ice has melted completely.

Then weigh and record the mass of the inner calorimeter cup with its contents (water and stirrer) so as to determine the mass of the melted ice water or mass of the ice m_i.

5. Compute the heat of fusion L_f using TI Eq. 3, and compare it with the accepted value, L_f = 80 kcal/kg = 80 cal/g = 3.33×10^5 J/kg, by finding the percent error.

B. Heat of Vaporization

6. Set up the steam generator as shown in ● TI Fig. 2 with the boiler about two-thirds full of water, and begin heating the boiler. A water trap is used in the steam line (which should be as short as practically possible) to prevent hot water condensed in the tube from entering the calorimeter.

It is important that the hot water condensed in the tube be prevented from entering the calorimeter—note the hose arrangement in TI Fig. 2.

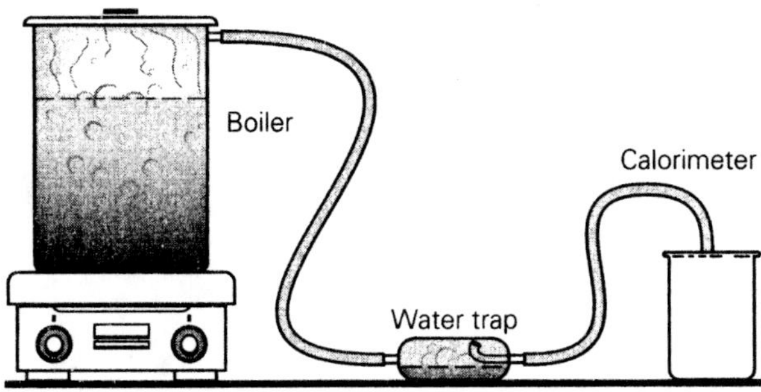

TI Figure 2 Steam generator arrangement. For the heat-of-vaporization measurement, steam from boiling water is transferred to the calorimeter through a water trap. The trap prevents hot water condensed in the tube from entering the calorimeter, which would introduce error.

7. Fill the inner calorimeter cup about two-thirds full of cool water at about 15°C below room temperature. Either the cool water from the heat-of-fusion experiment or fresh tap water may be used with some ice added to obtain the desired temperature. (Make sure that all the ice has melted, however.)

Weigh and record the mass of the calorimeter cup with the water and stirrer. Then place the cup in the calorimeter jacket and replace the lid. Gently stir the water, and read and record the equilibrium temperature T_c.

8. With the water in the steam generator boiling gently and steam flowing freely from the steam tube, as evidenced by water vapor coming from the tube (remember that steam itself is invisible), introduce steam into the calorimeter water and stir.

Caution: *Be careful not to get a steam burn when placing the steam line into, or removing it from, the cup.*

It is good procedure to stir the water and check its temperature again just before introducing the steam. If that temperature has changed, take the later reading as T_c.

When the temperature of the water is about 15°C above room temperature, turn off the heat source and carefully remove the steam line from the calorimeter. Stir gently, and read and record the equilibrium temperature T_f.

Finally, reweigh the inner calorimeter cup and its contents so as to determine the mass of the condensed steam m_s.

9. Compute the heat of vaporization L_v using TI Eq. 4 and compare it with the accepted value L_v = 540 kcal/kg = 540 cal/g = 2.26×10^6 J/kg by finding the percent error.

Name ______________________ Section ______________ Date ______________

Lab Partner(s) ____

EXPERIMENT 12

Latent Heats: Heats of Fusion and Vaporization of Water

TI *Laboratory Report*

Mass of calorimeter cup and stirrer m_{cs} ______________

Type of metal and specific heat of calorimeter cup and stirrer c_{cs} ______________

A. Heat of Fusion

Mass of calorimeter plus water ______________

Initial temperature of water T_h ______________

Mass of water m_w ______________

Final equilibrium temperature T_f ______________

Mass of calorimeter, water, and melted ice ______________

Mass of ice m_i ______________

Calculations (show work)

Experimental L_f ______________

Accepted L_f ______________

Percent error ______________

Don't forget units

(continued)

B. Heat of Vaporization

Mass of calorimeter plus water ____________________

Mass of water m_w ____________________

Mass of calorimeter, water, and condensed steam ____________________

Mass of steam m_s ____________________

Initial temperature of water T_c ____________________

Final equilibrium temperature T_f ____________________

Calculations (show work)

Experimental L_v ____________________

Accepted L_v ____________________

Percent error ____________________

Name ______________________ Section ______________ Date ______________

Lab Partner(s) ______________________

EXPERIMENT 12 *Laboratory Report*

TI QUESTIONS

1. Discuss the most important sources of error in the experimental procedures. If the temperature of the ice added to the calorimeter in the heat-of-fusion experiment were less than 0°C, how would this affect the results? Why should you use small pieces of ice rather than large pieces?

2. Explain why burns caused by steam at 100°C are more serious than those caused by an equal mass of boiling water at the same temperature.

3. How is the latent heat of water used in the cooling mechanism of our bodies?

4. What is the heat of sublimation? [*Hint:* Dry ice (solid CO_2) sublimes.]

(continued)

5. A piece of ice with a mass of 30 g at 0°C is added to 100 mL of water at 20°C. Assuming that no heat is lost to the surroundings, what is the situation when thermal equilibrium is reached? (Ignore the calorimeter or container.)

CI EXPERIMENT 12

CI Equipment Needed

- 1 Temperature sensor (PASCO CI-6505A)
- Calorimeter
- Hot water (~ 50° to 60°C)
- Ice
- Paper towels

CI Theory

In this experiment, we will measure the latent heat of fusion of water by finding how many calories of heat are needed to melt 1 g of ice completely. A temperature sensor will be used to monitor the temperature changes of a mixture of warm water and ice. The water (in a calorimeter cup) will lose heat when mixed with the ice. This heat will be used in melting the ice and in warming up the resulting water-ice mixture. By the conservation of energy, the heat lost by one part of the system must be equal to the heat gained by other parts of the system, if the system is isolated.

In this case, the amount of heat transferred will be determined by measuring the heat lost by the water and the calorimeter cup, as follows:

$$\begin{aligned} Q &= Q_{\substack{\text{lost by}\\ \text{water}}} + Q_{\substack{\text{lost by}\\ \text{cup}}} \\ &= m_{\text{water}} c_{\text{water}}\, \Delta T_{\text{water}} + m_{\text{cup}} c_{\text{cup}}\, \Delta T_{\text{cup}} \end{aligned} \qquad \text{(CI 1)}$$

Assuming that the water and the calorimeter cup both start at the same initial temperature, and assuming that they both reach the same final, equilibrium temperature as the rest of the mixture, $\Delta T_{\text{water}} = \Delta T_{\text{cup}}$ and

$$\begin{aligned} Q &= (m_{\text{water}} c_{\text{water}} + m_{\text{cup}} c_{\text{cup}})\Delta T \\ &= (m_{\text{water}} c_{\text{water}} + m_{\text{cup}} c_{\text{cup}})(T_{\text{initial}} - T_{\text{final}}) \end{aligned} \qquad \text{(CI 2)}$$

To determine how much of this heat goes into melting the ice, let's examine the other side of the heat transfer. When the ice melts and the resulting water-ice mixture warms up, the heat that is transferred can be expressed as

$$\begin{aligned} Q &= Q_{\substack{\text{to melt}\\ \text{the ice}}} + Q_{\substack{\text{gained by}\\ \text{ice water}}} \\ &= Q_{\substack{\text{to melt}\\ \text{the ice}}} + m_{\text{ice}} c_{\text{water}}\, \Delta T_{\text{ice}} \\ &= Q_{\substack{\text{to melt}\\ \text{the ice}}} + m_{\text{ice}} c_{\text{water}} (T_{\text{final}} - 0°\text{C}) \end{aligned} \qquad \text{(CI 3)}$$

Note that the initial temperature of the ice is 0°C but that the final temperature of the resulting water-ice mixture, which has the same mass, m_{ice}, as the original ice, is the same final equilibrium temperature of the water and cup.

By conservation of energy, the heat calculated with CI Eq. 2 is the same as that calculated with CI Eq. 3. Combining both expressions, we can find the heat needed to melt the ice completely:

$$Q_{\substack{\text{to melt}\\ \text{the ice}}} = Q - m_{\text{ice}} c_{\text{water}} T_{\text{final}} \qquad \text{(CI 4)}$$

For a particular mass of ice, m_{ice}, the heat used to melt each gram of the sample is easily calculated. This quantity is called the latent heat of fusion of water:

$$L_{\text{fusion}} = \frac{Q_{\substack{\text{to melt}\\ \text{the ice}}}}{m_{\text{ice}}} \qquad \text{(CI 5)}$$

Setting Up Data Studio

1. Open Data Studio and choose "Create Experiment."
2. From the sensor list, choose a temperature sensor. Connect the temperature sensor to channel A of the interface, as shown in the computer screen.
3. Double-click on the "Temperature Sensor" icon. The sensor properties window will open. Set the sample rate to slow, and set the timer to 5 s between samples. Click OK.
4. Drag the "Temperature, ChA" icon from the data list, and drop it on top of the "Digits" icon in the displays list. A digits display will open in a window called Digits 1.
5. Drag the "Temperature, ChA" icon from the data list, and drop it on top of the "Graph" icon in the displays list. A graph of temperature versus time will open in a window called Graph 1.
6. There should be a digits display and a graph on the screen. Adjust their sizes and locations so that they can be seen simultaneously. ● CI Fig. 1 shows what the screen should look like after the setup is complete.

CI Experimental Procedure

1. Measure the mass of the calorimeter cup, and record it in the laboratory report.*
2. Make a note, in the report, of the specific heat of the calorimeter cup, including units. It is usually printed on the cup by the manufacturer.
3. Set aside about 50 g of ice.† The ice has to be in pieces small enough to fit through the calorimeter lid. Wrap

* If the calorimeter comes with a stirrer, remove the stirrer. The temperature sensor will be the stirrer in this experiment.

† Anything from 40 g to 70 g will work fine; 50 g is just a suggestion.

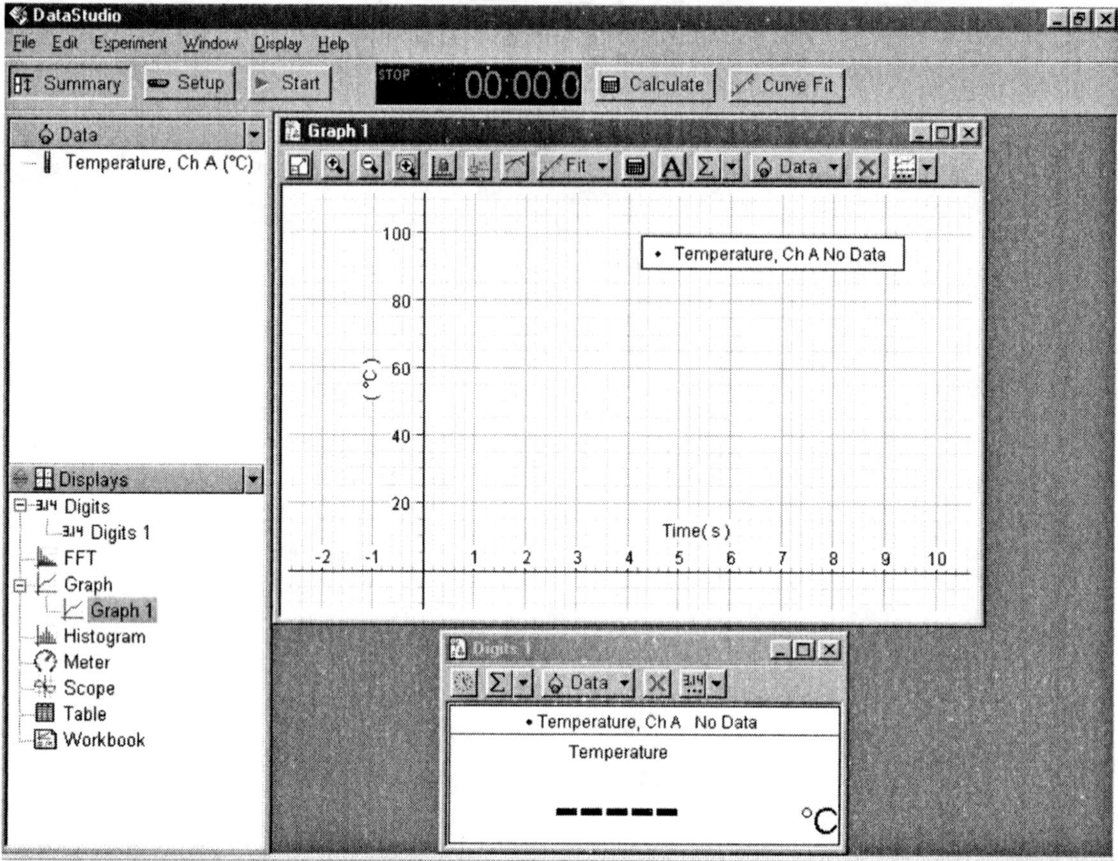

CI Figure 1 Data studio setup. The temperature of the water and ice mixture will be displayed simultaneously on a graph and on a digits display. A new data point will appear every 5 s. (Data displayed using DataStudio Software. Reprinted courtesy of PASCO scientific.)

the ice with paper towels to keep it dry until you are ready to use it. (Alternatively, keep it in the freezer or in a cooler until just before you use it.)

4. Put about 200 g of warm water (50 to 70° C) in the cup. Measure the mass of the cup with the water, and determine the mass of the water. Record it in CI Data Table 1.
5. Place the cup with the water in the calorimeter and put the lid on. Insert the temperature sensor into the cup through the hole in the lid, and gently stir the water for a few seconds with the sensor. This is to allow both the water and the cup to reach the same temperature.
6. While gently stirring the water, press the START button. (Keep stirring the water throughout the experiment.) The temperature readings will appear on the digits display and on the graph. Remember that a new data point for the graph will appear every 5 s.
7. Press the Scale-to-Fit button. This is the leftmost button on the graph toolbar. This will help scale the graph as data are collected.
8. If the temperature is observed to increase slightly, wait until the readings level off before going to the next step.
9. Add a few pieces of the ice to the water and continue stirring until it melts. Continue adding the ice and stirring until all the ice has melted.
10. Continue stirring for a few seconds after all the ice has melted, and observe the graph. The temperature plot should level out as the mixture reaches the equilibrium temperature. Press STOP.
11. Go to the digits display. On the toolbar there is a drop menu labeled with the Greek letter sigma (Σ). Choose "Maximum" from the menu. The display will show what was the maximum temperature measured during the experiment. Record this temperature as the initial temperature of the water and the cup.
12. Repeat, this time choosing "Minimum." Record the minimum temperature as the final temperature of the mixture. It should correspond to the temperature at which the plot leveled out at the end.
13. Carefully take the water cup out of the calorimeter and measure its mass again, with all of its contents. Record this value in CI Data Table 1.
14. Use the measured mass of the cup, the mass of the water, and the mass of the cup with water and with melted ice to determine the mass of ice, m_{ice}. Record it in CI Data Table 1.
15. Use CI Eq. 2 to determine the amount of heat lost by the water and the cup during the experiment.

16. Use CI Eq. 4 to calculate how much of the heat was used to melt the ice.
17. Use CI Eq. 5 to calculate the heat used per gram of water, L_f.
18. Repeat the experiment, this time using a little less water (or a little more water) and a little less ice (or a little more ice). Also vary the initial temperature of the water. Record all results and calculations as Trial 2 in the Laboratory Report.
19. Average the results for the latent heat of fusion from Trial 1 and Trial 2. Compare the average to the accepted value of the heat of fusion, 79.7 cal/g, by taking the percent error.

Name ______________________ Section ______________ Date ______________

Lab Partner(s) ____

EXPERIMENT 12

Latent Heat of Fusion of Water

CI *Laboratory Report*

CI DATA TABLE 1

Purpose: To determine the latent heat of fusion of water.

c_{cup} = ______ $c_{water} = \frac{1.0 \text{ cal}}{g \cdot \text{C}^\circ}$

	Trial 1	Trial 2
m_{cup}		
$m_{cup + water}$		
m_{water}		
$m_{cup + water + icewater}$		
m_{ice}		
$T_{initial}$		
T_{final}		
Heat lost by the water and the cup, Q		
Heat used to melt the ice, $Q_{to\ melt}$		
Latent heat of fusion of water, L_f		

Average L_f ______________ Percent error ______________

Don't forget units

(continued)

CI QUESTIONS

1. Was energy conserved in this experiment as theory predicts? Discuss your experimental results and the sources of uncertainty.

2. Why is it important that all the ice that is added to the water melt? How would the results of the experiment be affected if some ice remained in the mixture?

3. Why is it important that the ice be dry?

Name ______________________ Section ______________ Date ______________

Lab Partner(s) ____

EXPERIMENT 12 ADDENDUM

TI Calibration of a Thermometer

INTRODUCTION

With ice and a means to boil water available, you can quickly calibrate a thermometer, which is quite interesting and instructive.

EQUIPMENT NEEDED

- Uncalibrated thermometer (glass)
- Beaker (500 mL)
- Tripod stand and wire gauze pad (if Bunsen burner is used)
- Felt-tip pen or wax pencil
- Ruler
- Classroom Celsius thermometer

THEORY

A thermometer may be calibrated by using two fixed-point temperatures and then making a graduated scale between these points.* For example, the ice point and steam point of water are convenient fixed points (0°C or 32°F and 100°C or 212°F, respectively).

If the length between these two points is divided into 100 equal intervals, or degrees, the result corresponds with the Celsius temperature scale. Similarly, if the length between the fixed points is divided into 180 intervals, or degrees, the result corresponds to the Fahrenheit temperature scale.

By analogy, the meter standard was originally referenced to two marks on a metal bar. The length between the marks may be divided into 100 intervals, or centimeters. It could be divided into 180 intervals, but that would not produce a decimal scale.

* On the SI Kelvin (absolute) scale, the interval is known as the kelvin and is defined as 1/273.16 of the temperature of the triple point of water (the point where water coexists in three phases, 0.01°C and 4.58 mm Hg). Here the temperature scale fixed points are the triple point and absolute zero.

EXPERIMENTAL PROCEDURE

1. Start heating a *small* amount of water in the beaker. The water depth in the beaker should be several centimeters, enough to cover the thermometer bulb. (More water may be used, but it is unnecessary and will take longer to boil.)*

   While the water is heating, draw an outline of the thermometer on a sheet of paper. The temperature scale will be marked off on the paper, and the outline will allow the thermometer to be replaced on the paper in the proper position. (The scales on many thermometers are engraved not on the glass tube of the thermometer but on an attached frame.)

2. Place the uncalibrated thermometer into the heating water, and heat until the water boils vigorously. With the pen or pencil supplied, mark the height of the thermometer's liquid column on the stem. Turn off the burner. Remove the thermometer and place it on the outline, making a mark on the paper at the mark of the fixed steam point on the thermometer.

3. Pour the hot water from the beaker into a sink.

   Caution: *Use paper towels or tongs to transport the hot beaker, and pour carefully so as not to burn yourself. Recall that steam has a large latent heat.*

   Add a small amount of cold water to the beaker (1–2 cm in depth) and enough ice so that the beaker is one-third to one-half full.

4. Insert the uncalibrated thermometer into the water-ice mixture and stir. The liquid column of the thermometer should reach a low stationary point after a few minutes. Make a mark on the thermometer stem at this lowest point. (Leave the thermometer in the ice water for another minute or so to make sure the column goes

* The steam generator from the main experiment may also be used. Remove the cover, make sure there are several centimeters of water left in the bottom, and heat.

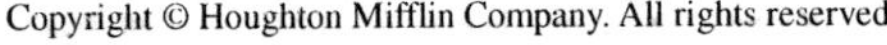

no lower. Adjust the mark accordingly if it does.) In thermal equilibrium, ice and water coexist at the ice point.

5. Remove the thermometer, place it on the outline, and mark the ice point on the paper. Lay the thermometer aside and, with a ruler, divide the length between the two fixed points into 10 equal intervals (deka-degree or 10-degree intervals). Using the Celsius values for the fixed points, label these marks on one side of the thermometer outline.

   Then divide the interval between the 20- and 30-degree marks into 10 equal intervals, or degrees. (The same could be done for the other 10-degree intervals, giving a centigrade, or 100-degree, scale, but this is unnecessary for the purpose of the experiment.)

6. Place the uncalibrated thermometer (which should now be at room temperature) on the outline and mark and read the temperature. Then, read the room temperature from the classroom thermometer and mark and record the value on the paper scale. Compare the temperature reading on your scale with the classroom (accepted) thermometer reading by finding the percent error. Show this calculation on the outline paper.

7. On the other side of the thermometer outline, make a graduated Fahrenheit scale with a fine scale in the vicinity of the room temperature reading. Note the value of your thermometer's room temperature reading on the Fahrenheit scale and record on the paper.

   Compare the experimental Fahrenheit reading with the experimental Celsius reading by computing T_F from $T_F = (9/5)T_C + 32$ using the experimental value of T_C in the equation. How close did you come?

8. Attach the outline paper to the Laboratory Report for the latent heat portion of the experiment.

Name ______________________ Section ______________ Date ______________

Lab Partner(s) ____

EXPERIMENT 13

Fields and Equipotentials

TI Advance Study Assignment

Read the experiment and answer the following questions.

A. *Electric Field*

1. What is an electric field, and what does it tell you?

2. What are "lines of force," and what force is it?

3. What are equipotentials, and how are they experimentally determined? What is their relationship to the electric field lines?

Don't forget units

(continued)

B. Magnetic Field

4. What is a magnetic field, how is it defined, and what does it tell you?

5. Does the magnetic **B** field have the same relationship to electric charge as the electric **E** field? Explain.

6. How may a magnetic pole be moved in a magnetic field without doing work?

Fields and Equipotentials

Introduction and Objectives

When buying groceries, we are often interested in the price per pound. Knowing this, we can determine the price for a given amount of an item. Analogously, it is convenient to know the electric force per unit charge at points in space due to an electric charge configuration, or the magnetic force per unit pole or "moving charge." Knowing these, we can easily calculate the electric force or magnetic force an interacting object would experience at different locations.

The electric force per unit charge is a vector quantity called the electric field intensity, or simply the **electric field (E)**. By determining the electric force on a test charge at various points in the vicinity of a charge configuration, the electric field may be "mapped," or represented graphically, by lines of force. The English scientist Michael Faraday (1791–1867) introduced the concept of lines of force as an aid in visualizing the magnitude and direction of an electric field.

Similarly, the magnetic force per unit pole is a vector quantity called the magnetic field intensity, or **magnetic field (B)**. In this case, the field is mapped out by using the pole of a magnetic compass.

In this experiment, the concept of fields will be investigated and some electric and magnetic field configurations will be determined experimentally.

After performing this experiment and analyzing the data, you should be able to:

1. Describe clearly the concept of a force field.
2. Explain lines of force and the associated physical interpretations.
3. Distinguish between lines of force and equipotentials, and describe their relationships to work.

Equipment Needed

A. *Electric Field*

- Field mapping board and probes
- Conducting sheets with grids
- Conducting paint
- Connecting wires
- 1.5-V battery (or 10-V dc source)
- Galvanometer [or high-resistance voltmeter or multimeter, or vacuum-tube voltmeter (VTVM) with two-point contact field probe*]
- Single-throw switch
- 3 sheets of Cartesian graph paper

B. *Magnetic Field*

- 2 bar magnets and one horseshoe magnet
- Iron filings
- 3 sheets of paper or overhead transparency material
- Small compass
- 3 sheets of Cartesian graph paper or regular paper

* Leads from the dc input of an oscilloscope work nicely.

Theory

A. *Electric Field*

The magnitude of the electrostatic force between two point charges q_1 and q_2 is given by Coulomb's law:

$$F = \frac{kq_1q_2}{r^2} \tag{1}$$

where r is the distance between the charges and the constant $k = 9.0 \times 10^9$ N-m^2/C^2. The direction of the force on a charge may be determined by the **law of charges** or **charge-force law:**

Like-charges repel, and unlike charges attract.

The magnitude E of the **electric field** is defined as the electrical force per unit charge, or $E = F/q_o$ (N/C). By convention, the electric field is determined by using a *positive* test charge q_o. In the case of the electric field associated with a single-source charge q, the magnitude of the electric field a distance r away from the charge is

$$E = \frac{F}{q_o} = \frac{kq_oq}{q_or^2} = \frac{kq}{r^2} \tag{2}$$

(electric field)

The direction of the electric field may be determined by the law of charges—that is, in the direction of the force experienced by the positive test charge.

The electric field vectors for several series of radial points from a positive source charge are illustrated in ● Fig. 1a. Notice that the lengths (magnitudes) of the vectors are smaller the greater the distance from the charge. (Why?)

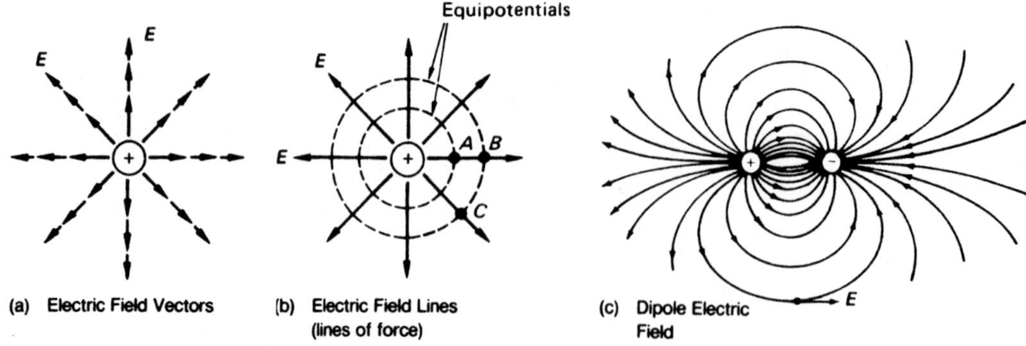

Figure 1 Electric field. (a) Electric field vectors near a positive charge. (b) Lines of force with equipotentials for a positive charge. (c) An electric dipole and its electric field. The direction of the electric field at a particular location is tangent to the line of force through that point, as illustrated on the bottom line of force.

By drawing lines through the points in the direction of the field vectors, we form lines of force (Fig. 1b), which give a graphical representation of the electric field. The direction of the electric field at a particular location is tangent to the line of force through that point (Fig. 1c). The magnitudes of the electric field are not customarily listed, only the direction of the field lines. However, the closer together the lines of force, the stronger the field.

If a positive charge were released in the vicinity of a stationary positive source charge, it would move along a line of force in the direction indicated (away from the source charge). A negative charge would move along the line of force in the opposite direction. Once the electric field for a particular charge configuration is known, we tend to neglect the charge configuration itself, since the effect of the configuration is given by the field.

Since a free charge moves in an electric field by the action of the electric force, we say that work ($W = Fd$) is done by the field in moving charges from one point to another (e.g., from A to B in Fig. 1b).

To move a positive charge from B to A would require work supplied by an external force to move the charge against the electric field (force). The work W per charge q_o in moving the charge between two points in an electric field is called the **potential difference** ΔV between the points:

$$\Delta V_{BA} = V_B - V_A = \frac{W}{q_o} \quad (3)$$

(It can be shown that the potential at a particular point a distance r from the source charge q is $V = kq/r$. See your textbook.)

If a charge is moved along a path at right angles or perpendicular to the field lines, no work is done ($W = 0$), since there is no force component along the path. Then along such a path (dashed-line paths in Fig. 1b), $\Delta V = V_B - V_C = W/q_o = 0$, and $V_C = V_B$. Hence, the potential is constant along paths perpendicular to the field lines. Such paths are called **equipotentials.** (In three dimensions, the path is along an equipotential surface.)

An electric field may be mapped experimentally by determining either the field lines (of force) or the equipotential lines. Static electric fields are difficult to measure, and field lines are more easily determined by measuring small electric currents (flow of charges) maintained in a conducting medium between charge configurations in the form of metal electrodes.

The steady-state electric field lines closely resemble the static field that a like configuration of static charges would produce. The current is measured in terms of the voltage (potential) difference by a high-resistance voltmeter or multimeter (or VTVM).

In other instances, equipotentials are determined, and hence the field lines, using a simple galvanometer as a detector. When no current flows between two probe points, as indicated by a zero deflection on the galvanometer, there is no potential difference between the points ($\Delta V = 0$), and the points are on an equipotential.

B. Magnetic Field

Analogous to an electric field, a **magnetic field** was originally defined as the magnetic force per unit pole. The direction of the force at a particular location is that of the force experienced by a north magnetic pole.

Just as we may map the electric field around an electric charge, we may draw magnetic lines of force around a magnet. A single magnetic pole, or magnetic monopole, has never been observed, so the magnetic field is mapped using the north pole (by convention) of a magnetic dipole, for example, the magnetic needle of a compass. The torque on the compass needle resulting from the magnetic force causes the needle to line up with the field, and the north pole of the compass points in the direction of the field (● Fig. 2). If the compass is moved in the direction indicated by the north pole, the path of the compass traces out a field line.

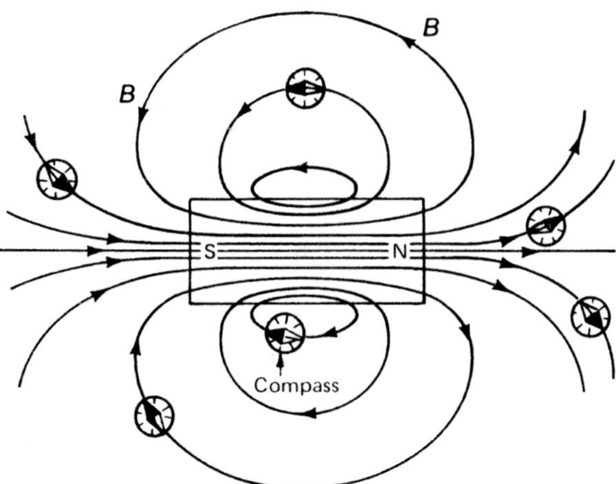

Figure 2 Magnetic field. The magnetic force causes a compass needle to line up with the field, and the north pole of the compass points in the direction of the field. If the compass is moved in the direction indicated by the north pole, the path of the compass needle traces out a field line.

Another observation is that an electric charge q moving nonparallel to a magnetic field experiences a force. For the special case in which the velocity vector $\mathbf{v}$ of the charge is perpendicular to the magnetic field $\mathbf{B}$, the magnitude of the force is given by

$$F = qvB$$

This gives an expression for the strength (magnitude) of the magnetic field in terms of familiar quantities:

$$\boxed{B = \frac{F}{qv}} \tag{4}$$

(magnetic field)

where the direction of $\mathbf{B}$ is perpendicular to the plane of $\mathbf{v}$ and $\mathbf{F}$. Note that the SI unit of magnetic field is N/A-m, or tesla (T).*

The magnetic field may then be thought of as the magnetic force "per unit charge" per velocity. The **B** field has the same form as that mapped out using compass-needle poles.

It is instructive for comparative purposes to draw equipotential lines perpendicular to the field lines, as in the electric field case. No work would be done on a magnetic pole (or electric charge) when it was moved along these equipotential lines. (Why?)

A common method of demonstrating a magnetic field is to sprinkle iron filings over a paper or transparency material covering a magnet (● Fig. 3). The iron filings become induced magnets and line up with the field as would a compass needle. This method allows one to visualize the magnetic field configuration quickly.

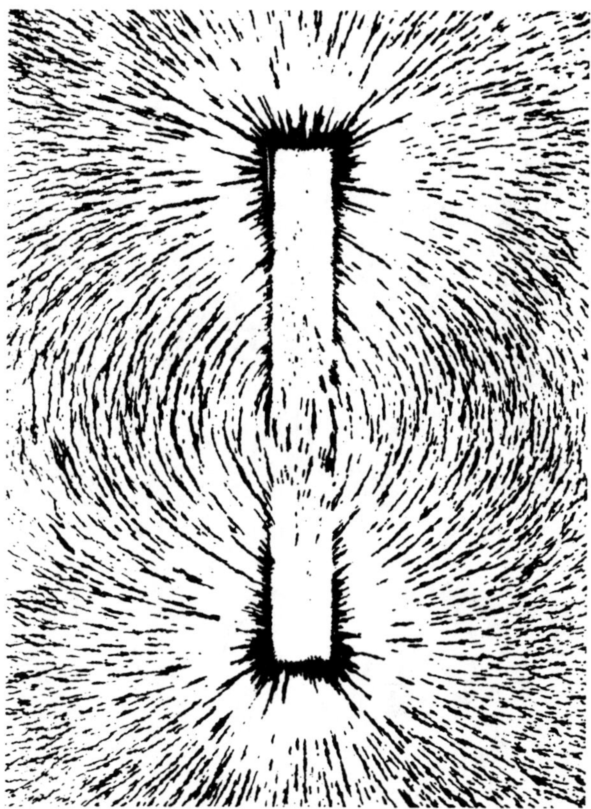

Figure 3 Iron filing pattern for a bar magnet. The iron filings become induced magnets and line up with the field, as would a compass needle. (Courtesy of *PSSC Physics,* D.C. Heath and Company with Educational Development Center, Inc., Newton, Massachusetts.)

EXPERIMENTAL PROCEDURE

A. *Electric Field*

1. An electric field mapping setup with a galvanometer is shown in ● Fig. 4a. The apparatus consists of a flat board on which is placed a sheet of carbonized conducting paper imprinted with a grid. The sheet has an electrode configuration of conducting silver paint, which provides an electric field when connected to a voltage source (e.g., a battery).

   The common electrode configurations ordinarily provided are two dots representing point charges of an electric dipole configuration (Fig. 1c) and two parallel linear electrodes representing a two-dimensional cross section of a parallel-plate capacitor (on the board in the photo in Fig. 4a).

2. Draw the electric dipole configuration on a sheet of graph paper to the same scale and coordinates as those

* Other units of magnetic field are the weber/m^2 (Wb/m^2) and the gauss (G). These units are named after early investigators of magnetic phenomena.

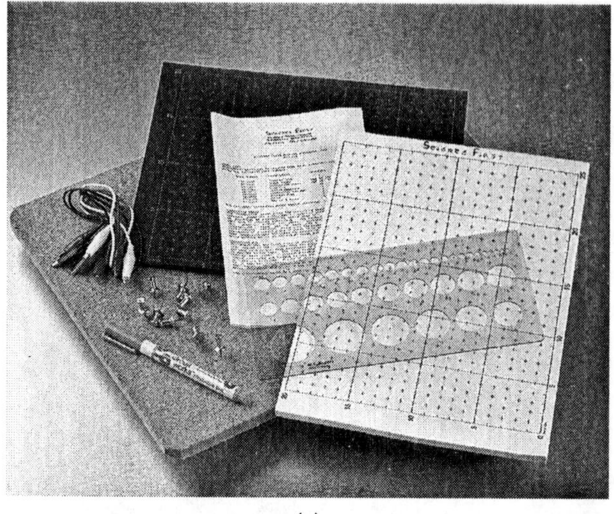

(a)

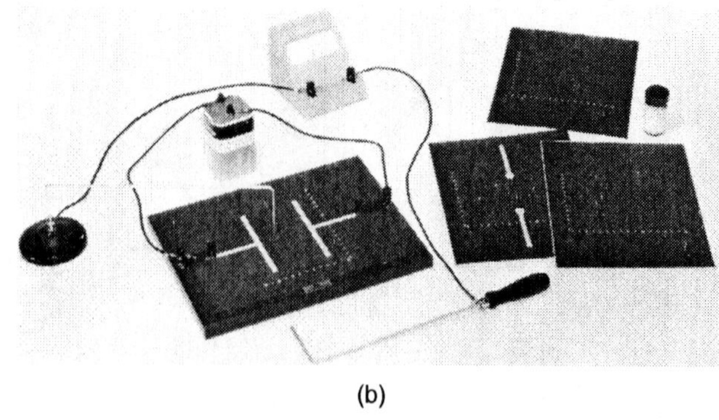

(b)

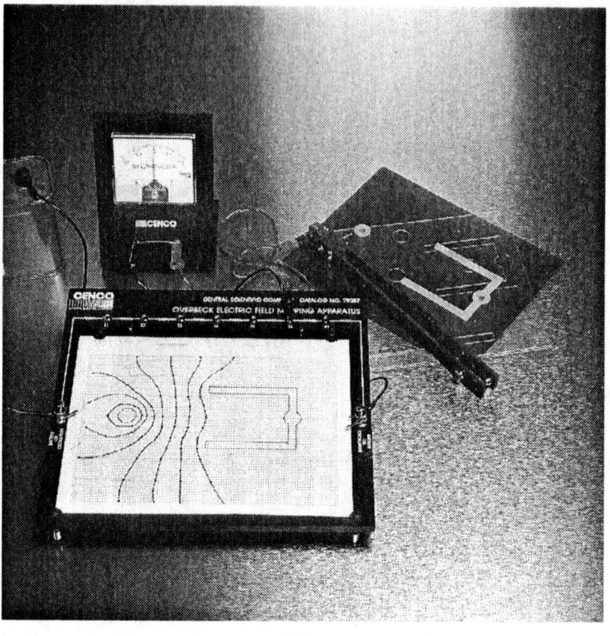

(c)

Figure 4 Electric field mapping equipment. (a) Equipment for painting electrodes on conductive paper in preparation for measuring voltages to map equipotentials. (b) A parallel-plate capacitor configuration on the board and an electric dipole configuration to right. (c) This apparatus uses conductive plates, and the mapping is done on graph paper. [Courtesy of Sargent-Welch.]

of the painted dipole on the imprinted grid on the conducting sheet. Then place the dipole conducting sheet on the board, and set the contact terminals firmly on the painted electrode connections. If you are using a galvanometer, do procedures 3 through 7. If you are using a voltmeter, do procedures 8 through 12.

Galvanometer Measurements

3. Connect the probes to the galvanometer as shown in Fig. 4b. The probes are used to locate points in the field that are at equipotential. Connect the voltage source (1.5-V battery) to the board terminals. Place a switch in the circuit (not shown in the figure) and leave it open until you are ready to take measurements.

   Place the stationary probe on the electric dipole sheet at some general point near the edge of the grid area in the region between the electrodes. The potential at this point will serve as a reference potential. Mark the probe position on your graph-paper map.

   The movable probe is then used to determine the location of a series of other points that have the same potential. When the movable probe is at a point with the same potential as that of the stationary reference probe, no deflection will be observed on the galvanometer.

4. Close the switch and place the movable probe on the conducting paper at some location an appreciable distance away from the stationary probe. Move the probe

until the galvanometer shows zero deflection (indicating a point of equipotential), and record this point on the graph-paper map.

Locate a series of 8 or 10 points of the same potential across the general field region, and draw a dashed-line curve through these points on the graph-paper map.

5. Choose a new location for the reference probe, 2 to 3 cm from the previous reference position, and locate another series of equipotential points. Continue this procedure until you have mapped the field region. Open the switch.

   Draw curves perpendicular to the equipotential lines on the graph-paper map to represent the electric field lines. Do not forget to indicate the field direction on the field lines.

6. Repeat the procedure for the parallel linear (plate) electrode configuration. Be sure to investigate the regions around the ends of the plate electrodes.

7. (*Optional*) Your instructor may wish to have you map the electric field for a nonsymmetric electrode configuration or a configuration of your own choosing. These can be prepared by painting the desired electrode configuration on a conducting sheet with silver paint.

Voltmeter Measurements

8. For the high-resistance voltmeter (or VTVM), the field probe should have two contacts mounted about 2 cm apart. Connect the voltage source (10-V dc) to the board terminals. Place a switch in the circuit (not shown in Fig. 4b) and leave it open until you are ready to take measurements.

   Close the switch, and with the zeroed voltmeter set on the 10-V scale, position the negative (−) contact of the field probe near the negative electrode. Using the negative probe point as a pivot, rotate the positive (+) contact around the fixed negative contact until the position with the maximum meter reading is found.

   Record the positions of the probe contacts on the graph-paper map. (The sensitivity of the voltmeter may be increased by switching to a lower scale. A mid-scale reading is desirable.

9. Using the second probe point as a new negative probe point, repeat the procedure to determine another point of maximum meter reading, and record. Continue this procedure until the positive electrode is approached. Draw a smooth curve through these points on the graph-paper map.

   Then, starting again at a new position near the negative electrode, repeat these procedures for another field line. Trace out four to six field lines in this manner. Do not forget to indicate the field direction on the lines.

10. Place the negative probe near the center of the field region, and rotate the positive contact until a position is found that gives a *zero* meter reading. Record several of these points on the graph paper with a symbol different from that used for the field lines. Check the zero on the voltmeter frequently, particularly when changing scales.

    Use the second point as a new pivot point, as before, and determine a series of null (zero) points. Draw a dashed-line curve through these equipotential points. Determine three to five equipotential lines in this manner.

11. Repeat this procedure for the parallel linear (plate) electrode configuration. Be sure to investigate the regions around the ends of the plate electrodes.

12. (*Optional*) Your instructor may wish to have you map the electric field for a nonsymmetric electrode configuration or a configuration of your own choosing. These can be prepared by painting the desired electrode configuration on a conducting sheet with silver paint.

B. Magnetic Field

13. Covering the magnets with sheets of paper or transparency material, sprinkle iron filings to obtain an iron filing pattern for each of the arrangements shown in ● Fig. 5.

    For the bar magnet arrangements, the magnets should be separated by several centimeters, depending on the pole strengths of the magnets. Experiment with this distance so that there is enough space between the ends of the magnets to get a good pattern.

14. Sketch the observed magnetic field patterns on Fig. 5 in the Laboratory Report. After the patterns have been sketched, collect the iron filings on a piece of paper and return them to the filing container (recycling them for someone else's later use). Economy in the laboratory is important.

15. Place the magnets for each arrangement on a piece of graph paper or regular paper. Draw an outline of the magnets for each arrangement on the paper, and label the poles N and S. Using a small compass, trace out (marking on the paper) the magnetic field lines as smooth curves. Draw enough field lines so that the pattern of the magnetic field can be clearly seen. Do not forget to indicate the field direction on the lines.

16. Draw dashed-line curves perpendicular to the field lines.

Name ______________________ Section ______________ Date ______________

Lab Partner(s) ____

EXPERIMENT 13

Fields and Equipotentials

TI Laboratory Report

Attach graphs to Laboratory Report.

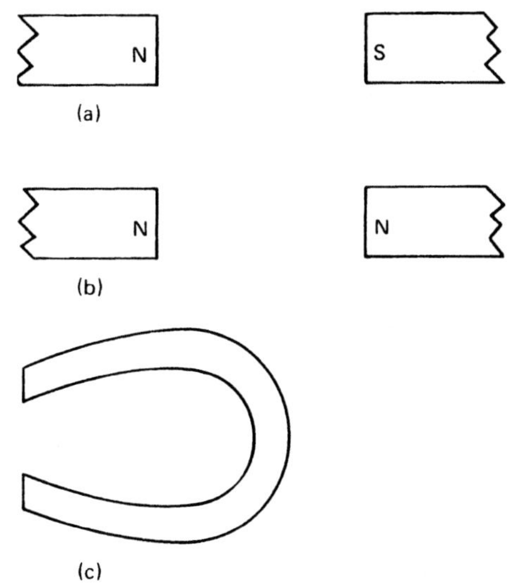

Figure 5 See Procedure Section B.

TI QUESTIONS

1. Directions of the fields are indicated on field lines. Why are no directions indicated on equipotential lines?

2. For the dipole configuration, in what region(s) does the electric field have the greatest intensity? Explain how you know from your map, and justify.

Don't forget units

(continued)

3. Comment on the electric field of the parallel plates (a) between the plates, and (b) near the edges of the plates.

4. Sketch the electric field for (a) a negative point charge near a positively charged plate, and (b) two positive point charges.

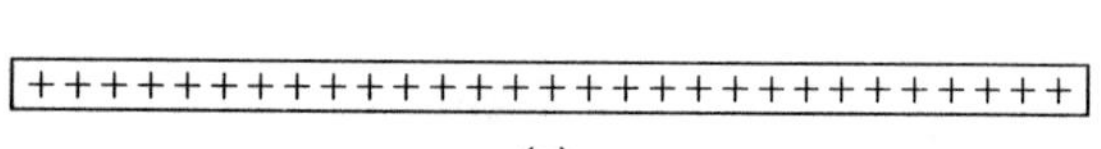

(a)

(b)

5. Compare the electric fields and magnetic fields of the experimental arrangements. Comment on any field similarities and differences.

6. Explain how a gravitational field might be mapped. Sketch the gravitational field for two point masses a short distance apart.

Name ______________________ Section ______________ Date ______________

Lab Partner(s) ____

EXPERIMENT 14

Ohm's Law

TI Advance Study Assignment

Read the experiment and answer the following questions.

1. What is the definition of *electrical resistance*?

2. What is an "ohmic" resistance? Are all resistances ohmic in nature?

3. In what ways are liquid and electrical circuits analogous?

4. For a series circuit, what is the terminal voltage of a battery or power supply equal to in terms of the potential differences or voltage drops across circuit components?

(continued)

CI *Advance Study Assignment*

Read the experiment and answer the following questions.

1. What is a triangle-wave voltage function?

2. What is a nonohmic resistance? How can we distinguish between an ohmic and a nonohmic resistance?

EXPERIMENT 14

Ohm's Law

OVERVIEW

Experiment examines Ohm's law by TI and CI procedures. In the TI procedure, an experimental circuit makes it possible to investigate (1) the variation of current with voltage, and (2) the variation of current and resistance (constant voltage). The CI procedure looks not only at the voltage-current relationship for an ohmic resistance but also at a nonohmic resistance. Steadily increasing and decreasing voltages are obtained by using a signal generator to produce a triangle-wave voltage.

INTRODUCTION AND OBJECTIVES

One of the most frequently applied relationships in current electricity is that known as **Ohm's law.** This relationship, discovered by the German physicist Georg Ohm (1787–1854), is fundamental to the analysis of electrical circuits. Basically, it relates the voltage (V) and current (I) associated with a resistance (R).

Ohm's law applies to many, but not all, materials. Many materials show a constant resistance over a wide range of applied voltages and are said to be "ohmic." Those which do not are said to be "nonohmic." Common circuit resistors are ohmic, which allows Ohm's law to be used in simple circuit analysis. As we shall see in the theory section, Ohm's law is really a special case of the definition of resistance.

In this experiment, Ohm's law will be investigated as applied to components in a simple circuit.

After performing this experiment and analyzing the data, you should be able to:

TI OBJECTIVES

1. Distinguish between ohmic and nonohmic resistances.
2. Explain current-voltage relationships by Ohm's law.
3. Apply Ohm's law to obtain values of current or voltage in investigating a circuit resistance.

CI OBJECTIVES

1. Verify Ohm's law experimentally.
2. Study the behavior of the current in both an ohmic and a nonohmic resistance.

TI EXPERIMENT 14

Ohm's Law

TI EQUIPMENT NEEDED*

- Ammeter (0 to 0.5 A)
- Voltmeter (0 to 10 V dc)
- (or multimeters)
- Decade resistance box (0.1 to 99.9 Ω)
- Rheostat (≈ 200 Ω)
- Unknown resistance
- Battery or power supply (6 V)
- Switch
- Connecting wires
- 2 sheets of Cartesian graph paper

* The ranges of the equipment are given as examples. These may be varied to apply to available equipment.

TI THEORY

When a voltage or potential difference (V) is applied across a material, the current (I) in the material is found to be proportional to the voltage, $I \propto V$. The resistance (R) of the material is defined as the ratio of the applied voltage and the resulting current—that is,

$$R = \frac{V}{I} \quad \textbf{(TI 1)}$$

(definition of electrical resistance)

For many materials, the resistance is constant, or at least approximately so, over a range of voltages. A resistor that has constant resistance is said to obey Ohm's law or to be "ohmic." From TI Eq. 1, it can be seen that the unit of resistance is volt/ampere (V/A). However, the combined unit is called the ohm (Ω), in honor of Georg Ohm. Note that to avoid confusion with a zero, the ohm is abbreviated with a capital omega (Ω) instead of a capital "O".

A plot of V versus I for an ohmic resistance is a straight line (● TI Fig. 1). Materials that do not obey Ohm's law are said to be "nonohmic" and have a nonlinear voltage-current relationship. Semiconductors and transistors are nonohmic.

In common practice, **Ohm's law** is written

$$V = IR \quad \textbf{(TI 2)}$$

where it is understood that R is independent of V. Keep in mind that Ohm's law is not a fundamental law such as Newton's law of gravitation. It is a special case, there being no law that materials must have constant resistance.

To understand the relationships of the quantities in Ohm's law, it is often helpful to consider the analogy of a liquid circuit. (● TI Fig. 2).* In a liquid circuit, the force

* Keep in mind that an analogy only illustrates a resemblance. Liquid and electrical circuits are physically quite different.

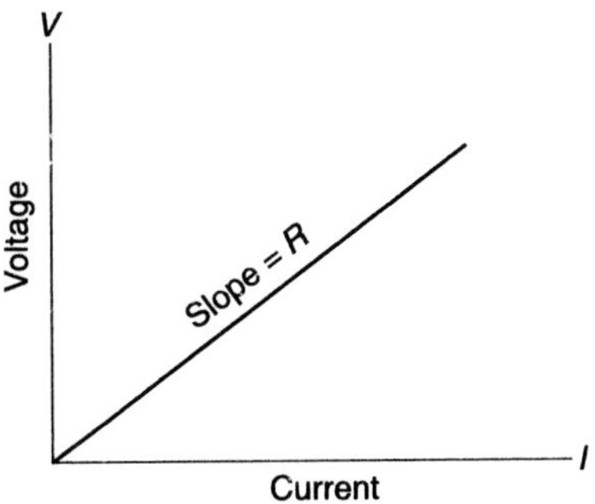

TI Figure 1 Ohmic resistance. A voltage-versus-current graph for an ohmic resistance is a straight line, the slope of which is equal to the value of the resistance ($R = V/I$).

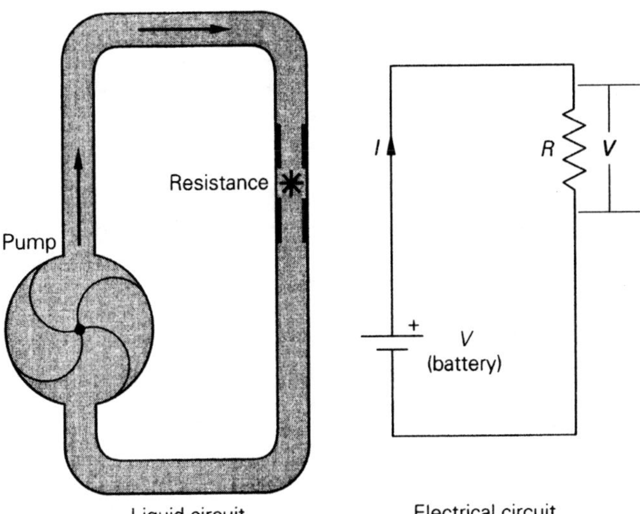

TI Figure 2 Analogy to a liquid circuit. In the analogy between a simple electric circuit and a liquid circuit, the pump corresponds to a voltage source, the liquid flow corresponds to electric current, and the paddle wheel hindrance to the flow is analogous to a resistor.

to move the liquid is supplied by a pump. The rate of liquid flow depends on the resistance to the flow (e.g., due to some partial obstruction in the circuit pipe, here a paddle wheel)—the greater the resistance, the less liquid flow.

Analogously, in an electrical circuit, a voltage source (e.g., a battery or power supply) supplies the voltage (potential difference) for charge flow, and the magnitude of the current is determined by the resistance R in the circuit. For a given voltage, the greater the resistance, the less current through the resistance, as may be seen from Ohm's law, $I = V/R$. Notice that the voltage source supplies a voltage "rise" that is equal to the voltage "drop" across the resistance and is given by $V = IR$ (Ohm's law).

In an electrical circuit with two or more resistances and a single voltage source, Ohm's law may be applied to the entire circuit or to any portion of the circuit. When it is applied to the entire circuit, the voltage is the terminal input voltage supplied by the voltage source, and the resistance is the total resistance of the circuit. When Ohm's law is applied to a particular portion of the circuit, the individual voltage drops, currents, and resistances are used for that part of the circuit.

Consider the circuit diagram shown in ● TI Fig. 3. This is a series circuit. The applied voltage is supplied by a power supply or battery. R_h is a rheostat, a variable resistor that allows the voltage across the resistance R_s to be varied. (This combination is sometimes called a *voltage divider* because the rheostat divides the applied voltage across itself and R_s.)

An ammeter Ⓐ measures the current through the resistor R_s, and a voltmeter Ⓥ registers the voltage drop across both R_s and the ammeter Ⓐ. S is a switch for closing and opening (activating and deactivating) the circuit.

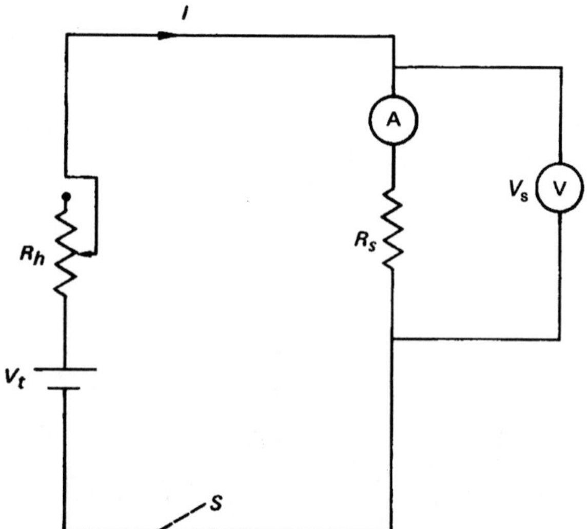

TI Figure 3 Circuit diagram. The voltmeter is connected in parallel across the ammeter and the resistance R_s. The other resistance, R_h, is that of the rheostat (continuously variable resistor).

Any component in a circuit that does not generate or supply a voltage acts as a resistance in the circuit. This is true for the connecting wires, the ammeter, and the voltmeter. However, the metallic connecting wires and the ammeter have negligibly small resistances, so they do not greatly affect the current.

A voltmeter has a high resistance, so there is little current through the voltmeter. Hence, to good approximations, the ammeter registers the current in the resistor, and the voltmeter reads the voltage drop across the resistance. These approximations are adequate for most practical applications.

Applying Ohm's law to the portion of the circuit with R_s only, we have

$$V_s = IR_s \qquad \textbf{(TI 3)}$$

where V_s and I are the voltmeter and ammeter readings, respectively. Notice that the same current I flows through the rheostat R_h and the resistance R_s. The voltage drop across R_h is then

$$V_h = IR_h \qquad \textbf{(TI 4)}$$

To apply Ohm's law to the entire circuit, we use the fact that the applied voltage "rise" or the terminal voltage V_t of the voltage source must equal the voltage "drops" of the components around the circuit. Then

$$V_t = V_h + V_s$$

or

$$V_t = IR_h + IR_s = I(R_h + R_s) \qquad \textbf{(TI 5)}$$

From TI Eq. 5, we see that for a constant R_s, the current through this resistance, and hence its voltage drop V_s, can be varied by varying the rheostat resistance R_h. (The terminal voltage, V_t, is constant.) Similarly, when R_s is varied, the voltage V_s can be maintained constant by adjusting R_h.

TI EXPERIMENTAL PROCEDURE

1. With the voltmeter, measure the terminal voltage of the power supply or battery, and record it in the Laboratory Report. Start with the voltmeter connection to the largest scale, and increase the sensitivity by changing to a smaller scale if necessary. Most common laboratory voltmeters and ammeters have three scale connections and one binding post common to all three scales.

   It is good practice to take measurements initially with the meters connected to the largest scales. This prevents the instruments from being "pegged" (the needle forced off scale in galvanometer-type meters) and possibly damaged, should the magnitude of the voltage or current exceed the smaller scale limits. A scale setting may be changed for greater sensitivity by moving the connection (or turning the switch on a multimeter) to a lower scale after the general magnitude and measurement are known.

Also, take care to ensure the proper polarity (+ and −); connect + to +, and − to −. Otherwise, the meter will be "pegged" in the opposite direction.

2. Set up the circuit shown in the circuit diagram (TI Fig. 3) with the switch open. A standard decade resistance box is used for R_s. Set the rheostat resistance R_h for maximum resistance and the value of the R_s to about 50 Ω. *Have the instructor check the circuit before closing the switch.*

A. *Variation of Current with Voltage*

3. After the instructor has checked the circuit, close the switch and read the voltage and current on the meters. Open the switch after the readings are taken, and record them in TI Data Table 1. Repeat this procedure for a series of four successively lower rheostat settings along the length of the rheostat.

   It is convenient for data analysis to adjust the rheostat (after closing the switch) so that evenly spaced and convenient ammeter readings are obtained. The switch should be closed only long enough to obtain the necessary readings. This prevents unnecessary heating in the circuit and running the battery down.

4. Repeat procedure 3 for another value of R_s (about 30 Ω).

5. Repeat procedure 3 for the unknown resistance, and record data in TI Data Table 2. Relatively low values of voltage may be required. Your instructor will discuss this and the proper connection. *Do not proceed with this procedure without instructions.*

6. Plot the results for both decade box resistances on a single V_s-versus-I_s graph, and draw straight lines that best fit the sets of data. Determine the slopes of the lines, and compare them with the constant values of R_s of the decade box by computing the percent errors. According to Ohm's law, the corresponding values should be equal.

7. Plot V_s versus I_s for the unknown resistance. What conclusions about the unknown resistance can you draw from the graphs?

B. *Variation of Current and Resistance (V_s constant)*

8. This portion of the experiment uses the same circuit arrangement as before. In this case, the voltage V_s is maintained constant by adjusting the rheostat resistance R_h when the R_s is varied.

   Initially, set the rheostat near maximum resistance and the resistance R_s of the decade box to about 100 Ω. Record the value of R_s in TI Data Table 3.

   Close the circuit and adjust the rheostat for a convenient voltmeter reading (about 4 V). Record the voltmeter reading as the constant voltage V_s in TI Data Table 3. Record the current and resistance in the table. Open the circuit after making the readings.

9. Repeat this procedure for four more successive steps of current by reducing the value of R_s of the decade box. Keep the voltage across R_s constant for each setting by adjusting the rheostat resistance R_h. Do not reduce R_s below 30 Ω.

10. Plot the results on an I_s-versus-$1/R_s$ graph and draw a straight line that best fits the data. (Reciprocal ohms, $1/R$, is commonly given the unit name "mhos.") Determine the slope of the line, and compare it with the constant value of V_s by computing the percent error. According to Ohm's law, these values should be equal.

Name ______________________ Section ______________ Date ______________

Lab Partner(s) ____

TI EXPERIMENT 14

Ohm's Law

TI Laboratory Report

A. *Variation of Current with Voltage*

TI DATA TABLE 1

Terminal voltage V_t ______________

Reading	Constant R_s ________		Constant R_s ________	
	Voltage V_s ( )	Current I_s ( )	Voltage V_s ( )	Current I_s ( )
1				
2				
3				
4				
5				

Calculations
(show work)

Slope of lines	Percent error from R_s
________	________
________	________

Don't forget units

(continued)

TI **DATA TABLE 2** Unknown Resistance

Reading	Voltage V_s ( )	Current I_s ( )
1		
2		
3		
4		
5		
6		
7		

Conclusions from graph:

Name ____________ Section ____________ Date ____________

Lab Partner(s) ____________

EXPERIMENT 14 **_Laboratory Report_**

B. Variation of Current with Resistance (V_s constant)

TI **DATA TABLE 3** Constant voltage V_s ____________

Reading	Current I_s ( )	Resistance R_s ( )	$1/R_s$ ( )
1			
2			
3			
4			
5			

Calculations (show work)

Slope of line ____________

Percent error from V_s ____________

TI QUESTIONS

1. If the switch were kept closed during the procedures and the circuit components heated up, how would this affect the measurements? (*Hint:* See Experiment 20.)

(continued)

2. Devise and draw a circuit using a long, straight wire resistor instead of a decade box that would allow the study of the variation of voltage with resistance (I_s constant). According to Ohm's law, what would a graph of the data from this circuit show?

3. Compute the values of R_h and the voltage drops across this resistance for the two situations in TI Data Table 1, reading 1.

CI EXPERIMENT 14

Equipment Needed

This activity is designed for the Science Workshop 750 Interface, which has a built in function generator. It is easily adapted to use with an external wave function generator. Just substitute the available triangle-function generator for the signal generator in the procedure.

- 100-Ω resistor
- 2 cables with alligator clips
- 6-V light bulb
- Voltage sensor (PASCO CI-6503)
- Science Workshop 750 Interface

Theory

As discussed in the TI Theory section, for many materials the resistance remains constant over a range of voltages. Such materials are called "ohmic" and they obey **Ohm's law:**

$$V = IR \qquad \text{(CI 1)}$$

For such a material, a graph of voltage versus current is a straight line, the slope of which is the value of the resistance, as shown in TI Fig. 1.

In this CI part of the experiment, we will investigate the relationship between current and voltage for both an ohmic and a nonohmic component of a circuit. The current will be measured as the voltage across a component is steadily increased and decreased. If the component is ohmic, the current should be directly proportional to the voltage.

To achieve a steadily increasing and decreasing voltage, we will use a signal generator, which can produce what is called a triangle-wave voltage. ● CI Fig. 1 shows how the voltage from such a source varies with time. Notice that it increases up to a maximum value, then drops steadily back to zero, and then, with a change of polarity, increases in the opposite direction. This repeats with a certain fixed frequency.

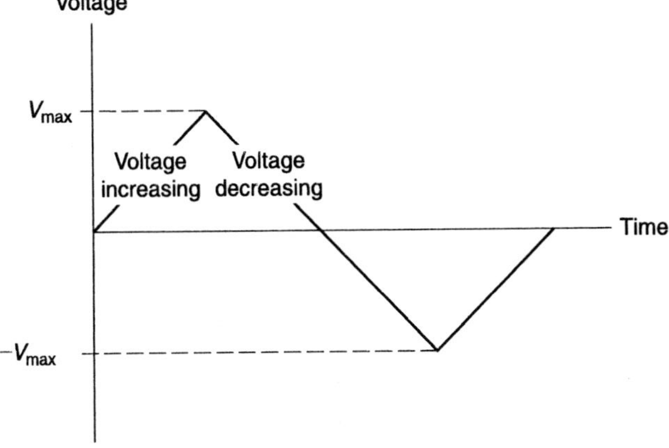

CI Figure 1 A triangle-wave voltage function. With a triangle-wave voltage function, the voltage will increase up to a maximum value, drop steadily back to zero, and then change the polarity and increase in the opposite direction. This will repeat with a certain fixed frequency.

Setting Up Data Studio

1. Open Data Studio and choose "Create Experiment."
2. From the sensor list, choose a Voltage Sensor. Connect the voltage sensor to the interface, as shown in the computer screen.
3. Right below the sensor list there is an icon for the Signal Output. Double-click on the icon. The signal generator window will open. (See ● CI Fig. 2.)
4. The default form of the signal generator function is a sine wave. Change it to a triangle wave by selecting from the drop menu.
5. Set the amplitude to 5.00 volts.
6. Set the frequency to 0.500 Hz. This will produce a triangle wave with a period of 2 seconds.
7. Click on the Measurement and Sample Rate button on the signal generator window. A list of measurements will open. Choose to measure the output current, and deselect all others.
8. Do not close the signal generator window. Move it toward the bottom of the screen.
9. The data list should now have two icons: one for the voltage reading of the sensor and one for the output current of the source.
10. Create a graph by dragging the "Voltage" icon from the Data list and dropping it on the "Graph" icon in the Displays list. A graph of voltage versus time will open. The graph window will be called Graph 1.
11. Drag the "Output Current" icon from the data list, and drop it on top of the X axis of the graph. The time axis should change to a current axis. Graph 1 is now a graph of voltage versus current.
12. ● CI Fig. 3 shows what the screen should look like once the setup is complete. The size of the graph window can be changed, if needed. The signal generator window will need to stay visible for procedure B of the experiment, where the output voltage will be manually controlled.

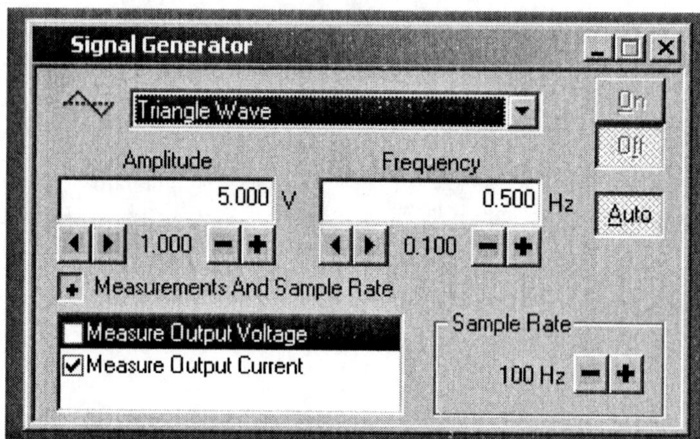

CI Figure 2 The signal generator window. Choose a triangle-wave function, adjust the amplitude and the frequency as specified in the setup procedure, and choose to measure the output current. (Data displayed using DataStudio Software. Reprinted courtesy of PASCO scientific.)

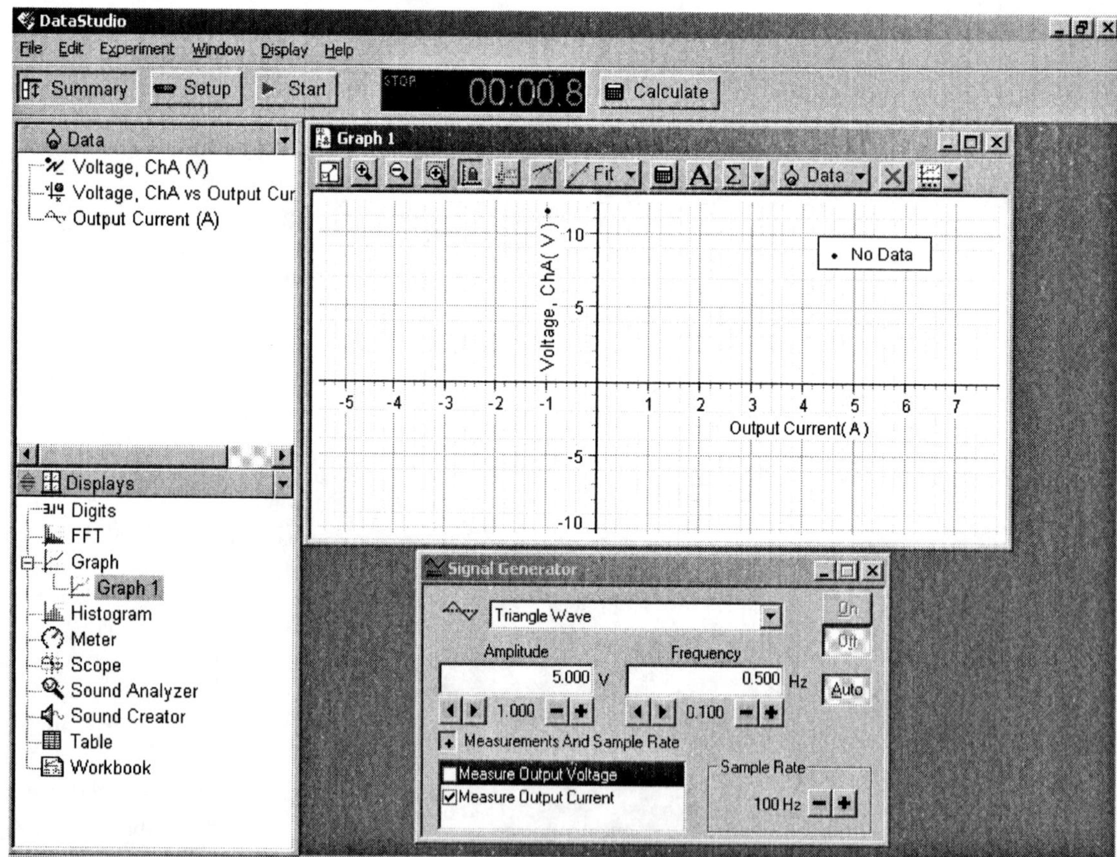

CI Figure 3 Data Studio setup. A graph of voltage versus current will show the variations for an ohmic and a nonohmic resistor. The signal generator window remains active to manually control the output during experimental procedure B. (Data displayed using DataStudio Software. Reprinted courtesy of PASCO scientific.)

CI EXPERIMENTAL PROCEDURE

A. *Ohmic Component*

1. Connect the signal generator to the 100-Ω resistor. The voltage sensor will measure the voltage drop across the resistor, as shown in the circuit of ● CI Fig. 4.
2. Press the START button and click on the Scale-to-Fit button of the graph toolbar. (That is the leftmost button of the graph toolbar.) After a few seconds, press the STOP button. A cycle is complete after 2 seconds, but it will not affect the experiment if it runs longer than that. In fact, let it run longer and follow the plot on the screen as it appears. What is happening to the current as the voltage changes?
3. Print a copy of the graph and paste it to the Laboratory Report.
4. As expected, the graph for the ohmic resistor is a straight line. Use the Fit drop menu (on the graph toolbar) to select a "Linear Fit" for the data. Record the slope of the line, and compare it to the known value of the resistance by calculating a percent error.

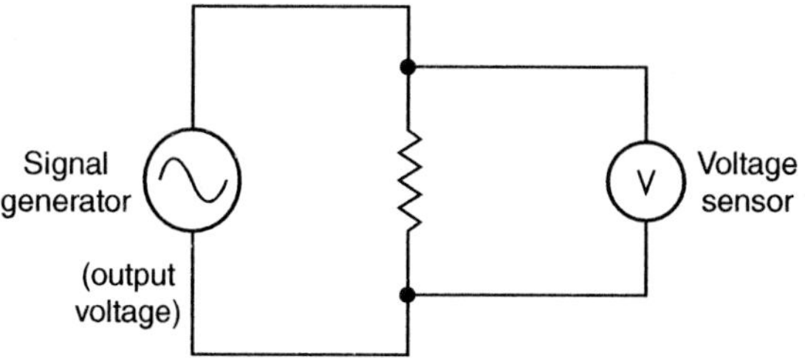

CI Figure 4 The experimental setup. The resistor (ohmic or nonohmic) is connected to the signal generator. The voltage sensor measures the voltage drop across the resistor.

B. *Nonohmic Component*

1. Change the 100-Ω resistor for a small 6-V light bulb.
2. Click on the button labeled "Auto" in the signal generator window. This will cancel the automatic ON/OFF feature of the generator and give manual control of the signal.
3. Press the "On" button of the signal generator.
4. Press the START button and collect data for a few seconds, enough to observe the pattern on the screen. Press the Scale-to-Fit button if needed to see the data better. What is happening to the current now, as the voltage changes?
5. Press the STOP button to end the data collection.
6. Press the "Off" button of the signal generator to turn off the output voltage.
7. Print a copy of the graph and paste it to the Laboratory Report.

Name ______________________ Section ______________ Date ______________

Lab Partner(s) ____

CI EXPERIMENT 14

Ohm's Law

CI *Laboratory Report*

A. *Ohmic Component*

Don't forget to attach the graph to the Laboratory Report.

Calculations
(show work)

Slope of line ______________

Percent error from *R* ______________

B. *Nonohmic Component*

Don't forget to attach the graph to the Laboratory Report.

CI QUESTIONS

1. The graph of voltage versus current for the nonohmic resistor was not a straight line. Describe what happened to the current as the voltage increased, compared to what happened for the ohmic resistor.

2. Why does the graph for the nonohmic resistor "loop"? *Hint:* What happens to the light bulb filament as the current increases?

Don't forget units

(continued)

3. Describe what is happening to the resistance of the light bulb as the voltage increases. (*Hint:* Look at the graph in segments, and treat each segment as though it were a straight line with slope equal to the resistance.)

Name ______________________ Section ______________ Date ______________

Lab Partner(s) ____

EXPERIMENT 15

The Voltmeter and Ammeter

TI Advance Study Assignment

Read the experiment and answer the following questions.

1. What is the function of the galvanometer in a voltmeter or ammeter?

2. What is the purpose of the "multiplier" resistor in a voltmeter? Is the voltmeter a high- or a low-resistance instrument?

3. How is the voltmeter connected in the circuit? Explain why.

(continued)

4. What is the purpose of the "shunt" resistance in an ammeter? Is the ammeter a high- or a low-resistance instrument?

5. How is the ammeter connected in a circuit? Explain why.

6. What would happen if the ammeter were connected in parallel with a circuit element?

EXPERIMENT 15

The Voltmeter and Ammeter*

Introduction and Objectives

Voltmeters and ammeters are widely used instruments for detecting and measuring voltages and currents. Electrical quantities cannot be seen directly by looking at a wire. Like a weather vane, these instruments are used to help us observe that which we cannot see directly.

This experiment is intended to provide a behind-the-scenes look at the construction of these meters and insight into their proper use. The design of a meter and the calculation of the appropriate series or parallel resistance not only illustrates the inner workings of the voltmeter and ammeter but also provides experience analyzing a circuit using Ohm's law.

An understanding of these instruments will be useful in future experiments to avoid the damage resulting from misuse and to recognize the conditions under which the meters introduce errors as their internal resistance becomes a part of the circuit.

In this experiment you will measure the characteristics of a galvanometer and use resistances to convert it into several voltmeters and a three-range ammeter. After performing the experiment, you should be able to:

1. Explain the principle of the galvanometer and how voltmeters and ammeters are made by combining galvanometers with resistors.
2. Understand why voltmeters are high-resistance instruments and ammeters are low-resistance instruments.
3. Describe how ammeters and voltmeters are correctly connected in circuits and tell what would happen if they were incorrectly connected.

Equipment Needed

- Galvanometer†
- Decade resistance box (1 to 999999 Ω)
- Voltmeter (≈ 10 V, triple-range preferred)
- Millivoltmeter (≈ 100 mV)
- Power supply or battery (≈ 1.5 V and 6 V)
- Wheatstone-bridge slide wire
- Triple-range milliammeter
- Single-pole switch
- Miscellaneous wires, including at least 6 clip leads

† A left-zero galvanometer like those used in meters is preferred. The galvanometer from an open bench-type voltmeter can be used by clipping directly to the galvanometer terminals on the back, or a microammeter can be used as a galvanometer.

Theory

The **galvanometer** is the chameleon of scientific instruments. With the addition of a resistor and a new face, it can become a voltmeter or ammeter of whatever scale you want. The galvanometer is the basic indicating component of all deflection-type meters. The galvanometer is an electromagnetic device capable of detecting very small currents. (How small depends on how much you want to pay.)

The basic design of a moving-coil galvanometer is shown in ● Fig. 1 (sometimes called a *D'Arsonval galvanometer,* after the French physicist who invented it around 1882). It consists of a coil of wire mounted on bearings between two poles of a permanent magnet. When a current passes through the coil, it experiences a torque and rotates the pointer along the scale until balanced by the torque supplied by two small springs. The deflection is proportional to the current in the coil.

Some galvanometers have a scale marked with zero at the center. These are used in circuits like the potentiometer and Wheatstone bridge to detect a balance point. The galvanometer used in most voltmeters and ammeters has the zero at the left.

The galvanometers used for meter construction are characterized by their coil resistance r and the coil current required to give a full-scale deflection of the pointer I_c. Once these are known, the resistances necessary to convert the galvanometer to the desired voltmeter or ammeter can be calculated.

A. The dc Voltmeter

The goal here is to design a circuit that can be connected across a resistance R that will allow a small current that is proportional to the voltage difference to flow through the galvanometer, and that will divert as little current as possible from the resistance R. The circuit in ● Fig. 2a accomplishes both of these goals. The series resistor R_m is called a *multiplier* resistor because it multiplies the voltage range of the galvanometer. The combination of the

* This experiment was written and designed by Professor Fred B. Otto, Maine Maritime Academy, Castine, Maine.

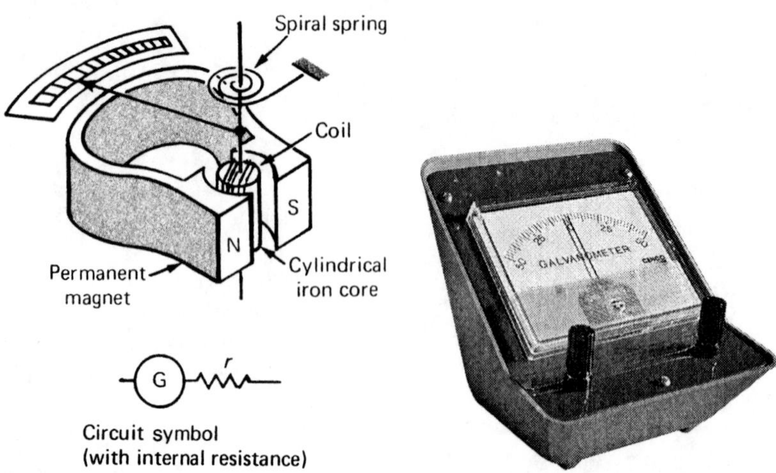

Figure 1 Galvanometer. The drawing shows the basic design of a moving-coil (D'Arsonval) galvanometer. An actual galvanometer is shown in the photo. (Photo courtesy of Sargent-Welch.)

multiplier resistance and the galvanometer is the voltmeter. These are usually combined in a single box.

The resistance of the voltmeter can be calculated using Ohm's law. If V_{max} is to be the maximum scale reading on the meter, the total resistance of the meter equals V_{max}/I_c. Since the galvanometer resistance, r, represents part of the total resistance of the voltmeter, it must be subtracted to give the value of the multiplier resistance R_m to be added in series to make a voltmeter.

$$R_m = \frac{V_{max}}{I_c} - r \tag{1}$$

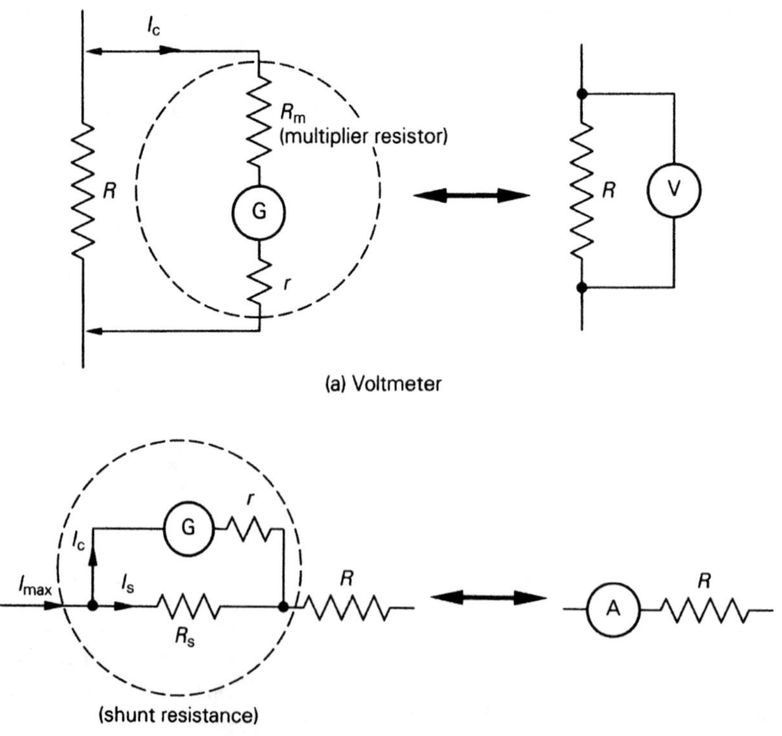

Figure 2 Circuit diagram for voltmeter and ammeter. (a) A voltmeter has a large "multiplier" resistor R_m in series with the galvanometer. (b) An ammeter has a "shunt" resistor R_s in parallel with the galvanometer.

Example 1 Suppose that we wish to calculate the multiplier resistor to convert a galvanometer with a full-scale current (I_c) of 2.0×10^{-3} A and a coil resistance of 100 Ω into a 3-V voltmeter—that is, a voltmeter with a $V_{max} = 3.0$ V.

Solution

$$R_m = \frac{V_{max}}{I_c} - r$$

$$= \frac{(3.0\ \text{V})}{(2.0 \times 10^{-3}\ \text{A})} - 100\ \Omega = 1400\ \Omega$$

The deflection is proportional to the voltage, and a scale is provided showing the value of V_{max} at the right end. The scale is subdivided and graduated so that the voltage can be read directly from the scale.

A voltmeter is ***always*** *connected "across," or in parallel with, a circuit component to measure the potential difference, or voltage, drop across the component.*

If a voltmeter were connected in series with a circuit component, its high resistance would reduce the current in the circuit and the voltage drop across that component.

B. The dc Ammeter

The challenge here is to design a circuit that will divert a small amount of current through the galvanometer that is proportional to the much larger current flowing through the resistor R. This diversion is accomplished by placing a small "shunt" resistance R_s in series with R as shown in Fig. 2b.

The small resistance connected in parallel with the galvanometer is called a *shunt* because it directs or "shunts" most of the current away from the galvanometer. As the current flows through the shunt resistance, a small voltage is developed that diverts a small amount of the current through the galvanometer, causing it to have a controlled deflection proportional to the current through the circuit. The galvanometer and shunt resistance combination is the ammeter.

As with the voltmeter, the value of the shunt resistance required to give a full-scale deflection for a desired maximum current can be calculated using Ohm's law. With the pointer reading full scale, the current through the galvanometer is I_c and the voltage drop across the galvanometer is $I_c r$. Because the galvanometer and the shunt resistor are in parallel, there must be the same voltage drop across the shunt, so

$$I_c r = I_s R_s \tag{2}$$

The current I_s through the shunt must be much larger than the current through the galvanometer coil; therefore the shunt resistance, R_s, must be much smaller than r of the coil. With the pointer deflecting to maximum, the current flowing in the resistor R is that of the maximum scale reading of the ammeter. Since $I_s = I_{max} - I_c$, Eq. 2 can be solved for R_s to give

$$R_s = \frac{I_c r}{I_{max} - I_c} \tag{3}$$

Example 2 Suppose that we wish to calculate the shunt resistor to convert a galvanometer with a full-scale current I_c of 2.0×10^{-3} A and a coil resistance of 100 Ω to a 3-A ammeter—that is, an ammeter with an $I_{max} = 3.0$ A.

Solution

$$R_s = \frac{I_c r}{I_{max} - I_c} = \frac{(2.0 \times 10^{-3}\ \text{A})(100\ \Omega)}{3.000\ \text{A} - 0.0020\ \text{A}}$$

$$= \frac{0.20\ \text{V}}{2.998\ \text{A}} = 0.067\ \Omega$$

(where any number of significant figures is assumed for I_{max}).

A scale is designed for the ammeter with the value of the maximum current marked at the right-hand end. The scale is subdivided so that we can read the current directly.

The low shunt resistance in parallel with the galvanometer makes the resistance of the ammeter small enough that, in calculating circuit currents, we can usually consider it negligible relative to R.

An ammeter is ***always*** *connected in line (in series) with a circuit component to measure the current flowing through that component.*

Since an ammeter is a low-resistance instrument, if an ammeter were connected in parallel with a circuit component, the meter would carry a large current and could burn out. Some meters have fuses to save the meter. Some others have diodes across the galvanometer that protect it from voltages above about 0.5 V.

EXPERIMENTAL PROCEDURE

1. Determine the full-scale current of the galvanometer by setting up the circuit as shown in ● Fig. 3. Set the resistance box to maximum. If you are using the galvanometer from a voltmeter, use clip leads to connect directly to the terminals on the back. Do not connect the meter to measure V_2 yet.

2. After the instructor has checked the circuit, close the switch and reduce the resistance box until the pointer of the meter is on the last mark. The full-scale current I_c is now flowing through both the resistance box and

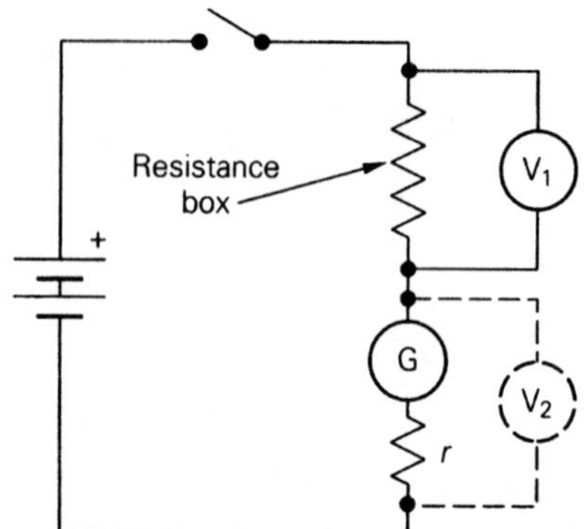

Figure 3 The circuit for measuring the full-scale current and the resistance of a galvanometer. See text for description.

the galvanometer. Record the resistance box setting and the voltmeter reading V_1. Open the switch after the reading is taken. Use Ohm's law to calculate the current I_c:

$$I_c = \frac{V_1}{R_{box}} \tag{4}$$

and record it in the Laboratory Report.

3. Connect the millivoltmeter or a low-range digital voltmeter to measure the voltage V_2. Millivoltmeters tend to have somewhat low resistance and may draw some current away from the galvanometer. If the galvanometer reading falls below the maximum, adjust the resistance box until the galvanometer needle indicates that the full maximum coil current is again flowing through the galvanometer.

   Record the voltage across the galvanometer V_2. Open the switch after the reading is taken. Use Ohm's law to calculate the resistance of the galvanometer coil:

$$r = \frac{V_2}{I_c} \tag{5}$$

and record it in the Laboratory Report.

A. *The dc Voltmeter*

4. Use Eq. 1 to calculate the multiplier resistance for a 1.5-V voltmeter (a voltmeter with a maximum reading of 1.5 V).

5. Set the resistance box as a multiplier resistor by setting it to the calculated value, and use this "home-grown" meter to measure the voltage of a dry cell. Compare this reading to the value read by the voltmeter provided and find the percent difference.

6. Design and build a 6-V and a 15-V voltmeter. Test each by using it to measure the voltage of the 6-V supply, and compare your measurement to that of the provided voltmeter.

7. Devise and draw a circuit for building a triple-scale voltmeter where the scale is changed by connecting to different terminals. If possible, look inside a triple-scale voltmeter and compare its circuit to yours.

B. *The dc Ammeter*

8. Use Eq. 3 to calculate the shunt resistance necessary to make a 300-mA (0.3-A) ammeter from your galvanometer. This can be recorded in Data Table 3 as the first scale of the three-scale meter you will be making later.

9. Small resistances like those used for ammeter shunts are hard to obtain from resistance boxes. The slide wire that is used for the Wheatstone bridge or the potentiometer experiments can be used for this purpose. We will measure the resistance of the 1-meter-long wire and then calculate the length required to provide the required shunt resistance.

   To measure the resistance of the wire, connect the voltmeter and ammeter as shown in ● Fig. 4a. Initially set the resistance box to 20 Ω. Use the 500-mA (0.5-A) scale of the ammeter.

10. After the instructor has checked your circuit, close the switch and carefully reduce the resistance until the ammeter reads about 500 mA (0.5 A). Record the current and voltage under slide-wire data. Open the switch and calculate the resistance of the wire using Ohm's law.

11. Compute the length of wire that will have a resistance equal to the required shunt resistance.

$$\text{Length} = \frac{\text{shunt } R}{R \text{ of one meter}} \tag{6}$$

12. Near the "zero" end of the wire, construct a shunt by attaching two clip leads as shown in Fig. 4b. Make the distance between the leads equal to the length computed above. Attach the other ends of these leads to your galvanometer. Your ammeter is complete.

13. Test your ammeter. Set the resistance box to 100 Ω. As you reduce the resistance, compare the readings of your meter with that of the ammeter at about 100, 200, and 300 mA, and record the results in Data Table 2. **Note:** Whenever a connection is made, there is an unpredictable amount of contact resistance. Contact resistance can give large errors when dealing with small resistances. The better high-current shunts are four-terminal resistors, providing separate terminals for the current-carrying wires and the wires to the galvanometer.

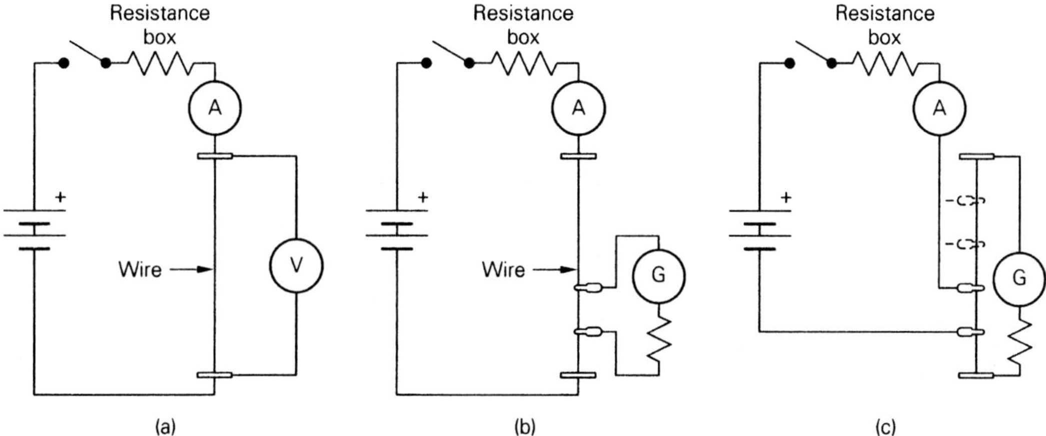

Figure 4 Experiment circuits. (a) Circuit to measure the resistance of a wire. (b) Single-range ammeter. (c) Multirange ammeter. See text for description.

This way, the extra voltage drop at the current-carrying connections is not included in the shunt voltage drop seen by the galvanometer. Our slide-wire shunt has provided us with these separate connections.

14. Making a three-range ammeter is a little more complex than making a three-range voltmeter. The first step toward expanding your ammeter into a three-range ammeter will be to reverse the connections as shown in Fig. 4c.

Connect the galvanometer to the ends of the wire, and connect the circuit so that the current flows in and out through the clip leads. It may be less obvious, but the contact resistance at the current connections is still not a part of the shunt resistance seen by the galvanometer.

15. Test your ammeter again against the laboratory meter. It will probably read a little lower this time. The extra wire of the slide wire in effect increases the r of the galvanometer. Adjust the length of the shunt by sliding the clip up the wire until both meters read the same. Record this as the experimental length in Data Table 3 and compute the percent difference.

16. To add a second scale to your meter, first calculate the shunt resistance and wire length for a 150-mA meter. Leave the first two clip leads in place. Attach a third lead at the calculated distance from the zero-end lead.

You now have a two-scale meter with the zero-end lead acting as the common terminal. Test your meter against the laboratory meter and adjust the length until the meters agree. Record the computed and experimental lengths.

17. Repeat the process, and add a third scale with a full-scale reading of 60 mA.

18. If possible, look inside a laboratory triple-scale ammeter and compare its circuit with yours. Draw the circuit for the triple-scale ammeter.

Name ______________________ Section ______________ Date ______________

Lab Partner(s) ____

EXPERIMENT 15

The Voltmeter and Ammeter

TI Laboratory Report

Galvanometer characteristics:

Resistance box setting ______________

V_1 ______________

Full-scale coil current I_c ______________

Full-scale voltage drop V_2 ______________

Galvanometer resistance r ______________

A. The dc Voltmeter

DATA TABLE 1

Scale	R_m ( )	Your meter ( )	Lab voltmeter ( )	Percent difference

Circuit diagram for a triple-scale voltmeter:

Don't forget units

(continued)

B. The dc Ammeter

Slide-wire data:

Current ____________ Voltage ____________

Computed resistance for one meter ____________

DATA TABLE 2

Your meter ( )	Lab voltmeter ( )	Percent difference

DATA TABLE 3

Scale	Shunt resistance ( )	Computed length ( )	Experimental length ( )	Percent difference

Circuit diagram for a triple-scale ammeter:

Name ______________________ Section ______________ Date ______________

Lab Partner(s) ____

 QUESTIONS

1. Indicate how the dial for the triple-scale voltmeter with 1.5-V, 6-V, and 15-V scales might be labeled.

2. What would be the lowest voltage scale that could be made using your galvanometer?

3. The sensitivity of a voltmeter is commonly expressed in *ohms per volt* (Ω/V), which is the total resistance of the meter ($r + R_m$) divided by the full-scale reading. Calculate the *ohms per volt* sensitivity for each of the three voltage scales that you designed for your galvanometer. Are they the same? Are they equal to $1/I_c$?

(continued)

4. Indicate how the dial for the triple-scale ammeter you designed might be labeled.

0
0
0

5. Ammeter shunts are rated in terms of the voltage drop when the rated full-scale current is flowing. For example, it might be 200 A, 50 mV. What would be the millivolt rating on shunts designed for use with your galvanometer?

6. **Challenge question:** If ρ is the linear resistivity of the slide wire used for the ammeter shunts, the shunt resistance in Eq. 3 is $\rho\ell$, and the resistance of the rest of the wire, $\rho(1 - \ell)$, is added to the galvanometer resistance r. Make these changes to Eq. 3, and solve for ℓ to obtain an equation that compensates for the extra wire length when the lengths for shunts are calculated.

Name ______________________ Section ______________ Date ______________

Lab Partner(s) ____

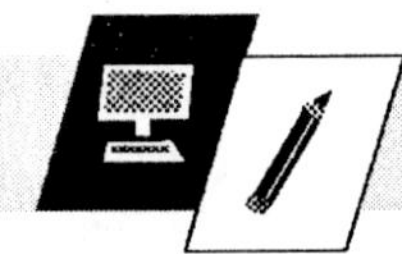

EXPERIMENT 16

Resistances in Series and Parallel

TI Advance Study Assignment

Read the experiment and answer the following questions.

1. Explain the difference between series and parallel connections.

2. Consider resistors are connected in series.
   a. How are the voltage drops across the individual resistors related to the voltage supplied by the battery?

   b. How are the currents through the individual resistors related to the current supplied by the battery?

3. Consider resistors are connected in parallel.
   a. How are the voltage drops across the individual resistors related to the voltage supplied by the battery?

   b. How are the currents through the individual resistors related to the current supplied by the battery?

(continued)

4. Give (draw and explain) an analogy to liquid flow for the series-parallel circuit in part C of the experiment.

5. How would the current divide in a parallel branch of a circuit containing two resistors R_1 and R_2 if (a) $R_1 = R_2$, and (b) $R_1 = 4R_2$?

Name ______________________ Section ______________ Date ______________

Lab Partner(s) ____

CI Advance Study Assignment

Read the experiment and answer the following questions.

1. Explain the difference between series and parallel connections.

2. Consider resistors are connected in series.
   a. How are the voltage drops across the individual resistors related to the voltage supplied by the battery?

   b. How are the currents through the individual resistors related to the current supplied by the battery?

3. Consider resistors are connected in parallel.
   a. How are the voltage drops across the individual resistors related to the voltage supplied by the battery?

   b. How are the currents through the individual resistors related to the current supplied by the battery?

(continued)

4. In a plot of voltage versus current, what physical quantity is represented by the slope of the graph?

EXPERIMENT 16

Resistances in Series and Parallel

OVERVIEW

Experiment examines resistances in parallel and series combinations with both TI and CI procedures. In the TI procedure, the resistances are measured using a voltmeter and ammeter. In the CI procedure, measurements are made with a voltage (and current) sensor, and graphs of V versus I are plotted, from which the resistances are given by the slopes.

INTRODUCTION AND OBJECTIVES

The components of simple circuits are connected in series and/or parallel arrangements. Each component may be represented as a resistance to the current in the circuit. In computing the voltage and current requirements of the circuit (or part of the circuit), it is necessary to know the equivalent resistances of the series and parallel arrangements.

In this experiment, the circuit characteristics of resistors in series and parallel will be investigated. A particular circuit will first be analyzed theoretically, and then those predictions will be checked experimentally.

After performing this experiment and analyzing the data, you should be able to:

TI OBJECTIVES

1. Describe the current-voltage relationships for resistances in series.
2. Describe the current-voltage relationships for resistances in parallel.
3. Reduce a simple series–parallel resistance circuit to a single equivalent resistance, and compute the voltage drops across and the currents through each resistance in the circuit.

CI OBJECTIVES

1. Describe the current-voltage relationships for resistances in series.
2. Describe the current-voltage relationships for resistances in parallel.
3. Describe the changes in the slopes of V-versus-I graphs as more resistors are connected in (a) series and (b) parallel.

TI EXPERIMENT 16

Resistances in Series and Parallel

TI EQUIPMENT NEEDED*

- Battery or power supply (3 V)
- Ammeter (0 to 500 mA)
- Voltmeter (0 to 3 V)
- Single-pole, single-throw (SPST) switch
- Four resistors (10 Ω, 20 Ω, 100 Ω, and 10 kΩ, composition type, 1 W)
- Connecting wires

* The ranges of the equipment are given as examples. These may be varied to apply to available equipment.

TI THEORY

A. Resistances in Series

Resistors are said to be **connected in series** when they are connected as in ● TI Fig. 1. (The resistors are connected in line or "head to tail," so to speak, although there is no distinction between the connecting ends of a resistor.) When they are connected to a voltage source V and the switch is closed, the source supplies a current I to the circuit.

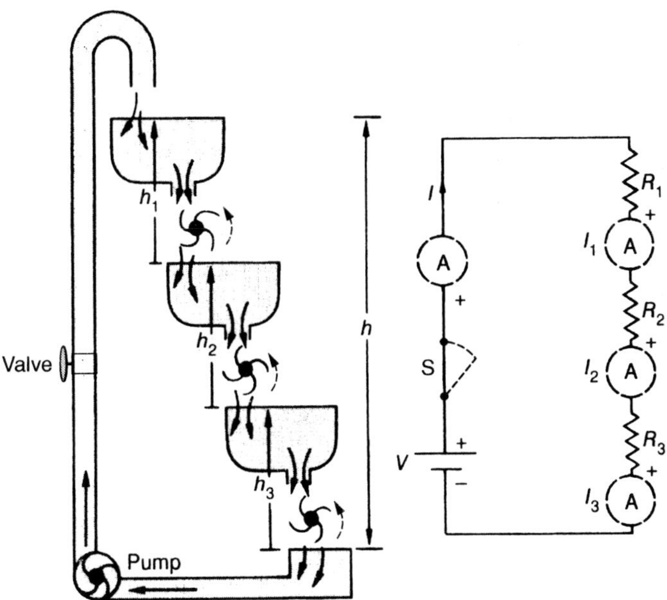

TI Figure 1 Series connection. A liquid analogy on the left for the circuit diagram of resistors in series on the right. The analogies are: pump–voltage source, valve–switch, liquid flow–current, and paddle wheels–resistors. See text for more description.

By the conservation of charge, this current I flows through each resistor. The voltage drop across each resistor is not equal to V, but the *sum* of the voltage drops is:

$$V = V_1 + V_2 + V_3 \qquad \textbf{(TI 1)}$$

In an analogous liquid-gravity circuit (TI Fig. 1), a pump, corresponding to the voltage source, raises the liquid a distance h. The liquid then falls or "drops" through three paddle wheel "resistors" and the distances h_1, h_2, and h_3. The liquid "rise" supplied by the pump is equal to the sum of the liquid "drops," $h = h_1 + h_2 + h_3$. Analogously, the voltage "rise" supplied by the source is equal to the sum of the voltage drops across the resistors (TI Eq. 1).*

The voltage drop across each resistor is given by Ohm's law (e.g., $V_1 = IR_1$). TI Eq. 1 may be written

$$\begin{aligned} V &= V_1 + V_2 + V_3 \\ &= IR_1 + IR_2 + IR_3 \\ &= I(R_1 + R_2 + R_3) \end{aligned} \qquad \textbf{(TI 2)}$$

For a voltage across a single resistance R_s in a circuit, $V = IR_s$, and by comparison,

$$\boxed{R_s = R_1 + R_2 + R_3} \qquad \textbf{(TI 3)}$$

(resistances in series)

where R_s *is the equivalent resistance of the resistors in series.* That is, the three resistors in series could be replaced by a single resistor with a value of R_s, and the same current I would be drawn from the battery.

* Keep in mind that an analogy represents only a resemblance. Liquid and electrical circuits are quite different physically.

B. Resistances in Parallel

Resistors are said to be **connected in parallel** when connected as in ● TI Fig. 2. (In this arrangement, all the "heads" are connected, as are all of the "tails.") The voltage drops across all the resistors are the same and equal to the voltage V of the source. However, the current I from the source divides among the resistors such that

$$I = I_1 + I_2 + I_3 \qquad \textbf{(TI 4)}$$

In the liquid circuit analogy (TI Fig. 2), the height h the pump raises the liquid is equal to the distance the liquid "drops" through each paddle wheel "resistor." The liquid flow coming into the junction of the parallel arrangement divides among the three pipe paths, analogously to the current dividing in the electrical circuit.

The current in an electrical parallel circuit divides according to the magnitudes of the resistances in the parallel branches—the smaller the resistance of a given branch, the greater the current through that branch. The current through each resistor is given by Ohm's law (e.g., $I_1 = V/R_1$), and TI Eq. 4 may be written

$$I = I_1 + I_2 + I_3 = \frac{V}{R_1} + \frac{V}{R_2} + \frac{V}{R_3}$$

$$= V\left(\frac{1}{R_1} + \frac{1}{R_2} + \frac{1}{R_3}\right) \qquad \textbf{(TI 5)}$$

For the current through a single resistance R_p in a circuit, $I = V/R_p$, and by comparison,

$$\boxed{\frac{1}{R_p} = \frac{1}{R_1} + \frac{1}{R_2} + \frac{1}{R_3}} \qquad \textbf{(TI 6)}$$

(resistances in parallel)

where R_p *is the equivalent resistance of the resistors in parallel.* That is, the three resistors in parallel could be replaced by a single resistor with a value of R_p, and the same current I would be drawn from the battery.

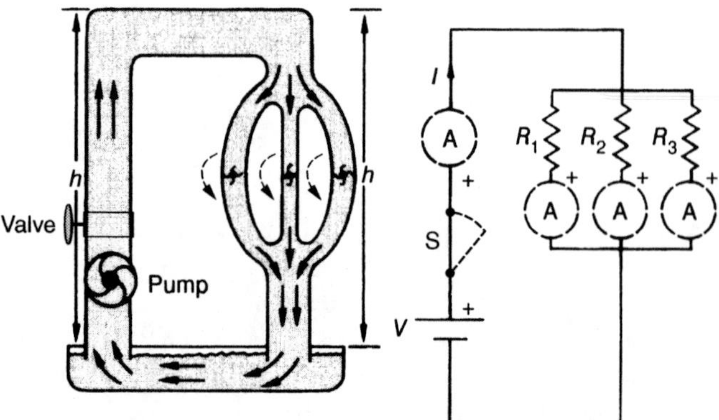

TI Figure 2 Parallel connection. A liquid analogy on the left for the circuit diagram of resistors in parallel on the right. See text for description.

The previous developments for equivalent resistances may be extended to any number of resistors (i.e., $R_s = R_1 + R_2 + R_3 + R_4 + \cdots$ and $1/R_p = 1/R_1 + 1/R_2 + 1/R_3 + 1/R_4 + \cdots$).

In many instances, two resistors are connected in parallel in a circuit, and

$$\frac{1}{R_p} = \frac{1}{R_1} + \frac{1}{R_2}$$

or

$$\boxed{R_p = \frac{R_1 R_2}{R_1 + R_2}} \qquad \textbf{(TI 7)}$$

(two resistances in parallel)

This particular form of R_p for two resistors may be more convenient for calculations than the reciprocal form.

Also, in a circuit with three resistors in parallel, the equivalent resistance of two of the resistors can be found by TI Eq. 7, and then the equation may be applied again to the equivalent resistance and the other resistance in parallel to find the total equivalent resistance of the three parallel resistors. However, if your calculator has a $1/x$ function, the reciprocal form may be easier to use.

Note that the voltage drops across R_1 and R_2 in parallel are the same, and by Ohm's law,

$$I_1 R_1 = I_2 R_2$$

or

$$\frac{I_1}{I_2} = \frac{R_2}{R_1} \qquad \textbf{(TI 8)}$$

TI Example 1 Given two resistors R_1 and R_2, with $R_2 = 2R_1$, in parallel in a circuit, what fraction of the current I from the voltage source goes through each resistor?

Solution With $R_2 = 2R_1$, or $R_2/R_1 = 2$, by TI Eq. 8

$$I_1 = \left(\frac{R_2}{R_1}\right) I_2 = 2I_2$$

Since $I = I_1 + I_2$, we have

$$I = I_1 + I_2 = 2I_2 + I_2 = 3I_2$$

or

$$I_2 = \frac{I}{3}$$

Hence, the current divides with one-third going through R_2 and two-thirds going through R_1.

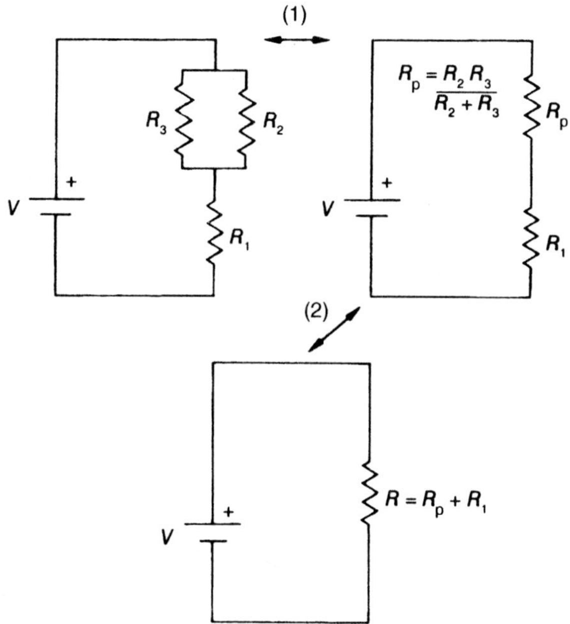

TI Figure 3 Circuit eduction. Series and parallel resistances are combined to find the equivalent resistance of a series-parallel circuit. See text for description.

Thus, the ratio of the resistances gives the relative magnitudes of the currents in the resistors.

Consider the circuit in ● TI Fig. 3. To find the equivalent resistance of this series–parallel circuit, one first "collapses" the parallel branch into a single equivalent resistance, which is given by TI Eq. 7. This equivalent resistance is in series with R_1, and the total equivalent resistance R of the circuit is $R = R_1 + R_p$.

TI Experimental Procedure

1. Examine the resistors. The colored bands conform to a color code that gives the value of a resistor. Look up the color code in Appendix A, Table A5, read the value of each resistor, and record in the Laboratory Report. Designate the smallest resistance as R_1 and consecutively larger values as R_2, R_3, and R_4.

2. In the following procedures, you will be asked to compute theoretically various quantities for a given circuit arrangement. The quantities are then determined by actual circuit measurements, and the calculated and experimental results are compared. Before initially activating each circuit arrangement, *have the circuit checked by the instructor, unless otherwise instructed.*

A. Resistors in Series

3. Set up a series circuit with R_1, R_2, and R_3, as in TI Fig. 1, with a switch and only one ammeter in the circuit next to the voltage source. A convenient way to check a circuit to see whether it is properly connected is to trace the path of the current (with your finger) through the circuit.

   Do this for the circuit under consideration to make sure that the current goes through each circuit component in series. Remember, an ammeter is *always* connected in series, and for proper polarity, + is connected to +.

   Connect the voltmeter across (in parallel with) the voltage source. After having the circuit checked by the instructor, close the switch. If using a variable power supply, adjust the voltage, if necessary, to the suggested value (3.0 V). Read and record the voltmeter value (V). This is the voltage "rise" of the source.

   (*Note:* If the needle of the ammeter goes in the wrong direction, reverse the polarity, i.e., reverse the hook-up of the leads of the ammeter.)

   Open the circuit after completing the reading.

4. Using the resistor values and the measured voltage, *compute* (a) the equivalent resistance R_s of the circuit, (b) the current in the circuit, and (c) the voltage drop across each resistor. Show your calculations in the Laboratory Report.

5. Returning to the experimental circuit, close the switch and read the current I. Compare this with the computed value by finding the percent difference. Open the switch and move the ammeter in the circuit to the position "after" the first resistor [i.e., on the opposite side of the resistor from the voltage source so as to measure the current through (coming from) the resistor]. Record this as I_1.

   Carry out this procedure for each resistor and record the currents in the Laboratory Report. The ammeter positions are shown in TI Fig. 1. Leave the switch closed only while readings are being taken.

6. Remove the ammeter from the circuit, and with the voltmeter, measure and record the voltage drop across each resistor and across all three resistors as a group. Remember, a voltmeter is *always* connected in parallel or "across" a circuit element to measure its voltage drop.

7. Compare the experimentally measured values with the theoretically computed values by finding the percent error. (Use the theoretical values as the accepted values.)

B. Resistors in Parallel

8. Set up a parallel circuit with R_1, R_2, and R_3, as in TI Fig. 2, with the ammeter and voltmeter connected as before in procedure 3. Check the circuit arrangement by tracing the current from the source through the circuit to see that it divides into three parallel

branches at the junction of the resistors and comes together again at the opposite junction.

Close the circuit (after it's been checked) and record the voltage and current readings in the Laboratory Report. (If using a variable power supply, adjust the voltage if necessary.)

Open the circuit after reading the voltage.

9. Using the resistor values and the measured voltage, *compute* (a) the equivalent resistance R_p of the circuit, (b) the current supplied by the source, and (c) the current through each resistor. Show your calculations in the Laboratory Report.

10. Returning to the experimental circuit, measure and record the voltage drops across each resistor and across all three resistors as a group.

Remove the voltmeter and connect the ammeter so as to measure the current I supplied by the source. Then move the ammeter to measure the current through each resistor by connecting the meter between a given resistor and one of the common junctions. The ammeter positions are shown in TI Fig. 2. Leave the switch closed only while readings are being taken.

11. Compare the theoretical and experimental values by computing the percent errors.

12. (*Optional*) Repeat procedures 8 through 11 with R_2 replaced by R_4.

C. *Resistors in Series–Parallel*

13. (Compute the following and record in the Laboratory Report.) If R_1 were connected in series with R_2 and R_3 in parallel (TI Fig. 3):

(a) What would be the equivalent resistance R_{sp} of the resistors?
(b) How much current would be supplied by the source?
(c) What would be the voltage drop across R_1?
(d) What would be the voltage drop across R_2 and R_3?
(e) What would be the voltage drop across all three resistors?
(f) What would be the currents through R_2 and R_3?

14. Set up the actual circuit and trace the current flow to check the circuit. With the voltmeter and ammeter, measure and record the calculated quantities.

You need not compute the percent errors in this case. However, make a mental comparison to satisfy yourself that the measured quantities agree with the computed values within experimental error.

Name ______ Section ______ Date ______

Lab Partner(s) ______

EXPERIMENT 16

Resistances in Series and Parallel

TI *Laboratory Report*

Resistor values R_1 ______ R_3 ______

R_2 ______ R_4 ______

A. Resistors in Series

Calculations (show work)

Source voltage V ______

Equivalent resistance R_s ______

Current I ______

Voltage drops across resistors V_1 ______

V_2 ______

V_3 ______

Don't forget units

(continued)

Experimental measurements

Percent error

I ______ ______

I_1 ______ V_1 ______ ______

I_2 ______ V_2 ______ ______

I_3 ______ V_3 ______ ______

$V_1 + V_2 + V_3$ ______

V across resistors as a group ______

B. Resistors in Parallel

Calculations (show work)

Source voltage V ______

Equivalent resistance R_p ______

Current I ______

Current through resistors I_1 ______

I_2 ______

I_3 ______

Experimental measurements

Percent error

I ______ ______

V_1 ______ I_1 ______ ______

V_2 ______ I_2 ______ ______

V_3 ______ I_3 ______ ______

$I_1 + I_2 + I_3$ ______

Name ____________ Section ____________ Date ____________

Lab Partner(s) ____________

EXPERIMENT 16 **_Laboratory Report_**

(Optional Procedure)

Calculations
(show work)

Source voltage V ____________

Equivalent resistance R_p ____________

Current I ____________

Current through resistors I_1 ____________

I_3 ____________

I_4 ____________

Experimental measurements

				Percent error
		I	____________	____________
V_1	____________	I_1	____________	____________
V_3	____________	I_3	____________	____________
V_4	____________	I_4	____________	____________

(continued)

C. Resistors in Series–Parallel

Calculations
(show work)

Source voltage V ______________

Equivalent resistance R_{sp} ______________

Current I ______________

Voltage drops

V_1 ______________

$V_2 = V_3$ ______________

Experimental measurements

Currents

I_2 ______________

I_3 ______________

I ______________

V_1 ______________

$V_2 = V_3$ ______________

I_2 ______________

I_3 ______________

TI QUESTIONS

1. Discuss the sources of error in the experiment.

Name ____________________ Section ____________ Date ____________

Lab Partner(s) ____________________

EXPERIMENT 16 *Laboratory Report*

2. Suppose that the resistors in the various circuit diagrams represented the resistances of light bulbs. When a light bulb "burns out," the circuit is open through that particular component, i.e., R is infinite. Would the remaining bulbs continue to burn for the following conditions? If so, would the bulbs burn more brightly (draw more current) or burn more dimly (draw less current), if:

   (a) R_2 burned out in the circuit in part A?

   (b) R_1 burned out in the circuit in part B?

   (c) Then R_3 also burned out in the circuit in part B?

   (d) R_3 burned out in the circuit in part C?

(continued)

(e) Then R_1 also burned out in the circuit in part C?

3. Explain the effect of replacing R_2 with R_4 in procedure 12. (Explain theoretically even if procedure 12 of the experiment was not done.)

4. For the circuit in Fig. 3, $V = 12$ V, $R_1 = 4\ \Omega$, $R_2 = 6\ \Omega$, and $R_3 = 3\ \Omega$. Show that the power supplied by the battery is equal to that dissipated in the resistors. What principle does this illustrate? Use the accompanying table. (Consider values significant to two decimal places.)

Circuit element	Current I	Power dissipated P
$R_1 = 4\ \Omega$		
$R_2 = 6\ \Omega$		
$R_3 = 3\ \Omega$		
		(total)
		Power supplied
Battery $V = 12$ V		

(Show calculations)

5. Given three resistors of different values, how many possible resistance values could be obtained by using one or more of the resistors? (List the specific combinations—for example, R_1 and R_2 in series.)

CI EXPERIMENT 16

Equipment Needed

This activity is designed for the Science Workshop 750 Interface, which has a built-in function generator.

- Voltage sensor (PASCO CI-6503)
- Science Workshop 750 Interface
- Cables and alligator clips
- Three 1000-Ω resistors

Theory

According to Ohm's law, the current through a resistor is proportional to the voltage but inversely proportional to the resistance:

$$I = \frac{V}{R} \tag{CI 1}$$

Thus if the resistance of a circuit increases, the current decreases, and if the resistance of a circuit decreases, the current increases. On the other hand, the larger the voltage, the larger the current. The overall current in a circuit thus depends on the interplay between the amount of voltage and the amount of resistance.

In this experiment, the total amount of resistance in a circuit will be varied by connecting resistors in series and then in parallel. An increasing voltage will be applied, and the overall current in the circuit (through the voltage source) will be measured.

Rewriting Ohm's law as $V = IR$, notice that a plot of voltage (in the y axis) versus current (in the x axis) must result in a straight line, with the slope equal to the overall resistance in the circuit:

$$\begin{array}{ccc} V & = & R\ I \\ \downarrow & & \downarrow\ \downarrow \\ y & = & m\ x \end{array}$$

Using voltage (and current) sensors, we will find the resistances of the circuits by measuring the slope of a voltage versus current plot.

Setting Up Data Studio

1. Open Data Studio and choose "Create Experiment."
2. From the sensor list, choose a Voltage Sensor. Connect the voltage sensor to the interface, as shown in the computer screen.
3. Double-click on the "Voltage Sensor" icon. The sensor properties window will open. Set the sample rate to 20 Hz, then click OK.
4. Press the Options button on the experiment setup window. The "Sampling Options" window will open. Under "Automatic Stop," set the time to 4.5 seconds. Click OK.
5. Directly below the sensor list there is an icon for Signal Output. Double-click on this icon. The signal generator window will open. (See ● CI Figure 1.)
6. The default form of the signal generator function is a sine wave. Change it to a "Positive Up Ramp Wave" by selecting from the drop menu.
7. Set the amplitude to 2.0 volts and the frequency to 0.20 Hz.
8. Click on the Measurements and Sample Rate button on the signal generator window. A list of measurements will open. Choose to measure the output current. Deselect the measurement of the output voltage.
9. Click on the Calculate button on the main toolbar. The calculator will open. Follow the next steps:
   a. Clear the definition box at the top, and enter the following formula in it:

      Voltage = smooth (20, x)

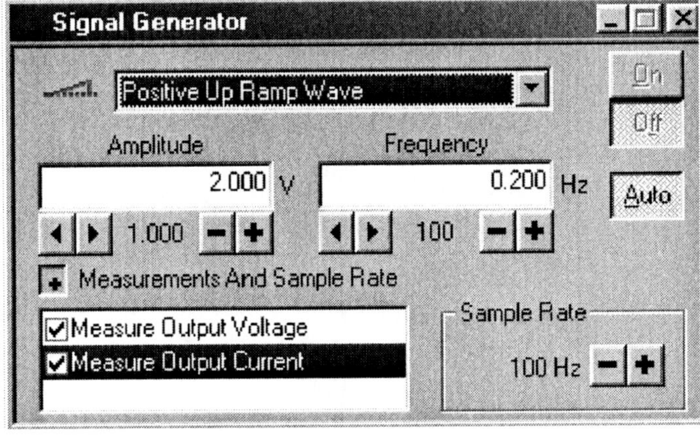

CI Figure 1 The Signal Generator Window. Choose a positive up ramp wave function, adjust the amplitude and the frequency as specified in the setup procedure, and choose to measure the output current. (Data displayed using DataStudio Software. Reprinted courtesy of PASCO scientific.)

b. Press the top Accept button after entering the formula. Notice that the variable x will appear, waiting to be defined.
c. To define the variable, click on the drop menu button on the side of the variable. Define x as a Data Measurement and when prompted choose Voltage (ChA).
d. Press the Accept button.
e. Click on the New button again to define another calculation.
f. Clear the definition box and enter the following formula in it:

Current = smooth (20, x)

g. Press the Accept button after entering the formula. Notice that the variable x will again appear, waiting to be defined.
h. This time define x as a Data Measurement and, when prompted, choose Output Current.
i. Press Accept again.

10. The data list on the top left of the screen should now have the following items: Voltage ChA, Output Current, Voltage, and Current, where a small calculator icon identifies the quantities that are calculated, not measured.
11. Drag the "Voltage" (calculator) icon from the data list and drop it on the "Graph" icon of the displays list. A graph of voltage versus time will open, in a window called Graph 1.
12. Drag the "Current" (calculator) icon from the data list and drop it on top of the time axis of Graph 1. The time axis will change into a current axis. The graph should now be of voltage versus current. ● CI Figure 2 shows what the screen should look like at this point.
13. Double-click anywhere on the graph. The graph settings window will open. Make the following selections:

Under the tab Appearance:

Data:

Connect data points in bold

Deselect the buttons marked "Show Data Points" and "Show Legend Symbols"

Click OK to accept the changes and exit the graph settings window.

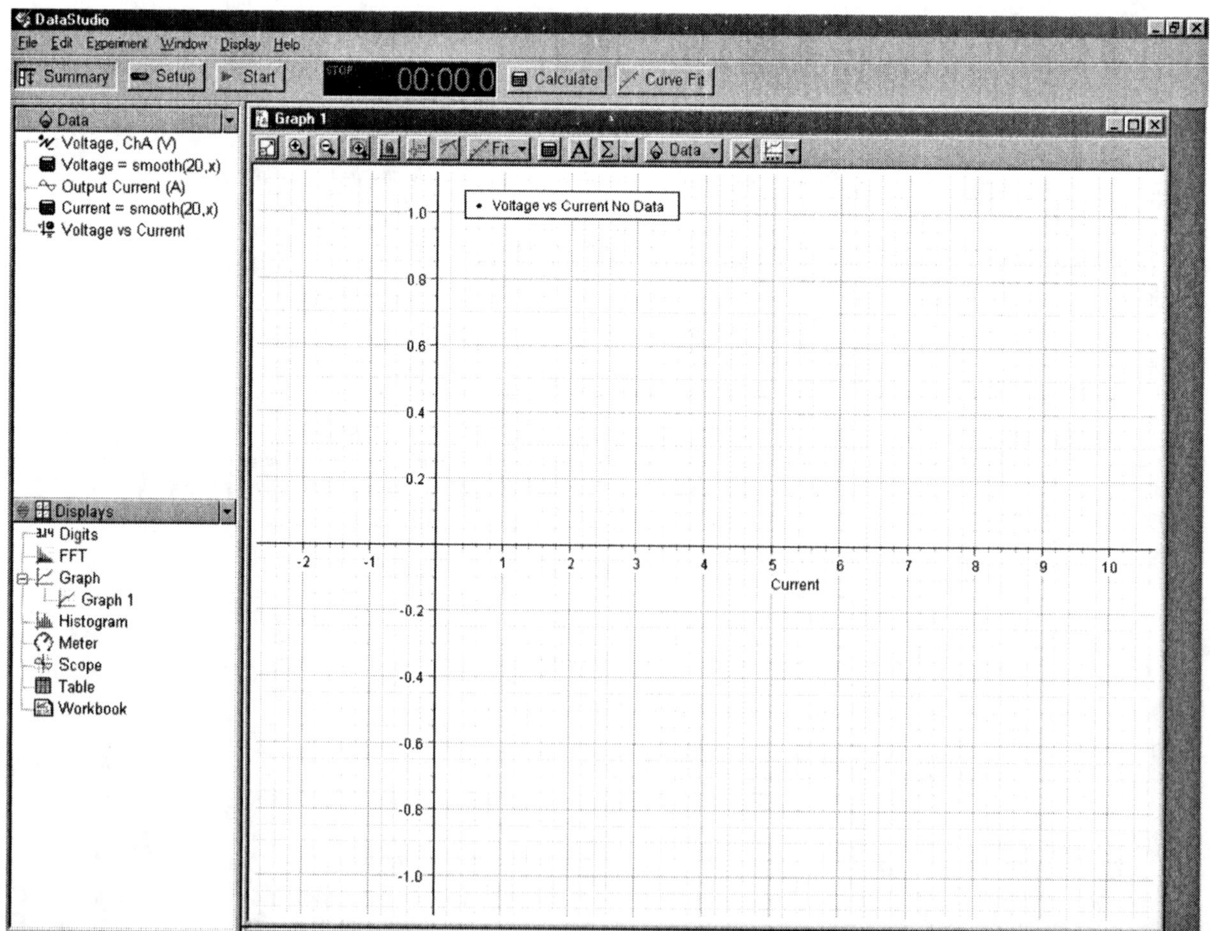

CI Figure 2 Data Studio setup. A graph of voltage versus current will be used to examine different simple circuits. The slope of the graph will represent the resistance of the circuit. (Data displayed using DataStudio Software. Reprinted courtesy of PASCO scientific.)

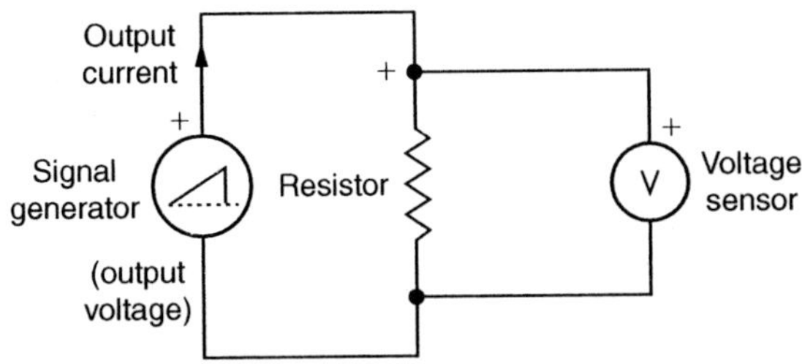

CI Figure 3 The experimental setup. A single resistor is connected to the source, with the voltage sensor connected across the resistor. The positive (red) lead of the voltage sensor must connect to the positive lead of the resistor.

CI EXPERIMENTAL PROCEDURE

A. *Measuring Resistance*

1. Get three resistors and label them R_1, R_2, and R_3.
2. Connect R_1 to the output source of the 750 Interface, using cables and alligator clips, if needed. A circuit diagram for this setup is shown in ● CI Figure 3.
3. Put alligator clips on the prongs of the voltage sensor, and connect the voltage sensor across the resistor. Make sure that the positive of the voltage sensor (red lead) is connected to the positive lead of the resistor.
4. Press the START button. Data collection will stop automatically after 4.5 seconds.
5. Press the Scale-to-Fit button of the graph toolbar. The Scale-to-Fit button is the leftmost button of the graph toolbar. This will scale all data to fit the full screen.
6. Use the Fit menu (on the graph toolbar) to do a "Linear Fit" of the data. A box with information about the fit will appear. Report the slope of the line in CI Data Table 1 as the value of R_1. Do not forget units.
7. Repeat the experiment two more times and determine an average value for R_1.
8. Repeat the process individually with R_2 and R_3.
9. If the graph window gets too crowded, go to "Experiment" (in the main menu, top of the screen) and choose "Delete all Data Runs." This will completely erase the data already collected. The fits can also be removed by deselecting them in the Fit menu.

B. *Resistances in Series*

1. Delete all the data to clear the graph. Also clear all the fits.
2. **Run 1:** Connect R_1 alone to the voltage source and take data, as before. Do a linear fit, and report the measured resistance in CI Data Table 2.
3. Introduce R_2 to the circuit by connecting it in series with R_1.
4. Connect the voltage sensor across both R_2 and R_1. (See ● CI Figure 4.)
5. **Run 2:** Press START and collect the data. Do a linear fit, and report the measured resistance in CI Data Table 2.
6. Now introduce R_3 to the circuit by connecting it in series with both R_2 and R_1.
7. Connect the voltage sensor across all three resistors. (See CI Figure 4.)
8. **Run 3:** Press START and collect the data. Do a linear fit, and report the measured resistance in CI Data Table 2.
9. Remove the fit information boxes and print the graph. Label it "Series Circuits" and attach it to the Laboratory Report.
10. Calculate the theoretical (expected) value of the equivalent resistance of each circuit. Compare the theoretical values with the measured ones by taking a percent difference.
11. Using the print-out of the graph or the Smart-Tool of the graph toolbar, determine the maximum value of the voltage and the maximum value of the current for each run. Report them in CI Data Table 2.

C. *Resistances in Parallel*

1. Delete all the data to clear the graph. Also clear all the fits.
2. **Run 1:** Connect R_1 alone to the voltage source and take data, as before. Do a linear fit, and report the measured resistance in CI Data Table 3.
3. Introduce R_2 to the circuit by connecting it in parallel with R_1.

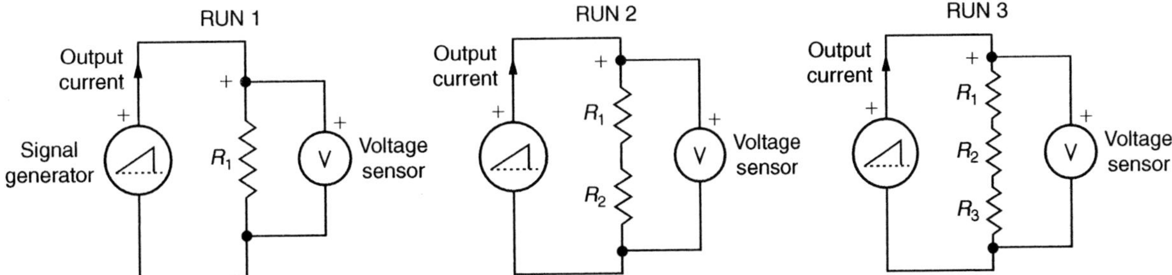

CI Figure 4 Resistors connected in series. Three different series circuits will be analyzed, each time adding an extra resistor to the series.

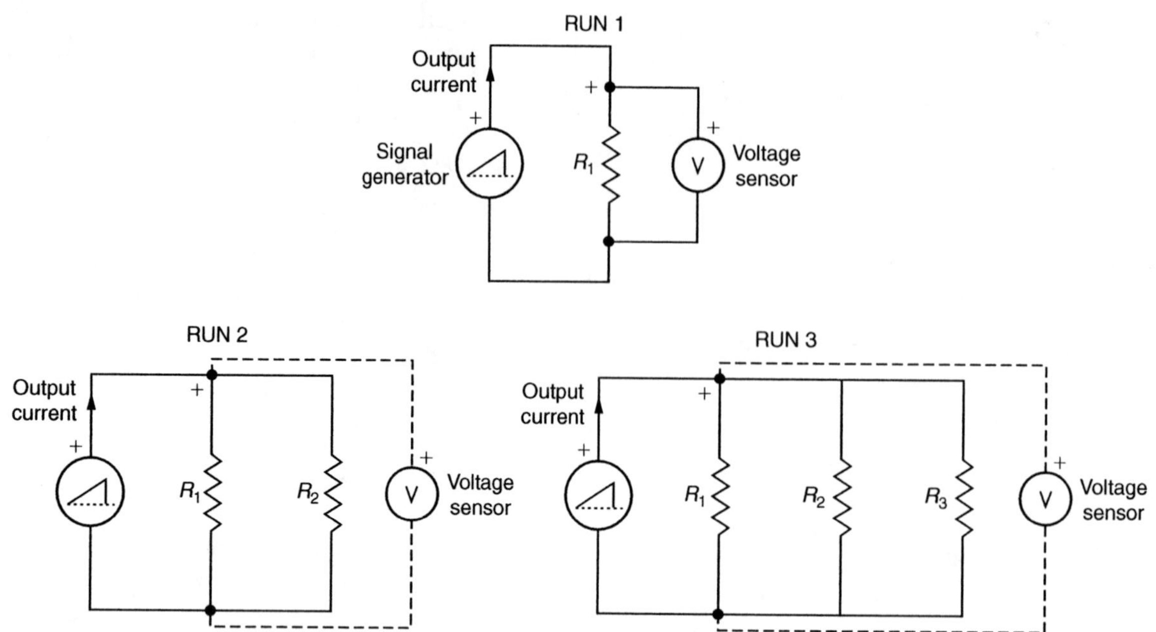

CI Figure 5 Resistors connected in parallel. Three different parallel circuits will be analyzed, each time adding an extra branch to the circuit.

4. Connect the voltage sensor across both R_2 and R_1. (See ● CI Figure 5.)
5. **Run 2:** Press START and collect the data. Do a linear fit, and report the measured resistance in CI Data Table 3.
6. Now introduce R_3 to the circuit by connecting it in parallel with both R_2 and R_1.
7. Connect the voltage sensor across the three resistors. (See CI Figure 5.)
8. **Run 3:** Press START and collect the data. Do a linear fit, and report the measured resistance in CI Data Table 3.
9. Remove the fit information boxes and print the graph. Label it "Parallel Circuits" and attach it to the Laboratory Report.
10. Calculate the theoretical (expected) value of the equivalent resistance of each circuit. Compare the theoretical values with the measured ones by taking a percent difference.
11. Using the print-out of the graph or the Smart-Tool of the graph toolbar, determine the maximum value of the voltage and the maximum value of the current for each run. Report them in CI Data Table 3.

Name ______________________ Section ______________ Date ______________

Lab Partner(s) ____

EXPERIMENT 16

Resistances in Series and Parallel

CI *Laboratory Report*

A. Measuring Resistance

CI DATA TABLE 1

Purpose: To measure the actual resistance of each of the three resistors.

Resistor	Slope measurements	Average resistance
R_1	1.	
	2.	
	3.	
R_2	1.	
	2.	
	3.	
R_3	1.	
	2.	
	3.	

Don't forget units

(continued)

B. *Resistances in Series*

CI **DATA TABLE 2**

Purpose: To experimentally measure the equivalent resistance of series circuits.

	Run 1 R_1 alone	Run 2 R_1 and R_2 in series	Run 3 R_1, R_2, and R_3 in series
Measured equivalent resistance			
Theoretical equivalent resistance $R_s = R_1 + R_2 + \cdots$			
Percent difference			
Maximum voltage			
Maximum current			

Name ______________________ Section ______________ Date ______________

Lab Partner(s) ____

C. *Resistances in Parallel*

CI DATA TABLE 3

Purpose: To experimentally measure the equivalent resistance of parallel circuits.

	Run 1 R_1 alone	Run 2 R_1 and R_2 in parallel	Run 3 R_1, R_2, and R_3 in parallel
Measured equivalent resistance			
Theoretical equivalent resistance $R_p = \left(\frac{1}{R_1} + \frac{1}{R_2} + \cdots\right)^{-1}$			
Percent difference			
Maximum voltage			
Maximum current			

Don't forget units

(continued)

CI QUESTIONS

1. As more resistors were added to the series circuit, what happened to the total resistance of the circuit?

2. For approximately the same maximum voltage, what happened to the maximum current as more resistors were added to the series circuit?

3. As more resistors were added to the parallel circuit, what happened to the total resistance of the circuit?

4. For approximately the same maximum voltage, what happened to the maximum current as more resistors were added to the parallel circuit?

Name ______________________ Section ______________ Date ______________

Lab Partner(s) ____

EXPERIMENT 17

Resistivity

TI Advance Study Assignment

Read the experiment and answer the following questions.

1. What are the factors that affect the resistance of an electrical conductor?

2. If the length and diameter of a wire conductor were both doubled, would the resistance be the same? Explain.

3. Why is resistivity called a material property? What are the units of resistivity, and what is specific resistance?

4. In the experiment, why is it important to close the circuit switch only long enough to obtain meter readings?

(continued)

5. In the Equipment Needed section, wires with American Wire Gauge (AWG) No. 24 and No. 30 are suggested. Given two wires of the same length and material with these AWG numbers, which one would have the greater resistance? Justify your answer. (*Hint:* Take a look in the Appendix.)

Resistivity

Introduction and Objectives

The resistance of an electrical conductor depends on several factors. Its physical shape is one factor. The type of conductor material is another, as might be expected. That is, two conductors with the same physical shape, but of different materials, have different resistances. This important material characteristic of resistance is expressed in terms of a quantity called **resistivity.**

Temperature is another factor that affects resistance. The factors of shape (or dimensions) and resistivity will be considered.

After performing this experiment and analyzing the data, you should be able to:

1. Explain on what factors the resistance of a wire depends and why.
2. Distinguish between resistance and resistivity.
3. Describe how the resistivity of a material may be measured.

Equipment Needed*

- Ammeter (0 to 0.5 A)
- Voltmeter (0 to 3 V)
- Rheostat (20 Ω)
- Single-pole, single-throw switch
- Battery or power supply (3 V)
- Meterstick
- Micrometer calipers
- Conductor board with wires of various types, lengths, and diameters.† For example, use two wires of the same material (No. 24 and 30) and two wires of different material.

* The ranges of the equipment are given as examples. These may be varied to apply to available equipment.

† If resistance spools or coils are used, either the coils should be provided with taps, or coils of different lengths should be provided.

Theory

The resistance of an electrical conductor depends on several factors. Consider a wire conductor. The resistance, of course, depends on the *type* of conductor material and also on (a) the length, (b) the cross-sectional area, and (c) the temperature of the wire.

As might be expected, the resistance of a wire conductor is directly proportional to its length ℓ and inversely proportional to its cross-sectional area A:

$$R \propto \frac{\ell}{A}$$

For example, a 4-m length of wire has twice as much resistance as a 2-m length of the same wire. Also, the larger the cross-sectional area, the greater the current flow (less resistance) for a given voltage.

These geometrical conditions are analogous to those for liquid flow in a pipe. The longer the pipe, the more resistance to flow. But the larger the cross-sectional area of the pipe, the greater the flow rate, or the smaller the resistance to flow.

The material property of resistance is characterized by the **resistivity** ρ, and for a given temperature,

$$R = \frac{\rho \ell}{A} \tag{1}$$

The resistivity is independent of the shape of the conductor, and rearranging Eq. 1 reveals that

$$\rho = \frac{RA}{\ell} \tag{2}$$

From this equation, resistivity can be seen to have the units Ω-m or Ω-cm. Common metal conductors have resistivities on the order of 10^{-6} Ω-cm. Another name sometimes used for resistivity is *specific resistance,* indicating that it is specific for a given material.

To determine the resistivities of some materials, we will use a circuit arrangement as illustrated in ● Fig. 1. The ammeter Ⓐ measures the current I in a wire conductor on the conductor board, and the voltmeter Ⓥ registers the voltage drop V across the conductor. Then the resistance of the wire, by Ohm's law, is $R = V/I$.

By measuring the length ℓ of the wire and its cross-sectional area A (from diameter d measurement, $d/2 = r$ and $A = \pi r^2$), we can calculate the resistivity of the conductor from Eq. 2. The rheostat R_h is used to limit the current in the circuit initially so as to protect the meters.

Experimental Procedure

1. Set up the circuit shown in Fig. 1 with one of the wires on the conductor board in the circuit. Leave the

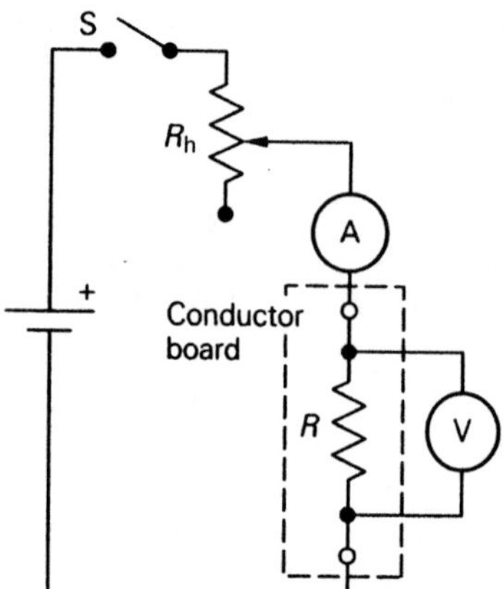

Figure 1 Resistivity measurement. The circuit diagram for the experimental procedure to measure resistivity. See text for description.

switch S open and set the rheostat at maximum resistance. *Have the instructor check the circuit before activating.**

* For best results, the voltmeter should make contact with the resistance wire (R) about 5 cm *in* from the terminals, not *at* the terminals. Also, the copper wire on the conductor board should be a single piece running back and forth several times the length of the board so that readings can be taken with various lengths of this wire (e.g., 1, 2, 3, . . . meters).

2. After the circuit has been checked, close the switch and adjust the rheostat until the current in the circuit as indicated on the ammeter is 0.5 A. Read and record the meter values, and open the switch as soon as possible to prevent heating and temperature change.

3. Measure (a) the length of the wire between the voltmeter connections and (b) the diameter of the wire. Record these in the data table.

4. Test the effect of length. Change the length of the wire being tested to about 0.50 m by moving one of the voltmeter contact points, and repeat the measurements.

5. Return the rheostat to its maximum resistance, and repeat the procedure for the other wires on the board.

6. **(a)** Compute the resistances and cross-sectional areas of the wires, and use these values to determine the resistivities of the materials.
   (b) Find the average resistivity for each material with more than one experimental value.

7. Compare the experimental values of the resistivities with the accepted values listed in Appendix A, Table A6, by computing the percent error.

Name ______________________ Section ____________ Date ____________

Lab Partner(s) ____

EXPERIMENT 17

Resistivity

TI Laboratory Report

DATA TABLE

Purpose: To determine the resistivities of various metals.

Wire	Type of material	Voltage V ( )	Current I ( )	Resistance $R = V/I$ ( )	Length ( )	Diameter ( )	Cross-sectional area ( )	Resistivity ( )
1								
2								
3								
4								

Type of material	Accepted value	Experimental value	Percent error
______	______	______	______
______	______	______	______
______	______	______	______

Calculations (show work)

Don't forget units

(continued)

TI QUESTIONS

1. Do the experimental data confirm that the resistance of a conductor is (a) directly proportional to its length and (b) inversely proportional to its cross-sectional area? Support your answers either graphically or mathematically with experimental results.

2. Give a definition of resistivity in terms of voltage and current.

3. An annealed copper wire (No. 15 AWG gauge) is to be replaced with an aluminum wire with approximately the same length and resistance. What gauge of aluminum wire would be required? (See Appendix A, Table A7, for wire gauges.)

Name ______________________ Section ______________ Date ______________

Lab Partner(s) ______________________

EXPERIMENT 18

Multiloop Circuits: Kirchhoff's Rules

TI Advance Study Assignment

Read the experiment and answer the following questions.

1. Do Kirchhoff's rules represent any new physical principles in the sense that Ohm's law does? Explain.

2. (a) What is a junction?

   (b) Distinguish between a branch and a loop.

3. A household wiring circuit consists of a voltage source (ac power from the electric company) connected across many loads (resistances) in parallel.
   (a) Draw a circuit diagram showing the voltage source and three loads—for example, a light bulb, a clock, and a TV set.

Don't forget units

(continued)

(b) The diagram has several loops. Are Kirchhoff's rules needed to analyze the current through each load? Explain.

4. (a) The direction one goes around a circuit loop makes no difference in the loop theorem equation obtained for the loop. Show this explicitly by going around the loops for the circuit in Example 1 in the opposite directions.

(b) Apply the loop theorem to loop 3 in Fig. 1 and show that it is redundant or unnecessary with the inside loop equations (Example 1).

EXPERIMENT 18

Multiloop Circuits: Kirchhoff's Rules

INTRODUCTION AND OBJECTIVES

The analysis of electrical circuits is the first step toward understanding their operation. By "analysis" we mean the process of calculating how the electrical currents in a circuit depend on the values of the voltage sources (or vice versa). For our discussion, we will refer to any voltage source as a battery with a terminal, or "operating," voltage V.

Many electrical circuits can be analyzed by using nothing more than Ohm's law. The simplest situation consists of one battery (V) and one resistor (R) connected in a single closed loop. In this case, $I = V/R$. Several batteries may appear in series, or several resistors may appear in series.

In these cases, a combination can be represented by a single equivalent element, and then Ohm's law can be used. Situations that look more complicated include the potentiometer and the Wheatstone bridge. These circuits contain more than one loop. However, the loops are independent; that is, there is no current flow between the loops when the bridge is balanced. Thus even these circuits can be analyzed with Ohm's law in this condition.

The more general electrical circuit contains several loops, with batteries and currents shared among the loops. Such a general circuit cannot be analyzed directly by using just Ohm's law. However, it can be analyzed using Kirchhoff's rules, or laws as they are sometimes called. These are named after Gustav Kirchhoff (1824–1887), the German physicist who developed them.

In this experiment,* we will investigate, use, and verify Kirchhoff's rules in analyzing multiloop circuits.

After performing this experiment and analyzing the data, you should be able to:

1. Clearly distinguish between circuit branches and junctions.
2. Apply Kirchhoff's rules to multiloop circuits.
3. Explain how Kirchhoff's rules are related to the conservation of charge and energy.

* Contributed in part by Professor I. L. Fischer, Bergen Community College, New Jersey.

EQUIPMENT NEEDED

- Ammeter (0 to 10/100/1000 mA)
- Voltmeter (0 to 5/25 V)
- Two batteries or voltage supplies (6 V and 12 V)
- Two single-pole, single-throw (SPST) switches
- Composition resistors, 2-W rating (100 Ω, 150 Ω, 220 Ω, 330 Ω, 470 Ω, 680 Ω, 1000 Ω)
- Connecting wires

Note: Items may be varied to apply to available equipment.

THEORY

The simple multiloop circuit shown in ● Fig. 1 will be used to illustrate the principles of Kirchhoff's rules and the terminology involved. The definitions of these terms vary among textbooks, even though the principles remain the same. Therefore, it is important to define terms carefully as they will be used here.

A **junction** is a point in a circuit at which three or more connecting wires are joined together, or a point where the current divides or comes together in a circuit. For example, in Fig. 1a, points B and D are junctions.

A **branch** is a path connecting two junctions, and it may contain one element or two or more elements. In Fig. 1a, there are three branches connecting junctions B and D. These are the left branch BAD, the center branch BCD, and the right branch BD with R_3.

A **loop** is a closed path of two or more branches. There are three loops in the circuit in Fig. 1 , as shown in Fig. 1b — two inside loops (loops 1 and 2) and one outside loop (loop 3). Notice that each loop in this case is a closed path of two branches.

Kirchhoff's Rules

These rules do not represent any new physical principles. They embody two fundamental conservation laws: conservation of electrical charge and conservation of (electrical) energy.

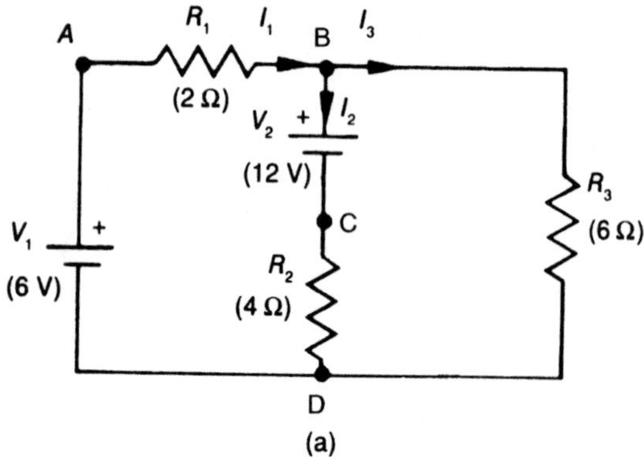

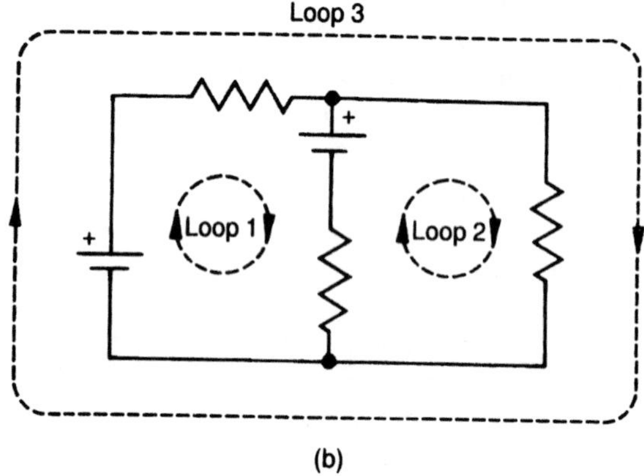

Figure 1 Multiloop circuit. (a) By Kirchhoff's junction theorem, the sum of the currents at a junction is zero; that is, the current into the junction equals the current out, or $I_1 = I_2 + I_3$, at junction B. (b) The circuit has three loops, about which the sum of the voltage changes is zero. (Kirchhoff's loop theorem.)

A current flows in each branch of a circuit. In Fig. 1a these are labeled I_1, I_2, and I_3. At a junction, *by the conservation of electrical charge,* the current (or currents) into a junction equal(s) the current(s) leaving the junction. For example, in Fig. 1a,

$$I_1 = I_2 + I_3$$
(current in = current out)

By the conservation of electrical charge, this means that charge cannot "pile up" or "vanish" at a junction. This current equation may be written

$$I_1 - I_2 - I_3 = 0 \quad (1)$$

Of course, we do not generally know whether a particular current flows into or out of a junction by looking at a multiloop circuit diagram. We simply assign labels and assume the directions in which the branch currents flow at a particular junction.

If these assumptions are wrong, a negative value for the current is obtained from the mathematics, as will be shown in a following example. Notice that once the directions of the branch currents are assigned at one junction, the currents at a common branch junction are fixed; for example, in Fig. 1 a, at junction D, $I_2 + I_3 = I_1$ [current(s) in = current out].

Equation 1 may be written in mathematical notation as

$$\sum_i I_i = 0 \quad (2)$$

which is a mathematical statement of **Kirchhoff's first rule** or **junction theorem:**

The algebraic sum of the currents at any junction is zero.

In a simple single-loop circuit, it is easy to see that *by the conservation of energy,* the voltage "drop" across the resistor must be equal to the voltage "rise" of the battery;* that is,

$$V_{\text{battery}} = V_{\text{resistor}}$$

where the voltage drop across the resistor is by Ohm's law equal to IR, i.e., $V_{\text{resistor}} = IR$.

By the conservation of energy, this means that the energy (per charge) delivered by the battery to the circuit is the same as that expended in the resistances. The conservation law holds for any loop in a multiloop circuit, although there may sometimes be more than one battery and more than one resistor in a particular loop.

In a manner similar to the summation of the currents in the first rule, we may write for the voltages **Kirchhoff's second rule** or **loop theorem:**

$$\sum_i V_i = 0 \quad (3)$$

or

The algebraic sum of the voltage changes around a closed loop is zero.

Since one may go around a circuit loop in either a clockwise or a counterclockwise direction, it is important to establish a sign convention for voltage changes. For example, if we went around a loop in one direction and crossed a resistor, this might be a voltage drop (depending on the current flow). However, if we went around the loop in the opposite direction, we would have a voltage "rise" in terms of potential.

We will use the sign convention illustrated in ● Fig. 2. The voltage change of a battery is taken as positive when the battery is traversed in the direction of the "positive" terminal (a voltage "rise") and as negative if the battery is traversed in the direction of the "negative" terminal. Note that the assigned branch currents have nothing to do with determining the voltage change of a battery; they affect only the direction one goes around a loop or through a battery.

* Here we take the terminal, or "operating," voltage of the battery instead of the emf ($\mathscr{E}$). The terminal, or "operating," voltage of the battery is $V = \mathscr{E} - Ir$, where r is the internal resistance of the battery (not usually known) and Ir is the internal voltage "drop" of the battery.

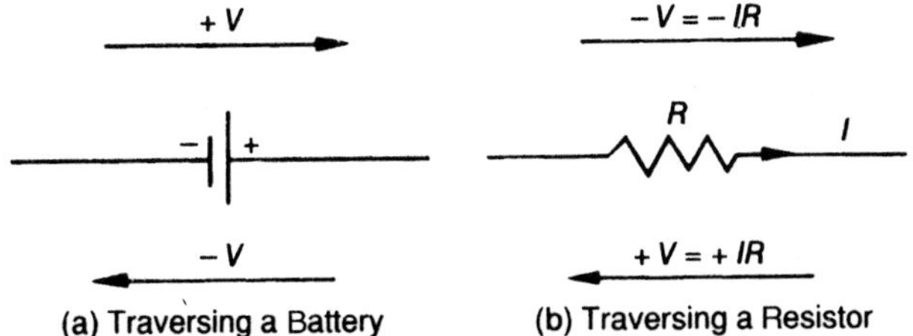

Figure 2 Sign convention for Kirchhoff's rules. (a) In going around a loop and passing through a battery, the voltage change is taken to be positive when the battery is traversed toward the positive terminal and to be negative when the battery is traversed toward the negative terminal. (b) When passing through a resistor in going around a loop, the voltage change across the resistor is taken to be negative ("voltage drop") if the resistor is traversed in the direction of the assigned branch current and as positive if the resistor is traversed in the opposite direction.

The voltage change across a resistor, on the other hand, involves the direction of the assigned current through the resistor. The voltage change is taken to be negative if the resistor is traversed in the direction of the assigned branch current (a voltage "drop") and as positive if the resistor is traversed in the opposite direction.

The sign convention allows you to go around a loop either clockwise or counterclockwise at your choice. Going in opposite directions merely makes all the signs opposite, and Eq. 2 is the same.

Kirchhoff's rules may be used in circuit analysis in several ways. We will consider two methods.

Branch (Current) Method

First, label a current for *each branch* in the circuit. This is done by a current arrowhead, which also indicates the current direction and is most conveniently done at a junction, as in Fig. 1 at junction B. Kirchhoff's first rule applies at any junction. Remember, the current directions are arbitrary, but there must be at least one current in and one current out. (Why?)

Then draw loops so that every branch is in at least one loop. This is shown for the circuit in Fig. 1, which has three loops. Again, the direction of a loop is arbitrary because of our sign convention.

With this done, current equations are written for each junction according to Kirchhoff's junction theorem (rule 1). In general, this gives a set of equations that includes all branch currents. For the simple circuit in Fig. 1, this is one equation, since the sum of the currents at junction D is the same as that at junction B.

Then Kirchhoff's loop theorem (rule 2) is applied to the circuit loops. This gives additional equations that, along with the junction equation, form a set of N equations with N unknowns, which can be solved for the unknowns. There may be more loops than necessary. Only the number of loops that include all branches is needed.

To illustrate this method, the circuit in Fig. 1 is analyzed in the following example. (Assume the component values in the circuit to be exact; that is, ignore the issue of significant figures.)

Example 1 Apply Kirchhoff's rules and the above sign convention to the circuit shown in Fig. 1, and find the value of the current in each branch.

Solution By rule 1 (junction theorem),

$$I_1 = I_2 + I_3 \tag{4}$$

with directions as assigned in the figure.

Going around loop 1 as indicated in the figure, with Kirchhoff's second rule (loop theorem) and our sign convention, we have, starting at battery 1,

$$V_1 - I_1R_1 - V_2 - I_2R_2 = 0$$

or, with known values (units omitted for convenience),

$$6 - I_1(2) - 12 - I_2(4) = 0$$

and

$$I_1 + 2I_2 = -3 \tag{5}$$

Similarly, around loop 2, starting at battery 2,

$$V_2 - I_3R_3 + I_2R_2 = 0$$

or

$$12 - I_3(6) + I_2(4) = 0$$

and

$$3I_3 - 2I_2 = 6 \tag{6}$$

Equations 4 – 6 constitute a set of three equations with three unknowns from which the values of I_1, I_2, and I_3 can be found. Solving these equations for the currents, we obtain

$$I_1 = -\tfrac{3}{11}\text{ A}$$
$$I_2 = -\tfrac{15}{11}\text{ A}$$
$$I_3 = \tfrac{12}{11}\text{ A}$$

The negative values of I_1 and I_2 indicate that the wrong directions were assumed for these currents. In the actual circuit, I_2 would flow into junction B, and I_1 would flow out of the junction as well as I_3 as assumed. Hence, if we had guessed correctly, we would have written, for junction B,

$$I_2 = I_1 + I_3$$
$$\tfrac{15}{11}\text{ A} = \tfrac{3}{11}\text{ A} + \tfrac{12}{11}\text{ A}$$
$$(\text{current in}) = (\text{current out})$$

and $\Sigma I_i = 0$ as required by rule 1.

In looking at Fig. 1 more carefully, one might have surmised this. Battery 2 (12 V) has twice the voltage of battery 1 (6 V), and it would have been a good guess that (conventional) current would flow out of battery 2 toward junction B. If battery 1 were a rechargeable battery, it would be recharging in the circuit. (Why?)

Notice that loop 3 was not used to solve the problem. This loop would have provided a redundant equation with the other two loop equations. However, loop 3 could have been used with one of the other loops to solve the problem.

Loop (Current) Method *(Optional)*

This method is similar to the previous branch method, but some consider it simpler mathematically. Loops are drawn as before so that every branch is in at least one loop. Then each loop is labeled as though it were a current, as shown in ● Fig. 3 for the circuit in Fig. 1. The "current loop" direction is arbitrary, but for simplicity and consistency, many choose to make all the currents clockwise. For resistors like R_2 that are part of two loops, the current down through the resistor is taken as $I_A - I_B$. This way the junction equations are automatically made part of the current equations, simplifying the solution by reducing the number of equations and unknowns.

We then use Kirchhoff's loop theorem (rule 2) to write an equation for each loop, applying the sign convention. For the circuit in Fig. 3, there are two loop equations for the "loop currents" I_A and I_B. These are, starting at V_1 and V_2, respectively,

$$\text{(loop A)} \quad V_1 - I_A R_1 - V_2 - I_A R_2 + I_B R_2 = 0$$

$$\text{(loop B)} \quad V_2 - I_B R_3 - I_B R_2 + I_A R_2 = 0$$

Traversing the current loops produces two equations for this circuit with two unknowns, I_A and I_B. (Note that in the branch method analysis in Example 1, the loop equations had three unknowns.) Putting in the known values, we can solve the equations simultaneously to find the value of each unknown:

$$\text{(loop A)} \quad 6 - I_A(2) - 12 - I_A(4) + I_B(4) = 0$$

$$\text{(loop B)} \quad 12 - I_B(6) - I_B(4) + I_A(4) = 0$$

These reduce to

$$-3I_A + 2I_B = 3$$

$$2I_A - 5I_B = -6$$

Solving for I_A and I_B, we find

$$I_A = -\tfrac{3}{11}\text{ A}$$

$$I_B = \tfrac{12}{11}\text{ A}$$

The computed values of the "loop currents" may then be utilized in a straightforward way to find the actual branch currents. Kirchhoff's junction theorem is applied to the various junctions in the circuit, and the branch currents are compared with the "loop currents." For example, compare the branch currents at junction B in Fig. 1 and the "loop currents" in Fig. 3. (The branch currents may be drawn directly on the current-loop diagram.)

It should be evident by comparison that

$$I_1 = I_A = -\tfrac{3}{11}\text{ A}$$

$$I_2 = I_A - I_B = -\tfrac{3}{11}\text{ A} - \tfrac{12}{11}\text{ A} = -\tfrac{15}{11}\text{ A}$$

$$I_3 = I_B = \tfrac{12}{11}\text{ A}$$

the same values obtained for the circuit by the branch method.

Experimental Procedure

1. Examine the resistors. The colored bands on composition resistors conform to a color code that gives the resistance value of the resistor. Look up the color code in Appendix A, Table A5, to identify each resistor. Note that the actual resistance value may vary according to the tolerance indicated by the last band (gold ±5%, silver ±10%, no band ±20%).

2. Connect the two-loop circuit as illustrated in ● Fig. 4. If you are using variable power supplies, adjust

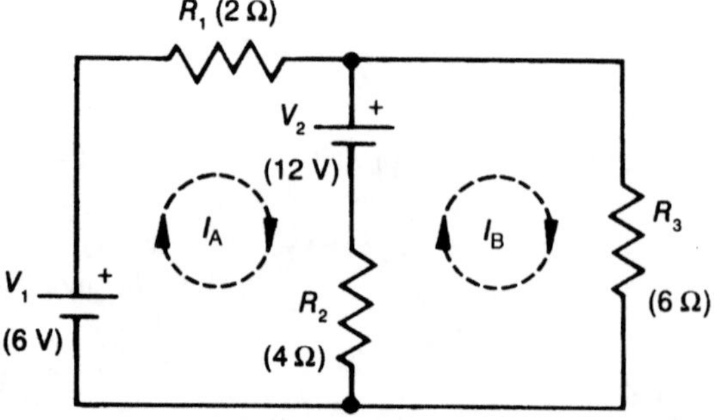

Figure 3 Loop method. In this method, the loops are taken to be "current" loops, with a particular current assigned to each loop.

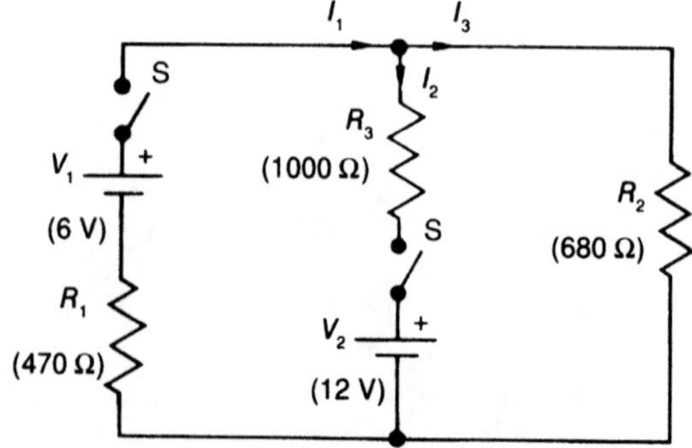

Figure 4 Multiloop circuit. Diagram for experimental two-loop circuit.

each power supply as closely as possible to the values specified in the figure. Leave the switches open until the circuit has been checked by the instructor.

Note: Lay out the circuit on your table exactly as shown in the diagram. This will help prevent errors and will facilitate your measurements.

3. After your circuit has been checked, close the switches and measure the "operating" value of each battery (V_1 and V_2) by temporarily connecting the voltmeter across it. Record these operating values in Data Table 1.

   Caution: *To avoid damage to the voltmeter, always start with the meter on its least sensitive scale. Increase the sensitivity of the meter only as needed for accurate measurement, and remember to return the meter to its least sensitive scale before proceeding.*

4. Temporarily open the switches. Insert the ammeter in series with one of the branches. Close the switches, measure and record the branch current, and then open the switches.

   Caution: *Observe the same precautions described under procedure 3 to avoid damage to the ammeter. Also, if the ammeter deflects downscale (below zero), open the switches before reversing the polarity of the meter.*

5. Repeat procedure 4 for each of the branches.

6. Compute the theoretical values of each branch current for this circuit. In the analysis, use the measured values of the batteries V_1 and V_2 and the labeled values of the resistors (procedure 1). Compare the measured values of the branch currents with the computed theoretical values by finding the percent error.

7. Connect the three-loop circuit as shown in ● Fig. 5. Repeat procedures 3 through 6 for this circuit. The instructor may wish to provide you with a different circuit to investigate. (In Fig. 5, why is there no current indicated between the two connection points on the bottom wire?)

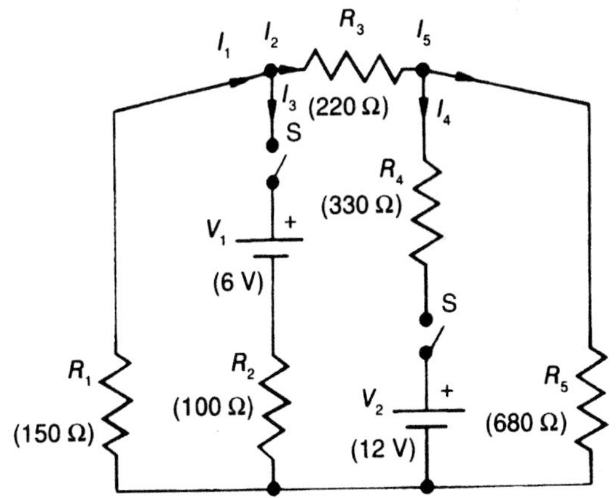

Figure 5 Multiloop circuit. Diagram for experimental three-loop circuit.

Name ______________________ Section ______________ Date ______________

Lab Partner(s) ____

EXPERIMENT 18

Multiloop Circuits: Kirchhoff's Rules

TI Laboratory Report

DATA TABLE 1

Purpose: To investigate Kirchhoff's rules by means of a two-loop circuit (Fig. 4).

R_1 ______________

R_2 ______________

R_3 ______________

	Measured value ( )	Theoretical value ( )	Percent error
V_1		X	X
V_2		X	X
I_1			
I_2			
I_3			

Calculations (show work)

DATA TABLE 2

Purpose: To investigate Kirchhoff's rules by means of a three-loop circuit (Fig. 5).

R_1 ______________ R_4 ______________

R_2 ______________ R_5 ______________

R_3 ______________

	Measured value ( )	Theoretical value ( )	Percent error
V_1		X	X
V_2		X	X
I_1			
I_2			
I_3			
I_4			
I_5			

Don't forget units

(continued)

TI QUESTIONS

1. Discuss the major sources of error in this experiment.

2. Using the values in Data Table 1, compare the power supplied by the batteries to that dissipated by the resistors. What would you expect, and what principle does this illustrate? Comment on your results.

3. Two batteries with emf's of 1.5 V and 1.2 V and internal resistances of 0.50 Ω and 0.80 Ω, respectively, are connected in parallel with + terminals together.
   (a) Determine the current they would deliver to an external resistance of 2.0 Ω.

   (b) Would more current be delivered if only one battery were used? If so, which one? Explain.

Name ______________________ Section ______________ Date ______________

Lab Partner(s) ____

EXPERIMENT 19

Reflection and Refraction

TI Advance Study Assignment

Read the experiment and answer the following questions.

1. What is the law of reflection, and does it apply to all reflecting surfaces?

2. Distinguish between regular and irregular reflection. Give an example of each.

3. Why is light refracted when it passes from one medium into an optically different medium?

(continued)

4. Show by Snell's law that if the speed of light is less in a particular medium, then a light ray is bent toward the normal when entering that medium. What happens if the speed of light is greater in the medium?

5. What is the difference between the relative index of refraction and the absolute index of refraction? Explain why we can experimentally determine the absolute index of refraction fairly accurately using air as a medium.

Reflection and Refraction

Introduction and Objectives

Reflection and refraction are two commonly observed properties of light. The reflection of light from smooth and polished surfaces, such as ponds of water and mirrors, enables us to view the images of objects. Also, when light passes from one medium into another, it is bent, or refracted. As a result, a stick in a pond or a spoon in a glass of water appears to be bent.

As part of geometrical optics, these phenomena are explained by the behavior of light rays. Through ray tracing, we can conveniently investigate the physical laws of reflection and refraction in the laboratory. In this experiment, we employ a plane mirror and a glass plate to study these laws and the parameters used in describing the reflection and refraction of light.

After performing this experiment and analyzing the data, you should be able to:

1. Describe the law of reflection and explain how it can be verified experimentally.
2. Explain Snell's law and its application to transparent materials.
3. Explain what the index of refraction tells you about a transparent material and how it can be measured experimentally.

Equipment Needed

- Pins
- Pin board (cardboard or poster board suffices)
- Sheets of white paper ($8\frac{1}{2} \times 11$ in.)
- Ruler and protractor
- Short candle (less than 5 cm) or some similar light source
- Rectangular mirror (and holder if available)
- Thick glass plate (approximately 8×10 cm)

Note: Ray boxes may be used if available.

Theory

A. Reflection

When light strikes the surface of a material, some light is usually reflected. The reflection of light rays from a plane surface such as a glass plate or a plane mirror is described by the **law of reflection:**

> *The angle of incidence is equal to the angle of reflection (that is, $\theta_i = \theta_r$).*

These angles are measured from a line perpendicular or *normal* to the reflecting surface at the point of incidence (● Fig. 1). Also, the incident and reflected rays and the normal lie in the same plane.

The rays from an object reflected by a smooth plane surface appear to come from an image behind the surface, as shown in the figure. From congruent triangles it can be seen that the image distance d_i from the reflecting surface is the same as the object distance d_o. Such reflection is called **regular** or **specular reflection.**

The law of reflection applies to any reflecting surface. If the surface is relatively rough, like the paper of this page, the reflection becomes diffused or mixed, and no image of the source or object will be produced. This type of reflection is called **irregular** or **diffuse reflection.**

B. Refraction

When light passes from one medium into an optically different medium at an angle other than normal to the surface,

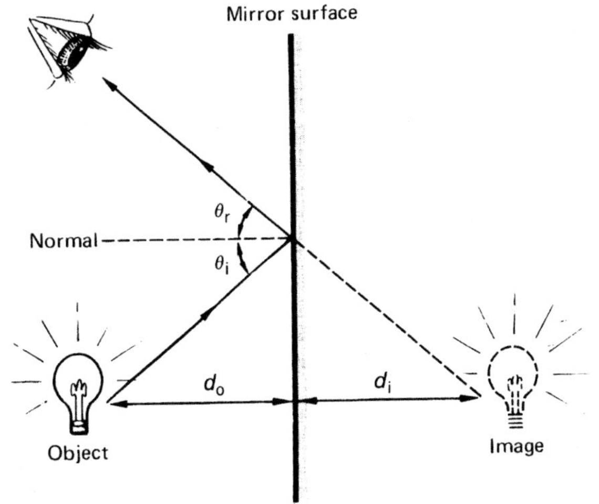

Figure 1 Law of reflection. The angle θ_i between the incident ray and the normal to the surface is equal to the angle θ_r between the reflected ray and the normal; that is, $\theta_i = \theta_r$. (Only a single ray is shown.) The object distance d_o is also equal to the image distance d_i for a plane mirror.

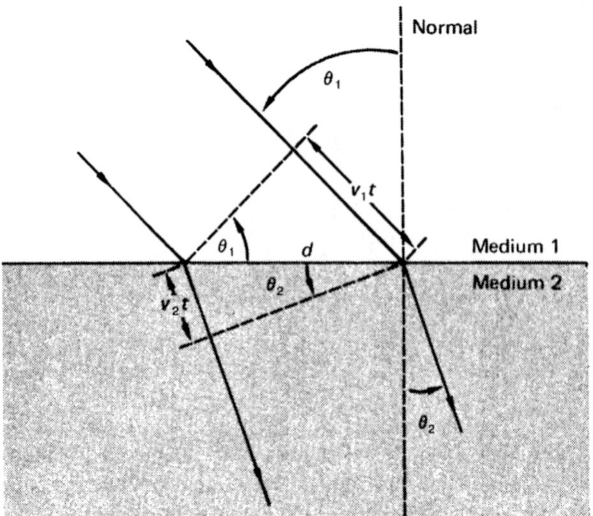

Figure 2 Refraction of two parallel rays. When medium 2 is more optically dense than medium 1, then $v_2 < v_1$ and the rays are bent toward the normal as shown here. If $v_2 > v_1$, the rays are bent away from the normal (as though the ray arrows were reversed in reverse ray tracing here).

it is "bent," or undergoes a change in direction, as illustrated in ● Fig. 2 for two parallel rays in a beam of light. This is due to the different velocities of light in the two media. In the case of refraction, θ_1 is the angle of incidence and θ_2 is the angle of refraction.

From the geometry of Fig. 2, where d is the distance between the parallel rays at the boundary, we have

$$\sin \theta_1 = \frac{v_1 t}{d} \quad \text{and} \quad \sin \theta_2 = \frac{v_2 t}{d}$$

or

$$\frac{\sin \theta_1}{\sin \theta_2} = \frac{v_1}{v_2} = n_{12} \tag{1}$$

where the ratio of the velocities n_{12} is called the **relative index of refraction.** Equation 1 is known as **Snell's law.** If $v_2 < v_1$ (as in Fig. 2), the rays are bent toward the normal in the second medium. And if $v_2 > v_1$, the rays are bent away from the normal (e.g., reversed rays in Fig. 2 with medium 2 taken as medium 1).

For light traveling initially in vacuum (or approximately for light traveling initially in air), the relative index of refraction is called the **absolute index of refraction** or simply the **index of refraction,** and

$$n = \frac{c}{v} \tag{2}$$

where c is the speed of light in vacuum and v is the speed of light in the medium. Hence, the index of refraction of vacuum is $n = c/c = 1$, and for air $n \simeq c/c = 1$. For water, $n = 1.33$.

Snell's law can then be written

$$\frac{\sin \theta_1}{\sin \theta_2} = \frac{v_1}{v_2} = \frac{c/n_1}{c/n_2} = \frac{n_2}{n_1}$$

or

$$n_1 \sin \theta_1 = n_2 \sin \theta_2 \tag{3}$$

where n_1 and n_2 are in indices of refraction of the first and second media, respectively.

We see from Eq. 2 that the index of refraction is a measure of the speed of light in a transparent material, or a measure of what is called the **optical density** of a material.* For example, the speed of light in water is less than that in air, so water is said to have a greater optical density than air. Thus the greater the index of refraction of a material, the greater its optical density and the lesser the speed of light in the material.

In terms of the indices of refraction and Snell's law (Eq. 3), we have the following relationships for refraction:

- If the second medium is more optically dense than the first medium ($n_2 > n_1$), the refracted ray is bent *toward* the normal ($\theta_2 < \theta_1$), as in Fig. 2.
- If the second medium is less optically dense than the first medium ($n_2 < n_1$), the refracted ray is bent *away from* the normal ($\theta_2 > \theta_1$), as for reverse ray tracing in Fig. 2.

Experimental Procedure

A. *Reflection*

Glass Plate as a Mirror

1. Place a sheet of white paper on the table. As illustrated in ● Fig. 3, draw a line where the candle (or object) will be placed. The line should be drawn parallel to the shorter edge of the page and about 3 to 4 cm from that edge. Make a mark near the center of the line, and place the candle on the mark.

* Optical density does not correlate directly with mass density. In some instances, a material with a greater optical density than another will have a lower mass density.

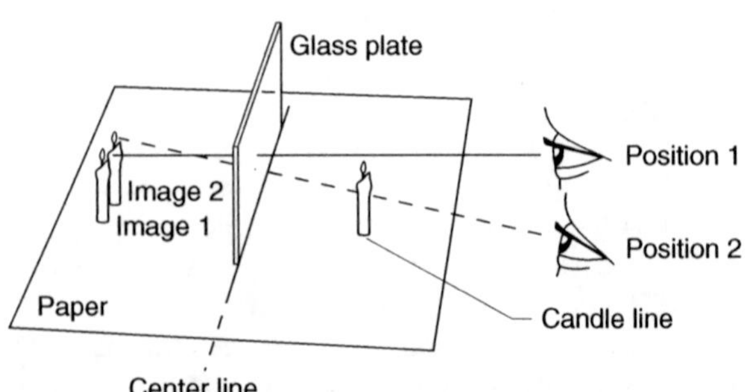

Figure 3 Glass plate as a mirror. The arrangement for the experimental procedure using a glass plate as a mirror. See text for description. (Images are displaced for illustration.)

Put the glass plate near the center of the paper, as shown in the figure. With the length of the plate parallel to the candle line, draw a line along the edge of the glass plate (side toward the candle). Light the candle.

Caution: *Take care not to burn yourself during the experimental procedure.*

Looking *directly over the candle* with your eye as in position 1 in Fig. 3, you will observe an image of the candle (image 1) in the glass plate. The glass plate reflects light and serves as a mirror. (Observing should be done with only one eye open.)

2. Observing the top of the flame from a side position (position 2 in Fig. 3), you will see a double image, one nearer than the other. Can you explain why?

   Place a pin in the pin board near the glass plate so that it is aligned (in the line of sight) with the front or nearer image of the candle (image 2 in Fig 3; double image not shown in figure). Place another pin closer to you or to the edge of the paper so that both pins and the candle image are aligned. Mark the locations of the pins.

   Repeat this procedure, viewing from a position on the other side of the candle.

3. Remove the equipment from the paper. Draw straight lines through the pair of pin points extending from the candle line through the glass-plate line. (Extend the candle line if necessary.) The lines will intersect on the opposite side of the plate line at the location of the candle image.

   Draw lines from the actual candle position or mark to the points of intersection of the previously drawn lines *and* the plate line. These lines from the candle (mark) to the glass-plate line and back to the observation positions are ray tracings of light rays.

4. Draw normal lines to the glass-plate line at the points of intersection of the ray lines. Label and measure the angles of incidence θ_i and reflection θ_r. Record the data in the Laboratory Report.

   Also, measure the perpendicular distances from the glass-plate line to the candle mark (the object distance d_o) and to the candle image position (the image distance d_i). Compute the percent differences of the quantities, as indicated in the Laboratory Report.

Plane Mirror

5. **(a)** Place the mirror near the center of a sheet of paper as with the glass plate used previously. (The mirror may be propped up by some means, or a holder may be used if available.) Draw a line along the silvered side of the mirror. Then lay an object pin about 10 cm in front of the mirror and parallel to its length (● Fig. 4).

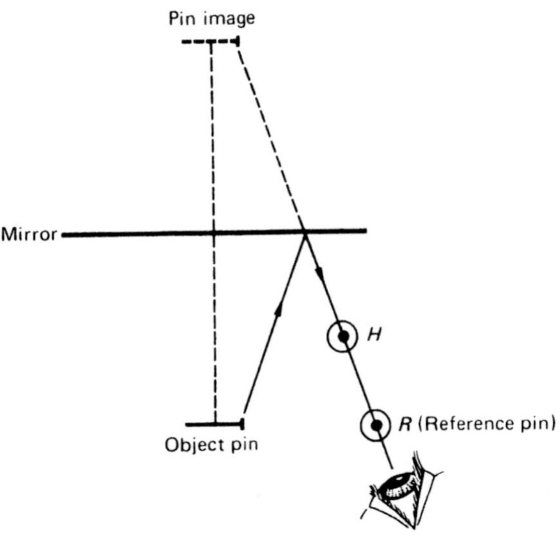

Figure 4 Plane mirror. The arrangement for the experimental procedure for a plane mirror. See text for description.

   Mark the locations of the ends of the object pin on the paper with a pencil.

   (b) Stick a reference pin R in the board to one side of the object pin and near the edge of the paper, as illustrated in Fig. 4, and mark its location.

   (c) Placing another pin nearer the mirror so that it is visually aligned with the reference pin and the head of the object pin's image in the mirror. Mark the position of this pin, and label it with an H. Then move this pin over so that it aligns with the reference pin and the "tail" of the image pin. Mark this location, and label it with a T.

   (d) Repeat this procedure on the opposite side of the object pin with another reference pin.

6. Remove the equipment from the paper, and draw straight lines from the reference points through each of the H and T locations and the mirror line. The H lines and T lines will intersect and define the locations of the head and tail of the pin image, respectively.

   Draw a line between the line intersections (the length of the pin image). Measure the length of this line and the length of the object pin, and record. Also, measure the object distance d_o and the image distance d_i from the mirror line, and record.

   Compute the percent differences of the respective measured quantities.

Rotation of a Mirror

7. Place the mirror near the center of a sheet of paper (as described above) and draw a line along the length of the silvered side of the mirror. Measure so as to find the center of the line, and mark that location.

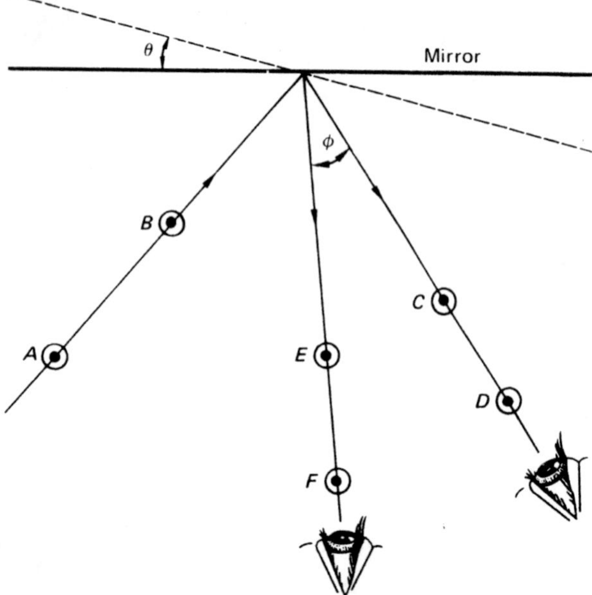

Figure 5 Mirror rotation. An illustration of the experimental arrangement and procedure for the rotation of a mirror. See text for description.

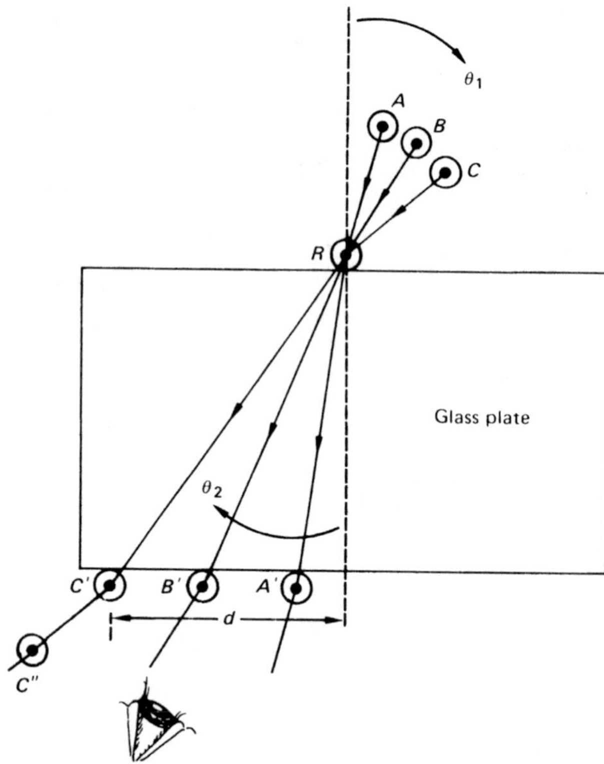

Figure 6 Index of refraction. An illustration (top view) of the experimental arrangement and procedure for determining the index of refraction of a glass plate. See text for description.

Stick two pins (*A* and *B*) in the board to one side and in front of and in line with the center of the mirror, as in ● Fig. 5. Viewing the aligned images of these pins from the other side of the page, place two more pins (*C* and *D*) in alignment. Label the locations of the pins.

8. Leaving pins *A* and *B* in place, rotate the mirror a small but measurable angle θ (approximately 10 to 15°) about its center point, and draw a line along the silvered side of the mirror.

   Align two pins (*E* and *F*) with the aligned images of *A* and *B*, and mark and label the locations of *E* and *F*.

9. Remove the equipment from the paper and draw the incident ray and the two reflected rays. Measure the angle of rotation θ of the mirror and the angle of deflection ϕ between the two reflected rays, and record in the Laboratory Report.

   Double θ, and compute the percent difference between 2θ and ϕ. Make a conclusion about the relationship between the angle of rotation of a mirror and the angle of deflection of a ray.

B. Refraction

Index of Refraction of a Glass Plate

10. Lay the glass plate in the center of a sheet of paper, and outline its shape with a pencil (● Fig. 6). Draw a line normal to one of the sides of the plate, and place a pin (*R*) at the intersection of this line and the face of the plate. Measure an angle θ_1 of 15° relative to this line, and place a pin (*A*) about 6 to 8 cm from the plate at this angle.

    Then, sighting through the edge of the plate from the eye position shown in Fig. 6, place a pin (A') adjacent to the face of the plate so that it is aligned with *R* and *A*. Mark and label the locations of the pins.

    Repeat with pins *B* and *C* at angles of 30° and 45°, respectively. For the 45°-angle case, align an additional pin (C'' Fig. 6).

11. Trace the various rays, and measure and record θ_1 and θ_2 for each case. Also measure and record the displacement *d* of ray $C'C''$ from the normal and the thickness of the plate. Using Eq. 3, compute the index of refraction of the glass.

    Compare the average experimental value of the index of refraction with the general range of the index of refraction of glass ($n = 1.5-1.7$, depending on type).

Name ____________ Section ____________ Date ____________

Lab Partner(s) ____________

EXPERIMENT 19

Reflection and Refraction

TI Laboratory Report

A. Reflection

Glass Plate as a Mirror

	θ_i	θ_r		
Ray 1	______	______	d_o	______
Ray 2	______	______	d_i	______

Percent differences between θ_i and θ_r

Ray 1 ______

Ray 2 ______

Percent difference between d_o and d_i ______

Plane Mirror

Length of pin ______ d_o ______

Length of image ______ d_i ______

Percent difference between pin length and image length ______

Percent difference between d_o and d_i ______

Rotation of a Mirror

Angle of rotation, θ ______ 2θ ______

Angle of deflection of ray, ϕ ______

Percent difference between ϕ and 2θ ______

Calculations
(show work)

Don't forget units

(continued)

B. Refraction

Index of Refraction of a Glass Plate

	θ_1	θ_2	Computed n
Ray ARA'	__________	__________	__________
Ray BRB'	__________	__________	__________
Ray CRC'	__________	__________	__________

Average n __________

General range of the index of refraction of glass __________

Displacement d of ray $C'C''$ __________

Thickness of glass plate __________

Calculations
(show work)

TI QUESTIONS

1. (a) Why are two images seen in the glass plate when it is viewed from position 2 in part A of the experiment? Why is only one image seen when it is viewed from position 1?

(b) Explain why reflection images are easily seen at night in a window pane from inside the house, whereas during the day they are not.

2. Judging on the basis of your experimental data, draw conclusions about (a) the relationship of the distance of the object in front of a plane mirror and the distance of its image "behind" the mirror; and (b) the image magnification (i.e., how much bigger the image is than the object).

3. Explain the situation shown in ● Fig. 7. How can this be done without hurting one's hand? (*Hint:* The author's hand extends inside the sliding glass-windowed door of a laboratory cabinet.)

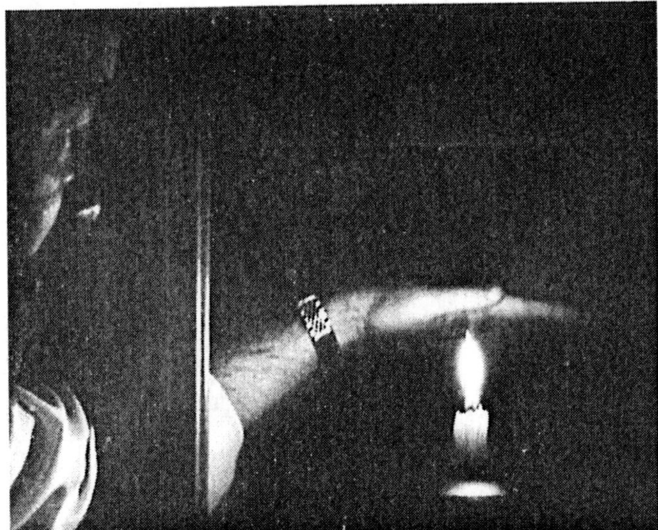

Figure 7 See Question 3.

(continued)

4. Prove mathematically that when a plane mirror is rotated an angle θ about an axis through its center (part A of the experiment), the angle of deflection ϕ of a light ray is equal to 2θ. Draw a diagram and show the work involved in your proof. Attach an additional sheet if necessary.

5. Referring to the situation in Fig. 6, show theoretically that ray $C'C''$ is parallel to ray CR. Compute the displacement d of the ray passing through the glass plate. Compare this with the measured experimental displacement.

6. Using the experimentally determined n for the glass plate, compute the speed of light in the glass plate.

Name ______________________ Section ______________ Date ______________

Lab Partner(s) ______________________

EXPERIMENT 20

Spherical Mirrors and Lenses

TI Advance Study Assignment

Read the experiment and answer the following questions.

1. Distinguish between concave and convex spherical mirrors.

2. What is the difference between a real image and a virtual image?

3. Distinguish between diverging and converging lenses.

4. What does the word *focal* mean with regard to the focal point of spherical mirrors and lenses?

(continued)

5. If an object is placed 15 cm in front of a concave mirror with a radius of curvature of 20 cm, what are the image characteristics? (Show your work.)

EXPERIMENT 20

Spherical Mirrors and Lenses

Introduction and Objectives

Mirrors and lenses are familiar objects that are used daily. The most common mirror is a plane mirror, the type we look into every morning to see our image. Spherical mirrors also have many common applications. For example, convex spherical mirrors are used in stores to monitor aisles and merchandise, and concave spherical mirrors are used as flashlight reflectors and as cosmetic mirrors that magnify.

Mirrors reflect light, whereas **lenses** transmit light. Spherical lenses are used to cause light rays to converge and hence focus them (biconvex spherical lenses) and to cause light rays to diverge (biconcave spherical lenses). Many of us wear lenses in the form of eyeglasses. Cameras and projectors use lens systems to form images. Cameras form reduced-size images on film or a chip (digital), and projectors form magnified images on a screen.

In this experiment, we will investigate the fundamental properties of spherical mirrors and lenses to learn the parameters that govern their use.

After performing this experiment and analyzing the data, you should be able to:

1. Distinguish among converging and diverging spherical mirrors and lenses.
2. Determine the image characteristics for spherical mirrors graphically using ray diagrams and analytically using the mirror equation and magnification factor.
3. Determine the image characteristics for spherical lenses graphically using ray diagrams and analytically using the thin-lens equation and magnification factor.

Equipment Needed

- Concave and convex spherical mirrors
- Convex lens (focal length 10 to 20 cm)
- Concave lens (focal length at least 5 cm longer than convex lens)
- Meterstick optical bench (or precision bench) with lens holder, screen, and screen holder (white cardboard can serve as the screen)
- Light source: candle and candle holder, or electric light source with object arrow

Theory

A. *Spherical Mirrors*

A **spherical mirror** is a section of a sphere and is characterized by a center of curvature C (● Fig. 1). The distance from the center of curvature to the vertex of the mirror along the optic axis is called the **radius of curvature** R. This also may be measured to any point on the surface of the mirror. (Why?)

The focal point F is midway between C and the vertex, and the **focal length** f is one-half the radius of curvature:

$$f = \frac{R}{2} \quad (1)$$

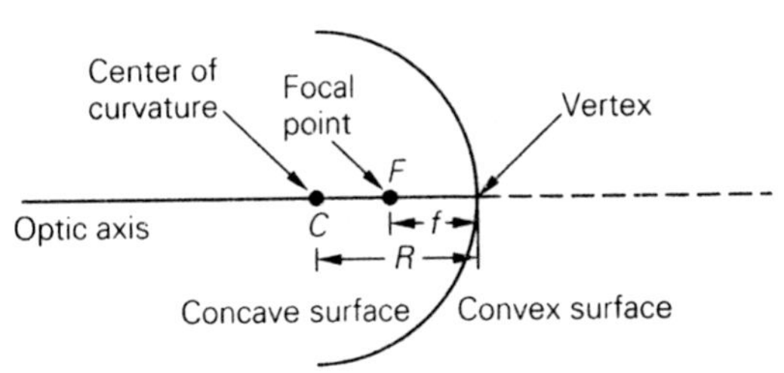

Figure 1 Spherical mirrors. The parameters used to describe spherical mirror surfaces. See text for description.

If the reflecting surface is on the inside of the spherical section, the mirror is said to be **concave.** For a **convex** mirror, the reflecting surface is on the outside of the spherical section.*

The characteristics of the images formed by spherical mirrors can be determined either graphically or analytically. Examples of the graphical ray method are shown in the ray diagrams in ● Fig. 2.

As illustrated for a concave mirror (Fig. 2a):

1. A **chief ray** from the object goes through the center of curvature C and is reflected back through C.
2. A **parallel ray** from the object is parallel to the optic axis and is reflected through the focal point F.
3. A **focal ray** from the object passes through the focal point F and is reflected parallel to the optic axis.

The intersection of these rays defines the location of the tip of the **image arrow,** which extends to the optic axis. The focal ray is a "mirror" image of the parallel ray and is not needed to locate the tip of the image. It is often

* To help remember the difference, note that a con*cave* mirror is recessed, as though one were looking into a *cave*.

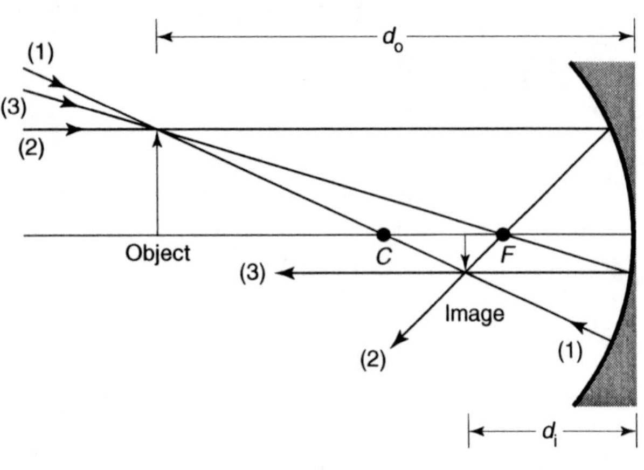

(a) Concave mirror

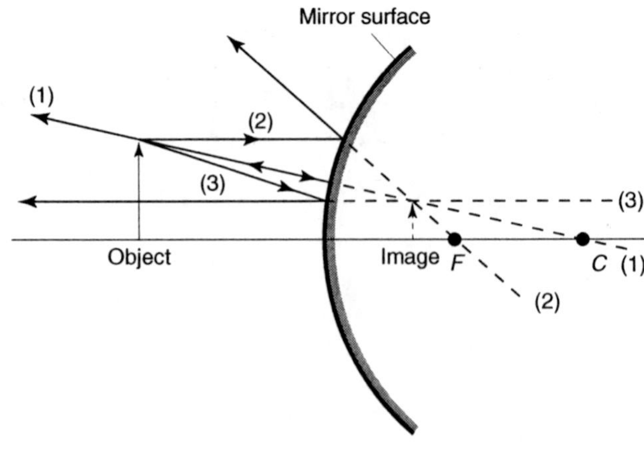

(b) Convex mirror

Figure 2 Mirror ray diagrams. Examples of the ray diagram method for determining the image characteristics for (a) a concave, or converging, spherical mirror and (b) a convex, or diverging, spherical mirror.

omitted but is helpful when the object is inside the center of curvature.

For a convex mirror, the chief and parallel rays appear to go through C and F, as illustrated in Fig. 2b.

A concave mirror is called a **converging mirror** because rays parallel to the optic axis converge at the focal point. Similarly, a convex mirror is called a **diverging mirror** because the rays parallel to the optic axis appear to diverge from the focal point.

If the image is formed on the same side of the mirror as the object, the image is said to be a **real image.** In this case, the light rays converge and are concentrated, and an image can be observed on a screen placed at the image distance. An image that is formed "behind" or "inside" the mirror is called a **virtual image.** Here, the rays appear to diverge from the image, and no image can be formed on a screen.

In general, an image is described in terms of whether it is:

1. Real or virtual,
2. Upright (erect) or inverted (relative to the object orientation), and
3. Magnified or reduced (or smaller)

In Fig. 2a the image is real, inverted, and reduced; in Fig. 2b the image is virtual, upright, and reduced.

The distance from the object to the vertex along the optic axis is called the **object distance** d_o, and the distance from the vertex to the image is the **image distance** d_i. Knowing the focal length f of the mirror, we can find the position of the image d_i from the **spherical mirror equation,**

$$\frac{1}{d_o} + \frac{1}{d_i} = \frac{1}{f} \qquad \textbf{(2a)}$$

Another convenient form of this equation is

$$d_i = \frac{d_o f}{d_o - f} \qquad \textbf{(2b)}$$

In the case of a concave mirror, the focal length is taken to be positive (+); for a convex mirror, the focal length is taken to be negative (−). The object distance d_o is taken to be positive in either case. The sign convention is as follows: If d_i is positive, the image is real, and if d_i is negative, the image is virtual. The **magnification factor** M is given by

$$M = -\frac{d_i}{d_o} \qquad \textbf{(3)}$$

If M is positive (d_i negative), the image is upright; if M is negative (d_i positive), the image is inverted. The sign convention is summarized in Table 1.

TABLE 1 Sign Convention for Spherical Mirrors and Lenses

Quantity	Conditions	Sign
Focal length f	Concave mirror	+
	Convex mirror	−
	Convex lens	+
	Concave lens	−
Object distance d_o	Usually* (Always in this experiment)	+
Image distance d_i	Image real	+
	Image virtual	−
Magnification M	Image upright	+
	Image inverted	−

* In some cases of lens combinations, d_o may be negative when the image of one lens is used as the object for the next lens.

Example 1 An object is placed 45 cm in front of a concave mirror with a focal length of 15 cm (corresponding to the case in Fig. 2a). Determine the image characteristics analytically. (Neglect significant figures.)

Solution With $d_o = 45$ cm and $f = 15$ cm, from Eq. .2a,

$$\frac{1}{45} + \frac{1}{d_i} = \frac{1}{15} = \frac{3}{45}$$

Then

$$\frac{1}{d_i} = \frac{2}{45} \quad \text{or} \quad d_i = \frac{45}{2} = 22.5 \text{ cm}$$

Then

$$M = -\frac{d_i}{d_o} = -\frac{22.5 \text{ cm}}{45 \text{ cm}} = -\frac{1}{2}$$

Thus the image is real (positive d_i), inverted (negative M), and reduced by a factor of $\frac{1}{2}$ (i.e., one-half as tall as the object).

B. Spherical Lenses

The shapes of biconvex and biconcave spherical lenses are illustrated in ● Fig. 3. A radius of curvature is defined for each spherical surface, but only the focal points (one for each spherical surface) are needed for ray diagrams.

A convex lens is called a **converging lens** because rays parallel to the principal axis converge at the focal point. A concave lens is called a **diverging lens** because rays parallel to the principal axis appear to diverge from the focal point.

As with spherical mirrors, the characteristics of the images formed by spherical lenses can be determined graphically or analytically. The chief (1) and parallel (2) rays for the graphical method are illustrated in the ray diagrams in ● Fig. 4. In the case of a convex lens (Fig. 4a), the chief ray (1) through the center of the lens passes straight through. A ray parallel (2) to the principal axis is refracted in such a way that it goes through the focal point on the far side of the lens. Also, a focal ray (3) through the near focal point is refracted by the lens so it leaves parallel to the axis. In the case of a concave lens (Fig. 4b), the chief ray (1) still goes straight through the centre of the lens. The ray parallel (2) to the principal axis is refracted upward so that it appears to have passed through the focal point on the object side of the lens. The focal ray (3), which is headed for the focal point on the far side of the lens, is refracted so that it leaves parallel to the principal axis.

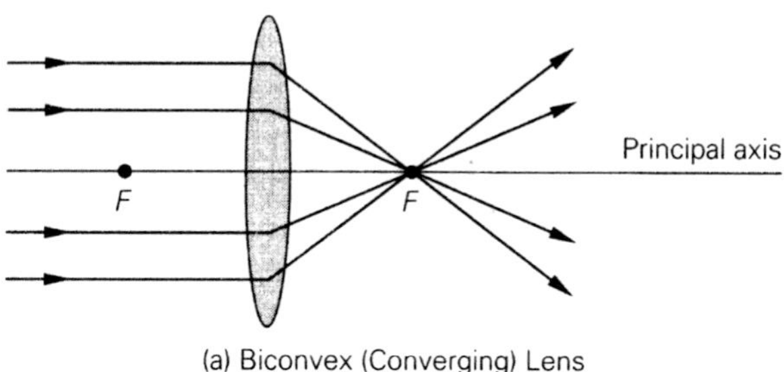

(a) Biconvex (Converging) Lens

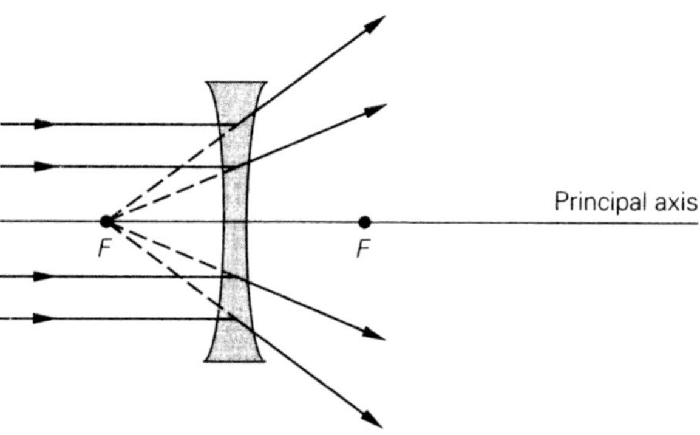

(b) Biconcave (Diverging) Lens

Figure 3 Spherical lenses. (a) A biconvex, or converging, lens and (b) a biconcave, or diverging, lens showing the refraction of parallel incident rays.

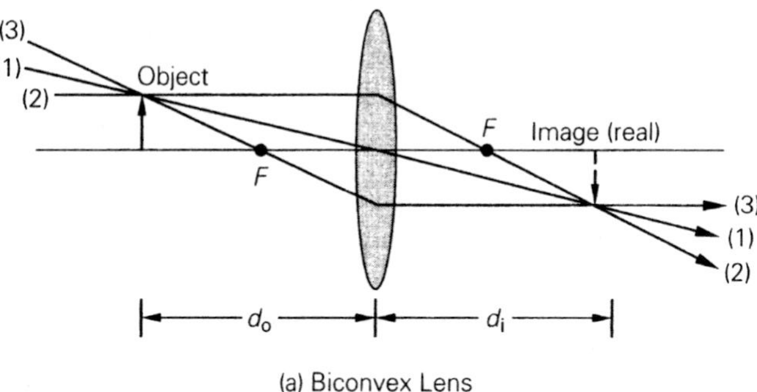

(a) Biconvex Lens

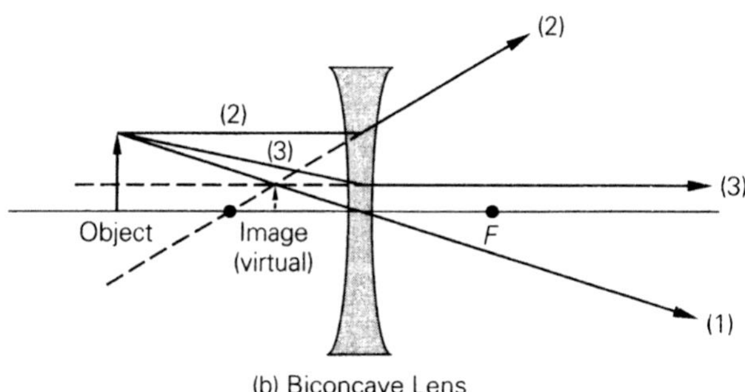

(b) Biconcave Lens

Figure 4 Lens ray diagrams. Examples of the ray diagram method for determining the image characteristics for (a) a biconvex, or converging, lens and (b) a biconcave, or diverging, lens.

If the image is formed on the side of the lens opposite to the object, it is real and can be observed on a screen. However, if the image is on the same side of the lens as the object, it is virtual and cannot be seen on a screen.

The spherical **thin-lens equation** and **magnification factor** for analytically determining the image characteristics are identical to the equations for spherical mirrors (Eqs. 2 and 3). The sign convention is also similar (see Table 1). It should be noted that this lens equation applies only to *thin* lenses.

Example 2 An object is placed 30 cm from a biconcave lens with a focal length of 10 cm (corresponding to the case in Fig. 4b). Determine the image characteristics analytically.

Solution With $d_o = 30$ cm and $f = -10$ cm (negative by convention for a concave lens), using Eq. 2b yields

$$d_i = \frac{d_o f}{d_o - f} = \frac{(30 \text{ cm})(-10 \text{ cm})}{30 \text{ cm} - (-10 \text{ cm})}$$

$$= \frac{-300 \text{ cm}}{40 \text{ cm}} = \frac{-30 \text{ cm}}{4} = -7.5 \text{ cm}$$

Then

$$M = -\frac{d_i}{d_o} = \frac{-(-30/4)}{30} = +\frac{1}{4}$$

Thus the image is virtual (negative d_i), upright (positive M), and reduced by a factor of $\frac{1}{4}$.

However, the relationship between the focal length and the radius of curvature for a spherical lens is not as simple as for a spherical mirror (Eq. 1). For a lens, the focal length is given by what is known as the *lensmaker's equation:*

$$\frac{1}{f} = (n - 1)\left(\frac{1}{R_1} + \frac{1}{R_2}\right) \quad \textbf{(4)}$$

where n is the index of refraction for the lens material and the R's are taken as positive for *convex* surfaces. (See your textbook.)

The index of refraction of glass varies, $n = 1.5$–1.7. For example, for glass with $n = 1.5$ and symmetric converging lenses ($R_1 = R$ and $R_2 = R$), Eq. 4 yields $f = R$.* Keep in mind, however, that the focal length of a lens depends in general on the R values, which can be different, as well as on n. In computations, the experimentally determined value of f will be used.

* For f to be equal to $R/2$ for a symmetric lens, as for a spherical mirror, requires $n = 2$, which is greater than the index of refraction of glass.

Experimental Procedure

A. *Spherical Mirrors*

Concave Mirror

1. (a) Construct a ray diagram for a concave mirror with an object located at its focal point. (Drawing provided in the Laboratory Report.) It should be observed from the diagram that the reflected rays are parallel. In this case we say that the rays "converge" at infinity or that the image is formed at infinity.

Inversely, rays coming from an object at infinity converge to form an image at the focal point or in the focal plane (the plane perpendicular to the optic axis).

(b) In the open area at the lower right corner of the Laboratory Report sheet, construct a ray diagram with several rays parallel to the optic axis to show they converge at f.

(c) Using the spherical-mirror equation, determine the image distance for an object at infinity (∞).

2. This focal property makes possible the experimental determination of the focal length of the mirror. An object a great distance from the mirror is essentially at infinity relative to the dimensions of the mirror.

Take the mirror and screen to a window. Holding the mirror in one hand and the screen in the other, adjust the distance of the screen from the mirror until the image of some outside distant object is observed on the screen (hence a real image).†

Measure the distance f from the mirror vertex to the screen, and record it in the Laboratory Report. Repeat this procedure twice, and take the average of the three measurements as the focal length of the mirror.

3. *Case 1: $d_o > R$.*

(a) Sketch a ray diagram for an object at a distance slightly beyond R (that is, $d_o > R$) and note the image characteristics.

(b) Set this situation up on the optical bench as illustrated in ● Fig. 5, with the object placed several centimeters beyond the radius of curvature (known from f determination in procedure 2, with $R = 2f$). Measure the object distance d_o, and record it in Data Table 1.

It is usually convenient to hold the mirror manually and adjust the object distance by moving the mirror rather than the object light source. Move the screen along the side of the optical bench until an image is observed on the screen.

† If a window is not available or it is a dark day, use procedure 4 to determine f experimentally. In this case, show first that $d_i = d_o = R$ and $M = 1$. Then, d_i having been measured, the focal length is $f = d_i/2 = R/2$.

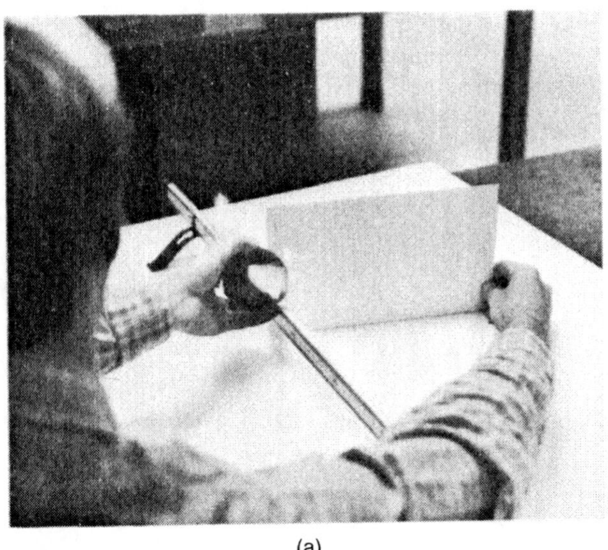

(a)

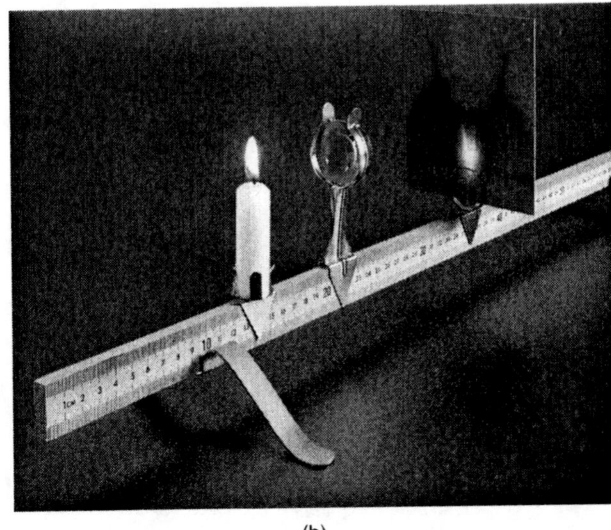

(b)

Figure 5 Experimental arrangements. Arrangements for experimental procedures for (a) spherical mirrors and (b) spherical lenses.

This is best observed in a darkened room. The mirror may have to be turned slightly to direct the rays toward the screen.

(c) Estimate the magnification factor M, and measure and record the image distance d_i.

(d) Using the mirror equation, compute the image distance and the magnification factor.

(e) Compare the computed value of d_i with the experimental value by computing the percent difference.

4. *Case 2:* $d_o = R$. Repeat procedure 3 for this case.

5. *Case 3:* $f < d_o < R$. Repeat procedure 3 for this case.

6. *Case 4:* $d_o < f$. Repeat procedure 3 for this case.

Convex Mirror

7. Sketch ray diagrams for objects at (1) $d_o > R$, (2) $f < d_o < R$, and (3) $d_o < f$, and draw conclusions about the characteristics of the image of a convex mirror. Experimentally verify that the image of a convex mirror is virtual (i.e., try to locate the image on the screen).

B. Spherical Lenses

Convex Lens

8. (a) Sketch a ray diagram for a convex lens with the object at its focal point. As with the concave mirror (procedure 1), the image is formed at infinity.

(b) Using the lens equation, determine the image characteristics for an object at infinity.

(c) Experimentally determine the focal length of the lens by a procedure similar to that used for the concave mirror. (The lens may be placed in a lens holder and mounted on a meterstick.)*

9. Repeat the four cases for the lens as was done for the concave mirror in procedures 3 to 6, with R replaced by $2f$ (see Fig. 5). It is initially instructive to move the lens continuously toward the object light source (decreasing d_o) from a $d_o > 2f$ and to observe the image on the screen, which also must be moved continuously to obtain a sharp image. In particular, notice the change in the size of the image as d_o approaches f.

Concave Lens

10. Repeat the procedures carried out for the convex mirror in procedure 7 for the concave lens, with R replaced by $2f$.

11. It is possible to determine the focal length of a concave lens experimentally by placing it in contact with a convex lens so as to form a lens combination. The combination forms a real image. If two lenses of focal lengths f_1 and f_2 are placed in contact, the lens combination has focal length f_c given by

$$\frac{1}{f_c} = \frac{1}{f_1} + \frac{1}{f_2} \qquad (5)$$

* In general for a lens, $f \neq R/2$. However, it can be shown for the case of $d_i = d_o$ that $d_o = 2f$. See Question 4 at the end of the experiment.

Place the concave lens in contact with the convex lens (convex surface to concave surface) in a lens holder, and determine the focal length of the lens combination f_c by finding the image of a distant object as in procedure 8. Record in the Laboratory Report.

Using Eq. 5 with the focal length of the convex lens determined in procedure 8, compute the focal length of the concave lens.

Name ____________________ Section ____________ Date ____________

Lab Partner(s) ____________________

EXPERIMENT 20

Spherical Mirrors and Lenses

TI Laboratory Report

A. Spherical Mirrors

Concave Mirror: Ray diagrams

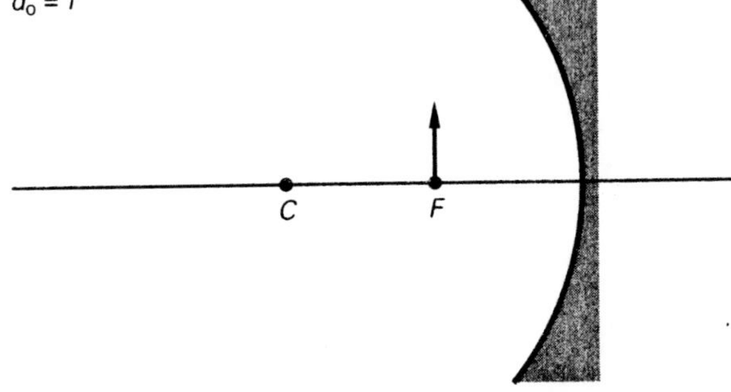

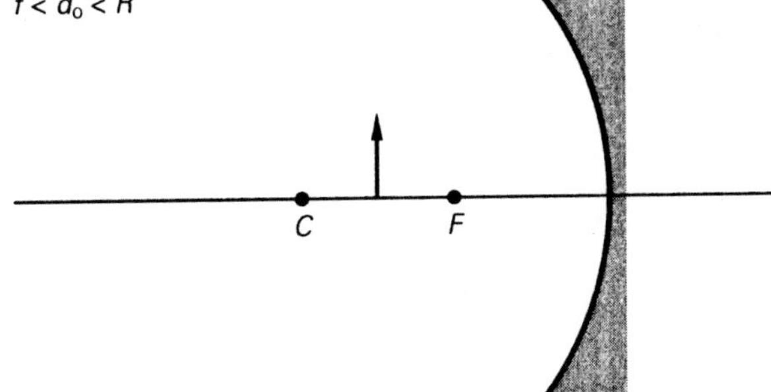

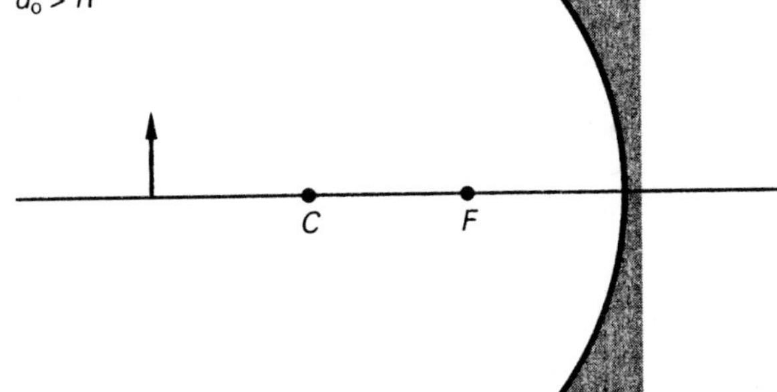

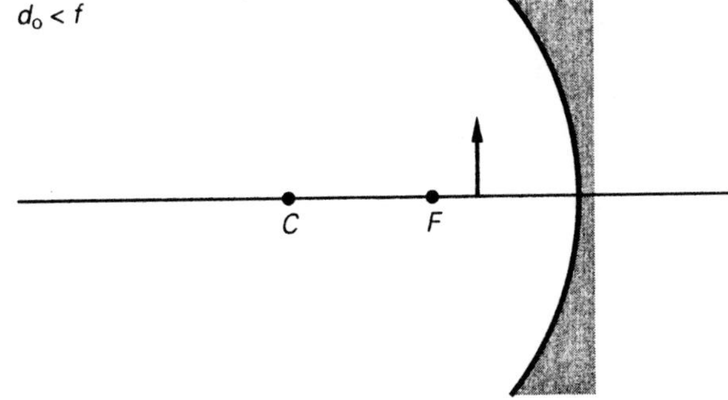

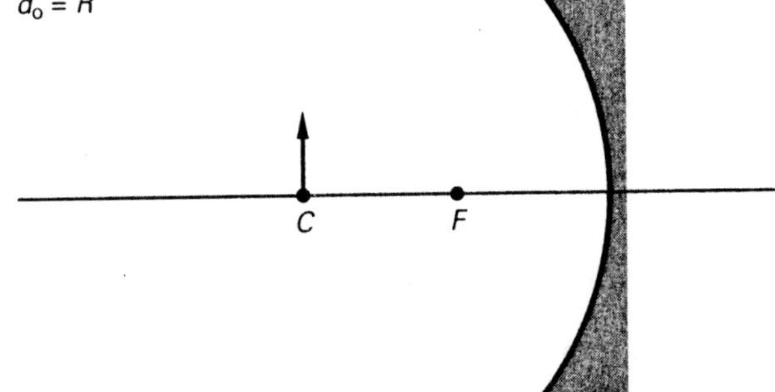

Don't forget units

(continued)

Calculation of d_i for object at ∞

Experimental focal length f ____________

____

____

Average ____________

DATA TABLE 1

Purpose: To determine the image distance and magnification.

	Experimental			Computed		d_i percent difference
	d_o ( )	d_i ( )	M factor (estimated)	d_i ( )	M	
$d_o > R$						
$d_o = R$						
$f < d_o < R$						
$d_o < f$						

Calculations
(show work)

Name ______________________ Section ______________ Date ______________

Lab Partner(s) ____

EXPERIMENT 20 — *Laboratory Report*

Convex mirror: Ray diagrams

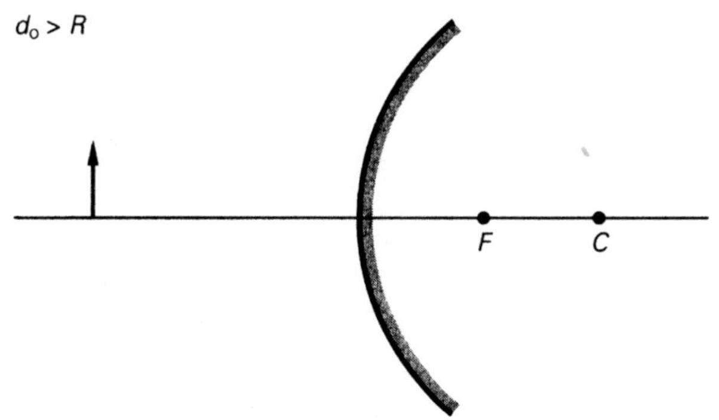

$f < d_o < R$

F C

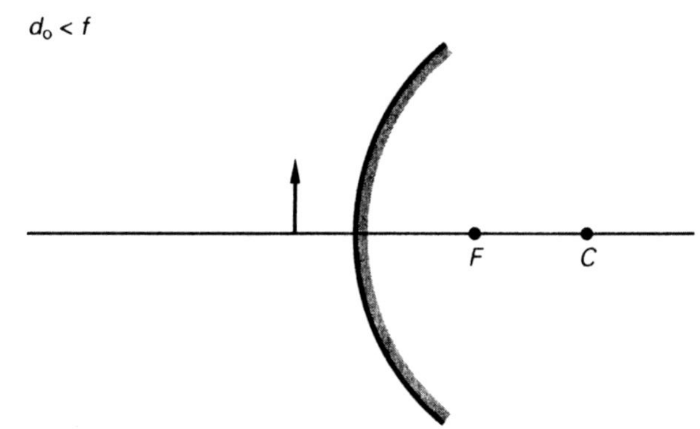

Conclusions

(continued)

B. Spherical Lenses

Convex lens: Ray diagrams

$d_o = f$

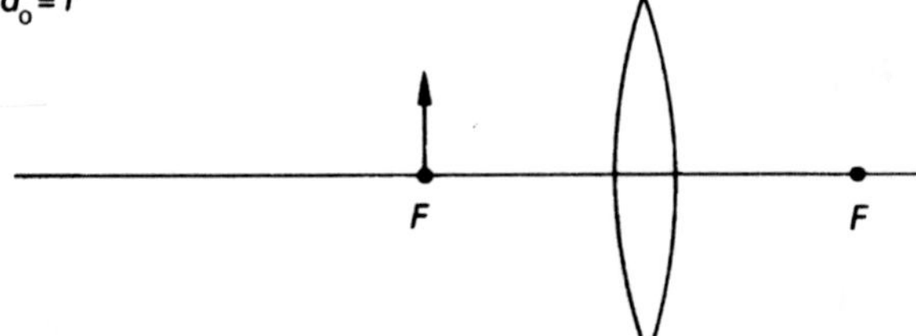

$f < d_o < 2f$

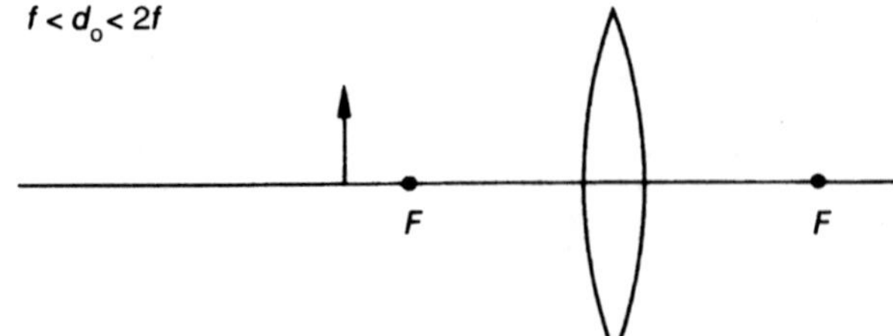

$d_o > 2f$

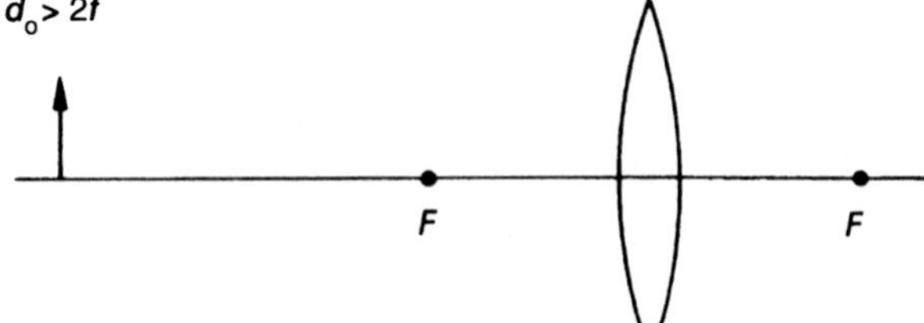

$d_o < f$

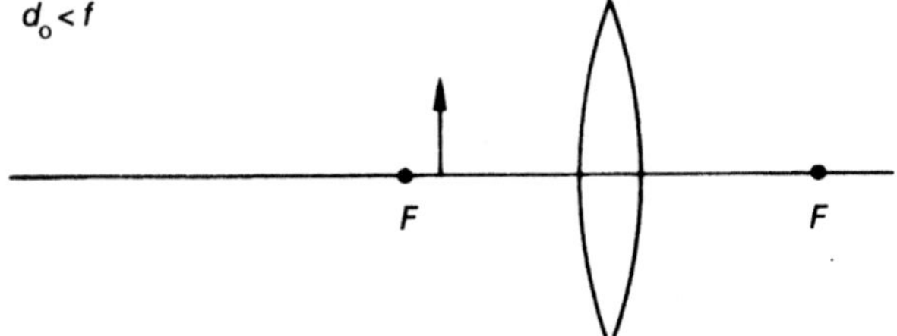

$d_o = 2f$

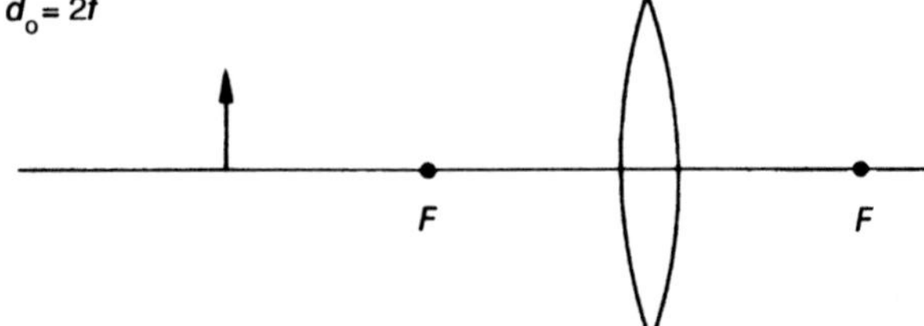

Calculation of d_i for object at ∞

Experimental focal length f ________________

____

____

Average ________________

Name ______________________ Section ______________ Date ______________

Lab Partner(s) ____

EXPERIMENT 20 *Laboratory Report*

DATA TABLE 2

Purpose: To determine the image distance and magnification.

	Experimental			Computed		d_i percent difference
	d_o ( )	d_i ( )	M factor (estimated)	d_i ( )	M	
$d_o > 2f$						
$d_o = 2f$						
$f < d_o < 2f$						
$d_o < f$						

Calculations
(show work)

(continued)

Concave lens: Ray diagrams

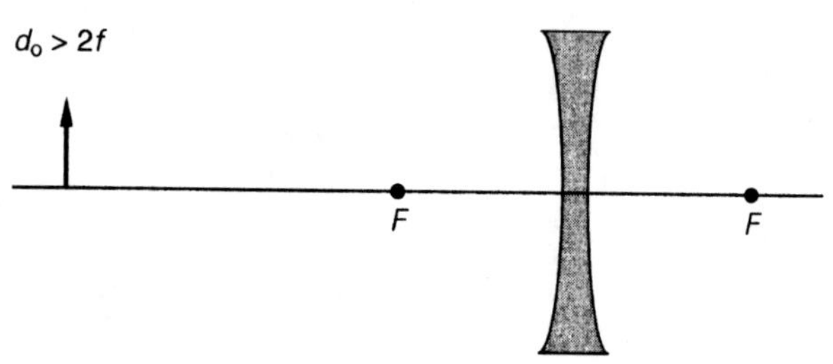

Conclusions

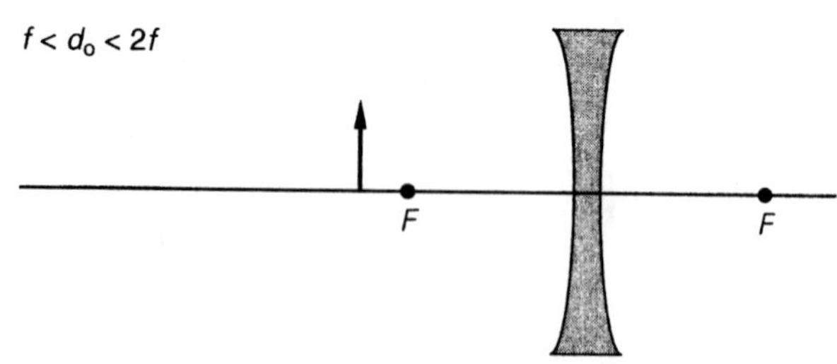

$d_o < f$

F F

Focal length determination:

f_c, focal length of the combination ____________

f, focal length of convex lens ____________

f, focal length of concave lens ____________

TI QUESTIONS

1. A plane mirror essentially has a radius of curvature of infinity. Using the mirror equation, show that (a) the image of a plane mirror is always virtual, (b) the image is "behind" the mirror the same distance as the object is in front of the mirror, and (c) the image is always upright.

Name ______ Section ______ Date ______

Lab Partner(s) ______

2. Show that the magnification factor for a mirror or lens $M = d_i/d_o$ (sign convention omitted) is the lateral magnification, or the ratio of the height (lateral size) of the image to that of the object. (*Hint:* Draw a ray diagram.)

3. Explain what characteristics make convex spherical mirrors applicable for store monitoring and concave spherical mirrors applicable as flashlight reflectors.

4. Prove that for a converging lens, for the case $d_i = d_o$, it is true that $d_i = d_o = 2f$.

(continued)

5. Using the thin-lens equation and the magnification factor, show that for a spherical diverging lens the image of a real object is always virtual, upright, and reduced. Does the same apply for a spherical diverging mirror?

6. (*Optional*) (a) Using the experimental value of f for the biconvex converging lens and $n = 1.5$, compute the radius of curvature of the lens's surfaces using the lensmaker's equation. (The radius of curvature for each surface is the same.)

(b) A student incorrectly assumes that $f = R/2$ for the lens and computes f using the value of R found in part (a). Compare this computed value of f with the experimental value.

(c) The index of refraction of the lens could have a different value (n of glass varies generally from 1.5 to 1.7). Would this make a difference? Explain.

APPENDIX A

Material Properties

TABLE A1 Densities of Materials

Substance	(g/cm^3)	(kg/m^3)
Solids		
Aluminum	2.7	2.7×10^3
Brass	8.4	8.4×10^3
Copper	8.9	8.9×10^3
Glass		
crown	2.5–2.7	$2.5–2.7 \times 10^3$
flint	3.0–3.6	$3.0–3.6 \times 10^3$
Gold	19.3	19.3×10^3
Iron and steel (general)	7.88	7.88×10^3
Lead	11.3	11.3×10^3
Nickel	8.8	8.8×10^3
Silver	10.5	10.5×10^3
Wood		
oak	0.60–0.90	$0.60–0.90 \times 10^3$
pine	0.35–0.50	$0.35–0.50 \times 10^3$
Zinc	7.1	7.1×10^3
Liquids		
Alcohol		
ethyl	0.79	0.79×10^3
methyl	0.81	0.81×10^3
Carbon tetra-chloride	1.60	1.60×10^3
Gasoline	0.68–0.75	$0.68–0.75 \times 10^3$
Glycerine	1.26	1.26×10^3
Mercury	13.6	13.6×10^3
Turpentine	0.87	0.87×10^3
Water	1.00	1.00×10^3
Gases (at STP):		
Air	0.001293	0.001293×10^3
Carbon dioxide	0.001975	0.001975×10^3
Helium	0.000179	0.000179×10^3
Hydrogen	0.000089	0.000089×10^3
Nitrogen	0.000125	0.000125×10^3
Oxygen	0.00143	0.00143×10^3

TABLE A2 Young's Modulus for Some Metals

Metals	(N/m^2)
Aluminum	6.5×10^{10}
Brass	9.0×10^{10}
Copper	12.0×10^{10}
Iron	
cast	9.0×10^{10}
wrought	19.0×10^{10}
Steel	19.2×10^{10}

TABLE A3 Coefficients of Linear Thermal Expansion

Substance	(1/C°)
Aluminum	24.0×10^{-6}
Brass	18.8×10^{-6}
Copper	16.8×10^{-6}
Glass	
window	8.5×10^{-6}
Pyrex	3.3×10^{-6}
Iron	11.4×10^{-6}
Lead	29.4×10^{-6}
Nickel	12.8×10^{-6}
Silver	18.8×10^{-6}
Steel	13.4×10^{-6}
Tin	26.9×10^{-6}
Zinc	26.4×10^{-6}

TABLE A4 Specific Heats

Substance	kcal/(kg-C°) or cal/(g-C°)	J/(kg-C°)
Aluminum	0.22	921
Brass	0.092	385
Copper	0.093	389
Glass	0.16	670
Iron	0.11	460
Lead	0.031	130
Mercury	0.033	138
Nickel	0.11	460
Silver	0.056	234
Steel	0.11	460
Tin	0.054	226
Water	1.00	4186
Zinc	0.093	389

TABLE A5 Color Code for Resistors (Composition Type)

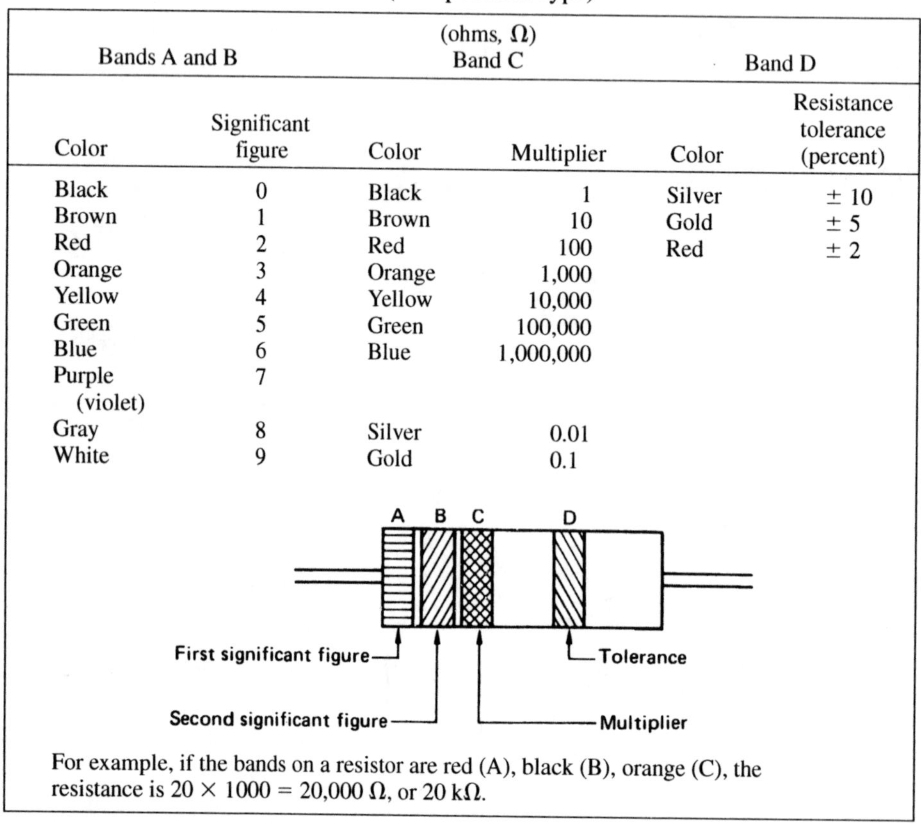

Bands A and B		(ohms, Ω) Band C		Band D	
Color	Significant figure	Color	Multiplier	Color	Resistance tolerance (percent)
Black	0	Black	1	Silver	± 10
Brown	1	Brown	10	Gold	± 5
Red	2	Red	100	Red	± 2
Orange	3	Orange	1,000		
Yellow	4	Yellow	10,000		
Green	5	Green	100,000		
Blue	6	Blue	1,000,000		
Purple (violet)	7				
Gray	8	Silver	0.01		
White	9	Gold	0.1		

For example, if the bands on a resistor are red (A), black (B), orange (C), the resistance is $20 \times 1000 = 20{,}000\ \Omega$, or 20 kΩ.

TABLE A6 Resistivities and Temperature Coefficients

Substance	Resistivity ρ (Ω-cm)	Temperature coefficient (1/C°)
Aluminum	2.8×10^{-6}	0.0039
Brass	7×10^{-6}	0.002
Constantan	49×10^{-6}	0.00001
Copper	1.72×10^{-6}	0.00393
German silver (18% Ni)	33×10^{-6}	0.0004
Iron	10×10^{-6}	0.005
Manganin	44×10^{-6}	0.00001
Mercury	95.8×10^{-6}	0.00089
Nichrome	100×10^{-6}	0.0004
Nickel	7.8×10^{-6}	0.006
Silver	1.6×10^{-6}	0.0038
Tin	11.5×10^{-6}	0.0042

TABLE A7 Wire Sizes [American Wire Gauge (AWG)]

Gauge No.	Diameter	
	in.	cm
0000	0.4600	1.168
000	0.4096	1.040
00	0.3648	0.9266
0	0.3249	0.8252
1	0.2893	0.7348
2	0.2576	0.6543
3	0.2294	0.5827
4	0.2043	0.5189
5	0.1819	0.4620
6	0.1620	0.4115
7	0.1443	0.3665
8	0.1285	0.3264
9	0.1144	0.2906
10	0.1019	0.2588
11	0.09074	0.2305
12	0.08081	0.2053
13	0.07196	0.1828
14	0.06408	0.1628
15	0.05707	0.1450
16	0.05082	0.1291
17	0.04526	0.1150
18	0.04030	0.1024
19	0.03589	0.09116
20	0.03196	0.08118
21	0.02846	0.07229
22	0.02535	0.06439
23	0.02257	0.05733
24	0.02010	0.05105
25	0.01790	0.04547
26	0.01594	0.04049
27	0.01419	0.03604
28	0.01264	0.03211
29	0.01126	0.02860
30	0.01003	0.02548
31	0.008928	0.02268
32	0.007950	0.02019
33	0.007080	0.01798
34	0.006304	0.01601
35	0.005614	0.01426
36	0.005000	0.01270
37	0.004453	0.01131
38	0.003965	0.01007
39	0.003531	0.008969
40	0.003145	0.007988

TABLE A8 Major Visible Spectral Lines of Some Elements

Element	Wavelength (nm)	Color	Relative intensity
Helium	388.9	Violet	1000
	396.5 (near)	Violet	50
	402.6 (near)	Violet	70
	438.8	Blue-violet	30
	447.1	Dark blue	100
	471.3	Blue	40
	492.2	Blue-green	50
	501.5	Green	100
	587.6	Yellow	1000
	667.8	Red	100
	706.5	Red	70
Mercury	404.7	Violet	300
	407.8	Violet	150
	435.8	Blue	500
	491.6	Blue-green	50
	546.1	Green	2000
	577.0	Yellow	200
	579.0	Yellow	1000
	690.7	Red	125
Sodium	449.4	Blue	60
	449.8	Blue	70
	466.5	Blue	80
	466.9	Blue	200
	498.3	Green	200
	514.9	Green	400
	515.3	Green	600
	567.0	Green	100
	567.5	Green	150
	568.3	Green	80
	568.8	Green	300
	589.0	Yellow-orange	9000
	589.6	Yellow-orange	5000
	615.4	Orange	500
	616.1	Orange	500

Wavelengths of various colors

Color	Representative (nm)	General ranges (nm)
Red	650.0	647.0–700.0
Orange	600.0	584.0–647.0
Yellow	580.0	575.0–585.0
Green	520.0	491.2–575.0
Blue	470.0	424.0–491.2
Violet	410.0	400.0–420.0

Visible spectrum ≈ 400.0–700.0 nm

TABLE A9 Radioisotopes

Isotope	Half-life	Principal Radiations (MeV)		
		Alpha	Beta	Gamma
Barium-133	10.4 years			0.356
Bismuth-210	5.01 days	4.654, 4.691	1.161	
Carbon-14	5730 years		0.156	
Cesium-137	30.1 years		0.512, 1.173	
Barium-137m	2.6 min			0.662
Cobalt-60	5.26 years		0.315	
Iodine-131	8.07 days		0.606	
Lead-210	22.3 years		0.017, 0.061	0.0465
Manganese-54	312.5 days			0.835
Phosphorus-32	14.3 days		1.710	
Polonium-210	138.4 days	5.305		
Potassium-42	12.4 hours		3.52 1.97	
Radium-226	1600 years	4.781 4.598		0.186
Sodium-22	2.60 years	0.545 1.82		1.275
Strontium-90	28.1 years		0.546	
Thallium-204	3.78 years		0.763	
Uranium-238	4.5×10^6 years	4.195		0.48
Yttrium-90	64.0 hours		2.27	
Zinc-65	243.6 days		0.329	1.116

TABLE A10 Elements: Atomic Numbers and Atomic Weights

The atomic weights are based on $^{12}C = 12.0000$. If the element does not occur naturally, the mass number of the most stable isotope is given in parentheses.

	Symbol	Atomic number	Atomic weight		Symbol	Atomic number	Atomic weight
Actinium	Ac	89	(227)	Mercury	Hg	80	200.59
Aluminum	Al	13	26.9815	Molybdenum	Mo	42	95.94
Americium	Am	95	(243)	Neodymium	Nd	60	144.24
Antimony	Sb	51	121.75	Neon	Ne	10	20.179
Argon	Ar	18	39.948	Neptunium	Np	93	(237)
Arsenic	As	33	74.9216	Nickel	Ni	28	58.71
Astatine	At	85	(210)	Niobium	Nb	41	92.9064
Barium	Ba	56	137.34	Nitrogen	N	7	14.0067
Berkelium	Bk	97	(247)	Nobelium	No	102	(253)
Beryllium	Be	4	9.01218	Osmium	Os	76	190.2
Bismuth	Bi	83	208.9806	Oxygen	O	8	15.9994
Boron	B	5	10.81	Palladium	Pd	46	106.4
Bromine	Br	35	79.90	Phosphorus	P	15	30.9738
Cadmium	Cd	48	112.40	Platinum	Pt	78	195.09
Calcium	Ca	20	40.08	Plutonium	Pu	94	(224)
Californium	Cf	98	(251)	Polonium	Po	84	(209)
Carbon	C	6	12.011	Potassium	K	19	39.102
Cerium	Ce	58	140.12	Praseodymium	Pr	59	140.9077
Cesium	Cs	55	132.9055	Promethium	Pm	61	(145)
Chlorine	Cl	17	35.453	Protactinium	Pa	91	(231)
Chromium	Cr	24	51.996	Radium	Ra	88	(226)
Cobalt	Co	27	58.9332	Radon	Rn	86	(222)
Copper	Cu	29	63.545	Rhenium	Re	75	186.2
Curium	Cm	96	(247)	Rhodium	Rh	45	102.9055
Dysprosium	Dy	66	162.50	Rubidium	Rb	37	85.4678
Einsteinium	Es	99	(254)	Ruthenium	Ru	44	101.07
Erbium	Er	68	167.26	Rutherfordium	Rf	104	(257)
Europium	Eu	63	151.96	Samarium	Sm	62	150.4
Fermium	Fm	100	(253)	Scandium	Sc	21	44.9559
Fluorine	F	9	18.9984	Selenium	Se	34	78.96
Francium	Fr	87	(223)	Silicon	Si	14	28.086
Gadolinium	Gd	64	157.25	Silver	Ag	47	107.868
Gallium	Ga	31	69.72	Sodium	Na	11	22.9898
Germanium	Ge	32	72.59	Strontium	Sr	38	87.62
Gold	Au	79	196.967	Sulfur	S	16	32.06
Hafnium	Hf	72	178.49	Tantalum	Ta	73	180.9479
Hahnium	Ha	105	(260)	Technetium	Tc	43	(99)
Helium	He	2	4.00260	Tellerium	Te	52	127.60
Holmium	Ho	67	164.9303	Terbium	Tb	65	158.9254
Hydrogen	H	1	1.0080	Thallium	Tl	81	204.37
Indium	In	49	114.82	Thorium	Th	90	232.0381
Iodine	I	53	126.9045	Thulium	Tm	69	168.9342
Iridium	Ir	77	192.22	Tin	Sn	50	118.69
Iron	Fe	26	55.847	Titanium	Ti	22	47.90
Krypton	Kr	36	83.80	Tungsten	W	74	183.85
Lanthanium	La	57	138.9055	Uranium	U	92	238.029
Lawrencium	Lr	103	(257)	Vanadium	Vy	23	50.9414
Lead	Pb	82	207.12	Xenon	Xe	54	131.30
Lithium	Li	3	6.941	Ytterbium	Yb	70	173.04
Lutetium	Lu	71	174.97	Yttrium	Y	39	88.9059
Magnesium	Mg	12	24.305	Zinc	Zn	30	65.37
Manganese	Mn	25	54.9380	Zirconium	Zr	40	91.22
Mendelevium	Md	101	(256)				

Mathematical and Physical Constants

TABLE B1 Metric Prefixes

Multiple		Name	Abbreviation
1,000,000,000,000,000,000	10^{18}	exa	E
1,000,000,000,000,000	10^{15}	peta	P
1,000,000,000,000	10^{12}	tera	T
1,000,000,000	10^{9}	giga	G
1,000,000	10^{6}	mega	M
1,000	10^{3}	kilo	k
100	10^{2}	hecto	h
10	10^{1}	deka	da
1	1	—	—
0.1	10^{-1}	deci	d
0.01	10^{-2}	centi	c
0.001	10^{-3}	milli	m
0.000001	10^{-6}	micro	μ
0.000000001	10^{-9}	nano	n
0.000000000001	10^{-12}	pico	p
0.000000000000001	10^{-15}	femto	f
0.000000000000000001	10^{-18}	atto	a

TABLE B2 Physical Constants

Quantity	Symbol	Value
Acceleration due to gravity	g	$9.8 \text{ m/s}^2 = 980 \text{ cm/s}^2 = 32.2 \text{ ft/s}^2$
Universal gravitational constant	G	$6.67 \times 10^{-11} \dfrac{\text{N-m}^2}{\text{kg}^2}$
Electron charge	e	1.60×10^{-19} C
Speed of light	c	$3.0 \times 10^{8} \text{ m/s} = 3.0 \times 10^{10} \text{ cm/s} = 1.86 \times 10^{5} \text{ mi/s}$
Boltzmann's constant	k	1.38×10^{-23} J/K
Planck's constant	h	$6.63 \times 10^{-34} \text{ J-s} = 4.14 \times 10^{-15} \text{ eV-s}$
	$\hbar$	$h/2\pi = 1.05 \times 10^{-34} \text{ J-s} = 6.58 \times 10^{-16} \text{ eV-s}$
Electron rest mass	m_e	$9.11 \times 10^{-31} \text{ kg} = 5.49 \times 10^{-4} \text{ u} \leftrightarrow 0.511 \text{ MeV}$
Proton rest mass	m_p	$1.672 \times 10^{-27} \text{ kg} = 1.00783 \text{ u} \leftrightarrow 938.3 \text{ MeV}$
Neutron rest mass	m_n	$1.674 \times 10^{-27} \text{ kg} = 1.00867 \text{ u} \leftrightarrow 939.1 \text{ MeV}$
Coulomb's law constant	k	$1/4\pi\varepsilon_0 = 9.0 \times 10^{9} \text{ N-m}^2/\text{C}^2$
Permittivity of free space	ε_0	$8.85 \times 10^{-12} \text{ C}^2/\text{N-m}^2$
Permeability of free space	μ_0	$4\pi \times 10^{-7} = 1.26 \times 10^{-6}$ Wb/A-m (T-M/A)
Astronomical and Earth data		
Radius of Earth		
equatorial		$3963 \text{ mi} = 6.378 \times 10^{6} \text{ m}$
polar		$3950 \text{ mi} = 6.357 \times 10^{6} \text{ m}$
Mass of Earth		6.0×10^{24} kg
Mass of Moon		$7.4 \times 10^{22} \text{ kg} = \frac{1}{81}$ mass of Earth
Mass of Sun		2.0×10^{30} kg
Average distance of Earth from Sun		$93 \times 10^{6} \text{ mi} = 1.5 \times 10^{8} \text{ km}$
Average distance of Moon from Earth		$2.4 \times 10^{5} \text{ mi} = 3.8 \times 10^{5} \text{ km}$
Diameter of Moon		$2160 \text{ mi} \approx 3500 \text{ km}$
Diameter of Sun		$864{,}000 \text{ mi} \approx 1.4 \times 10^{6} \text{ km}$

TABLE B3 Conversion Factors

Mass	1 g = 10^{-3} kg 1 kg = 10^3 g 1 metric ton = 1000 kg 1 u = 1.66 × 10^{-24} g = 1.66 × 10^{-27} kg
Length	1 cm = 10^{-2} m = 0.394 in. 1 m = 10^{-3} km = 3.28 ft = 39.4 in. 1 km = 10^3 m = 0.621 mi 1 in. = 2.54 cm = 2.54 × 10^{-2} m 1 ft = 12 in. = 30.48 cm = 0.3048 m 1 mi = 5280 ft = 609 m = 1.609 km
Area	1 cm^2 = 10^{-4} m^2 = 0.1550 in^2 = 1.08 × 10^{-3} ft^2 1 m^2 = 10^4 cm^2 = 10.76 ft^2 = 1550 in^2 1 in^2 = 6.94 × 10^{-3} ft^2 = 6.45 cm^2 = 6.45 × 10^{-4} m^2 1 ft^2 = 144 in^2 = 9.29 × 10^{-2} m^2 = 929 cm^2
Volume	1 cm^3 = 10^{-6} m^3 = 3.53 × 10^{-5} ft^3 = 6.10 × 10^{-2} in^3 1 m^3 = 10^6 cm^3 = 10^3 liters = 35.3 ft^3 = 6.10 × 10^4 in^3 = 264 gal 1 liter = 10^3 cm^3 = 10^{-3} m^3 = 1.056 qt = 0.264 gal 1 in^3 = 5.79 × 10^{-4} ft^3 = 16.4 cm^3 = 1.64 × 10^{-5} m^3 1 ft^3 = 1728 in^3 = 7.48 gal = 0.0283 m^3 = 28.3 liters 1 qt = 2 pt = 946.5 cm^3 = 0.946 liter 1 gal = 4 qt = 231 in^3 = 3.785 liters
Time	1 h = 60 min = 3600 s 1 day = 24 h = 1440 min = 8.64 × 10^4 s 1 year = 365 days = 8.76 × 10^3 h = 5.26 × 10^5 min = 3.16 × 10^7 s
Angle	360° = 2π rad 180° = π rad 1 rad = 57.3° 90° = $\pi/2$ rad 60° = $\pi/3$ rad 1° = 0.0175 rad 45° = $\pi/4$ rad 30° = $\pi/6$ rad
Speed	1 m/s = 3.6 km/h = 3.28 ft/s = 2.24 mi/h 1 km/h = 0.278 m/s = 0.621 mi/h = 0.911 ft/s 1 ft/s = 0.682 mi/h = 0.305 m/s = 1.10 km/h 1 mi/h = 1.467 ft/s = 1.609 km/h = 0.447 m/s 60 mi/h = 88 ft/s
Force	1 newton = 10^5 dynes = 0.225 lb 1 lb = 4.45 N Equivalent weight of 1-kg mass on Earth's surface = 2.2 lb = 9.8 N
Pressure	1 Pa (N/m^2) = 1.45 × 10^{-4} lb/in^2 = 7.4 × 10^{-3} torr (mm Hg) 1 tor (mm Hg) = 133 Pa (N/m^2) = 0.02 lb/in^2 1 atm = 14.7 lb/in^2 = 1.013 × 10^5 N/m^2 (Pa) = 30 in. Hg = 76 cm Hg 1 bar = 10^5 N/m^2 (Pa) 1 millibar = 10^2 N/m^2 (Pa)
Energy	1 J = 10^7 ergs = 0.738 ft-lb = 0.239 cal = 9.48 × 10^{-4} Btu = 6.24 × 10^{18} eV 1 kcal = 4186 J = 3.968 Btu 1 Btu = 1055 J = 778 ft-lb = 0.252 kcal 1 cal = 4.186 J = 3.97 × 10^{-3} Btu = 3.09 ft-lb 1 ft-lb = 1.356 J = 1.29 × 10^{-3} Btu 1 eV = 1.60 × 10^{-19} J
Power	1 W = 0.738 ft-lb/s = 1.34 × 10^{-3} hp = 3.41 Btu/h 1 ft-lb/s = 1.36 W = 1.82 × 10^{-3} hp 1 hp = 550 ft-lb/s = 745.7 W = 2545 Btu/h
Rest mass-energy equivalents	1 u = 1.66 × 10^{-27} kg ↔ 931 MeV 1 electron mass = 9.11 × 10^{-31} kg = 5.49 × 10^{-4} u ↔ 0.511 MeV 1 proton mass = 1.672 × 10^{-27} kg = 1.00728 u ↔ 938.3 MeV 1 neutron mass = 1.674 × 10^{-27} kg = 1.00867 u ↔ 939.1 MeV

TABLE B4 Trigonometric Relationships

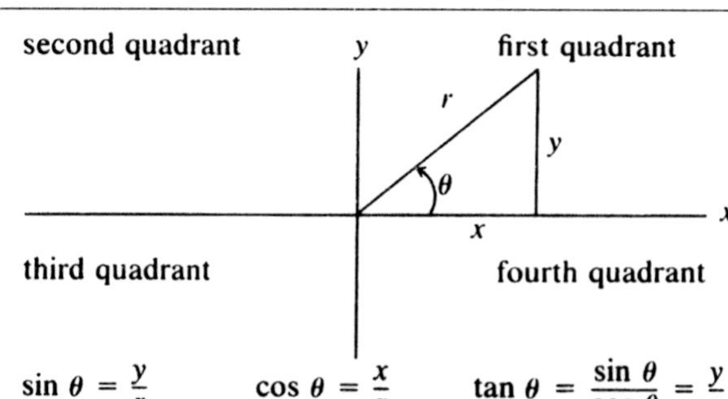

$\sin \theta = \frac{y}{r}$ $\cos \theta = \frac{x}{r}$ $\tan \theta = \frac{\sin \theta}{\cos \theta} = \frac{y}{x}$

$\theta°$ (rad)	$\sin \theta$	$\cos \theta$	$\tan \theta$
0° (0)	0	1	0
30° ($\pi/6$)	0.500	0.866	0.577
45° ($\pi/4$)	0.707	0.707	1.00
60° ($\pi/3$)	0.866	0.500	1.73
90° ($\pi/2$)	1	0	$\rightarrow \infty$

The sign of trigonometric functions depends on the quadrant, or sign of x and y, e.g., in the second quadrant $(-x, y)$, $-x/r = \cos \theta$ and $x/r = \sin \theta$, or by:

Reduction Formulas

	(θ in second quadrant)		(θ in third quadrant)		(θ in fourth quadrant)
$\sin \theta =$	$\cos (\theta - 90°)$	$=$	$-\sin (\theta - 180°)$	$=$	$-\cos (\theta - 270°)$
$\cos \theta =$	$-\sin (\theta - 90°)$	$=$	$-\cos (\theta - 180°)$	$=$	$\sin (\theta - 270°)$

Fundamental Identities

$$\sin^2\theta + \cos^2\theta = 1$$
$$\sin 2\theta = 2 \sin \theta \cos \theta$$
$$\cos 2\theta = \cos^2\theta - \sin^2\theta = 2 \cos^2\theta - 1 = 1 - 2 \sin^2\theta$$
$$\sin^2\theta = \tfrac{1}{2}(1 - \cos 2\theta)$$
$$\cos^2\theta = \tfrac{1}{2}(1 + \cos 2\theta)$$

For half-angle ($\theta/2$) identities, replace θ with $\theta/2$, e.g.,

$$\sin^2\theta/2 = \tfrac{1}{2}(1 - \cos \theta) \qquad \cos^2 \theta/2 = \tfrac{1}{2}(1 + \cos \theta)$$

$$\sin (\alpha \pm \beta) = \sin \alpha \cos \beta \pm \cos \alpha \sin \beta$$

$$\cos (\alpha \pm \beta) = \cos \alpha \cos \beta \mp \sin \alpha \sin \beta$$

For very small angles:

$$\cos \theta \approx 1$$

$$\sin \theta \approx \theta \text{ (radians)} \qquad \tan \theta = \frac{\sin \theta}{\cos \theta} \approx \theta$$

Law of sines:

$$\frac{a}{\sin \alpha} = \frac{b}{\sin \beta} = \frac{c}{\sin \gamma}$$

Law of cosines:

$$a^2 = b^2 + c^2 - 2bc \cos \alpha$$
$$b^2 = a^2 + c^2 - 2ac \cos \beta$$
$$c^2 = a^2 + b^2 - 2ab \cos \gamma$$

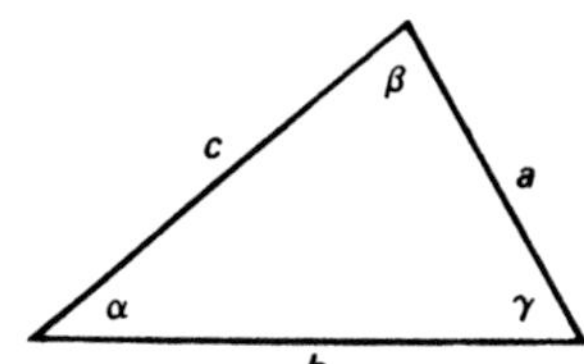

Standard Deviation and Method of Least Squares

STANDARD DEVIATION

To avoid the problem of negative deviations and absolute values, it is statistically convenient to use the square of the deviation.

The **variance** σ^2 of a set of measurements is the average of the squares of the deviations:

$$\sigma^2 = \frac{(x_1 - \bar{x})^2 + (x_2 - \bar{x})^2 + (x_3 - \bar{x})^2 + \cdots + (x_N - \bar{x})^2}{N}$$

$$= d_1^2 + d_2^2 + d_3^2 + \cdots d_N^2$$

$$= \frac{1}{N}\sum_{i=1}^{N}(x_i - \bar{x})^2 = \frac{1}{N}\sum_{i=1}^{N} d_i^2 \qquad \text{(C.1)}$$

The square root of the variance σ is called the **standard deviation***:

$$\sigma = \sqrt{\frac{1}{N}\sum_{i=1}^{N}(x_i - \bar{x})^2} = \sqrt{\frac{1}{N}\sum_{i=1}^{N} d_i^2} \qquad \text{(C.2)}$$

Because we take the average of the squares of the deviations and then the square root, the standard deviation is sometimes called the **root-mean-square deviation,** or simply the **root mean square.** Notice that σ always has the same units as x_i and that it is always positive.

Example C.1 What is the standard deviation of the set of numbers given in Example 1.6 in Experiment 1?

Solution First find the square of the deviation of each of the numbers.

$$d_1^2 = (5.42 - 5.93)^2 = 0.26$$
$$d_2^2 = (6.18 - 5.93)^2 = 0.06$$
$$d_3^2 = (5.70 - 5.93)^2 = 0.05$$
$$d_4^2 = (6.01 - 5.93)^2 = 0.01$$
$$d_5^2 = (6.32 - 5.93)^2 = 0.15$$

Then

$$\sigma = \sqrt{\frac{1}{N}\sum_{i=1}^{5} d_i^2}$$

$$= \left(\frac{0.26 + 0.06 + 0.05 + 0.01 + 0.15}{5}\right)^{1/2}$$

$$= 0.33$$

The experimental value E is then commonly reported as

$$E = \bar{x} \pm \sigma = 5.93 \pm 0.33$$

The standard deviation is used to describe the precision of the mean of a set of measurements. For a normal distribution of random errors,† it can be statistically shown that the probability that an individual measurement will fall within one standard deviation of the mean, which is assumed to be the true value, is 68% (● Fig. C.1). The probability of a measurement falling within two standard deviations is 95%.

METHOD OF LEAST SQUARES

Let $y' = m'x + b'$ be the predicted equation of the best-fitting straight line for a set of data. The vertical deviation of the ith data point from this line is then $(y_i - y_i')$.

The principle of least squares may be stated as follows: The "best-fitting" straight line is the one that minimizes the

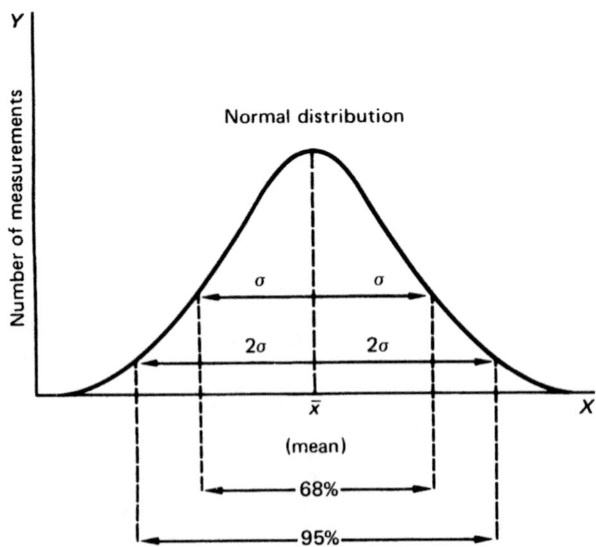

Figure C.1

* For a small number of measurements, it can be statistically shown that a better value of the standard deviation is given by $\sigma = \sqrt{[1/(N-1)]\Sigma d_i^2}$, where N is replaced by $N - 1$. Your instructor may want you to use this form of the standard deviation.

† This *normal,* or *Gaussian, distribution* is represented by a "bell-shaped" curve (Fig. C.1). That is, the scatter, or dispersion, of the measurements is assumed to be symmetric about the true value of a quantity.

sum of the squares of the deviations of the measured y values from those of the predicted equation $y' = m'x + b'$.

The numerical values of the slope m' and intercept b' that minimize the sum of the squares of the deviations, $\sum_{i=1}^{N} (y_i - y_i')^2$, may be found using differential calculus. The results are as follows:

$$m' = \frac{M_{xy}}{M_{xx}}$$

and

$$b' = \bar{y} - m'\bar{x}$$

where $\bar{x}$ and $\bar{y}$ are the mean values, $\bar{x} = \sum_{i=1}^{N} x_i$ and $\bar{y} = \sum_{i=1}^{N} y_i$,

and

$$M_{xy} = \sum_{i=1}^{N} (x_i - \bar{x})(y_i - \bar{y})$$

$$= \sum_{i=1}^{N} x_i y_i - \frac{\left(\sum_{i=1}^{N} x_i\right)\left(\sum_{i=1}^{N} y_i\right)}{N}$$

$$M_{xx} = \sum_{i=1}^{N} (x_i - \bar{x})^2 = \sum_{i=1}^{N} x_i^2 - \frac{\left(\sum_{i=1}^{N} x_i\right)^2}{N}$$

where the sums of the deviations, e.g., $\sum_{i=1}^{N} (x_i - \bar{x})$, are zero.

Exercises

1. Plot the data given in Data Table 1 on a sheet of graph paper, and draw the straight line you judge to fit the data best.
2. Using the method of least squares, find the slope and intercept of the "best-fitting" straight line, and compare them with the slope and intercept of the line you drew in Exercise 1. Plot this "best-fitting" line on the graph. (Recall that the slope of a line is the change in y for a one-unit increase in x.)

DATA TABLE 1

	y_i	x_i	x_i^2	$x_i y_i$
	25	12		
	44	28		
	78	47		
	80	70		
	43	16		
	58	53		
	95	72		
	67	38		
Sums (Σ)				

APPENDIX D

Graphing Exponential Functions

In some cases, exponential functions of the form

$$N = N_o e^{\lambda t} \quad \textbf{(D.1)}$$

$$(\text{or } y = Ae^{ax})$$

are plotted on Cartesian coordinates in linear form by first taking the natural, or Naperian, logarithm (base e) of both sides of the equation. For example, for $N = N_o e^{\lambda t}$,

$$\ln N = \ln (N_o e^{\lambda t}) = \ln N_o + \ln e^{\lambda t} = \ln N_o + \lambda t$$

or

$$\ln N = \lambda t + \ln N_o \quad \textbf{(D.2)}$$

Similarly, for $y = Ae^{ax}$,

$$\ln y = \ln A + \ln e^{ax} = \ln A + ax$$

or

$$\ln y = ax + \ln A \quad \textbf{(D.3)}$$

These equations have the general form of a straight line when plotted on a Cartesian graph ($y = mx + b$). For example, when we plot $\ln N$ versus t as Cartesian coordinates, the slope of the line is λ and the intercept is $\ln N_o$. The value of N_o is obtained by taking the *antilog* of the intercept value $\ln N_o$. (For a decaying exponential, $N = N_o e^{-\lambda t}$, the slope would be negative. Note that before plotting $\ln N$ versus t on Cartesian graph paper, we must find $\ln N$ for each value of N.)

Because logarithmic functions occur quite often in physics, special graph paper, called *semi-log graph paper,* is printed with graduations along the y or ordinate axis that are spaced logarithmically rather than linearly. The x or abscissa axis is graduated linearly. (Look at a sheet of semi-log graph paper.)

If a quantity is plotted on the ordinate axis of semi-log paper, the logarithmic graduated scale automatically takes the logarithm, so it is not necessary to look up the logarithm for each y value. However, commercial logarithmic graph paper is set up for common (base 10) logarithms rather than natural (base e) logarithms. Exponential functions may be treated as follows. Taking the (common) log of each side of $y = Ae^{ax}$ yields

$$\begin{aligned} \log y &= \log A + \log e^{ax} \\ &= \log A + ax \log e \\ &= \log A + (0.4343)ax \end{aligned} \quad \textbf{(D.4)}$$

where $\log e = 0.4343$.

Hence the slope of the resulting straight line is (0.4343)*a* rather than simply *a*.

The logarithmic ordinate scale is called "one-cycle," "two-cycle," and so on, depending on the number of powers of 10 covered on the axis. The beginnings of the cycles are consecutively labeled in multiples of 10 (e.g., 0.1, 1.0, 10, or 1.0, 10, 100, etc.), depending on the range (cycles) of the function. (Common logarithms can also be plotted on semi-log paper.)

Care must be taken in determining the slope of the line on a semi-log plot. On an ordinary Cartesian graph, the slope of a line is given by $\Delta y/\Delta x = (y_2 - y_1)/(x_2 - x_1)$. However, on a semi-log graph, the slope of a line is given by

$$\text{slope} = \frac{\Delta \log y}{\Delta x} \quad \left(\text{or } \frac{\Delta \log N}{\Delta t}\right) \quad \textbf{(D.5)}$$

On a semi-log plot, the listed ordinate values are y, not $\ln y$. Hence, one must explicitly take the logs of the ordinate values of the endpoints of the slope interval, y_2 and y_1, or the log of their ratio:

$$\begin{aligned} \text{slope} &= \frac{\Delta \log y}{\Delta x} = \frac{\log y_2 - \log y_1}{x_2 - x_1} \\ &= \frac{\log y_2/y_1}{x_2 - x_1} \end{aligned} \quad \textbf{(D.6)}$$

The value of N_o can be read directly from the y-intercept of the graph.

Another common equation form in physics is

$$y = ax^n \quad \textbf{(D.7)}$$

For example, the electric field, $E = kq/r^2 = kqr^{-2}$, is of this form, with $a = kq$ and $n = -2$. By plotting y versus x^n on Cartesian graph paper, we obtain a straight line with a slope of a. However, in an experiment the measured values are usually y and x, so computation of the x^n's is required.

But in some instances the exponent n may not be known. This constant, along with the constant a, may be found by plotting y versus x on log graph paper. (This is commonly called *log-log graph paper* because of the logarithmic graduations on both axes. Look at a sheet of log-log graph paper.)

At logarithmic graduations on axes, we again automatically take the logarithms of x and y. Working with common logarithms (base 10) in this instance, we find that the log-log plot of y versus x yields a straight line, as can be seen by taking the (common) log of both sides of Eq. D.7.

$$\log y = \log (ax^n) = \log a + \log x^n$$
$$= \log a + n \log x$$

or

$$\log y = n \log x + \log a \qquad \textbf{(D.8)}$$

which has the general form of a straight line with a slope of n and an intercept of log a. For the electric field example, this would be

$$E = \frac{kq}{r^2} = kqr^{-2}$$
$$\log E = -2 \log r + \log kq$$

Again, care must be taken in determining the slope of a straight line on a log-log graph. In this case,

$$\text{slope} = \frac{\Delta \log y}{\Delta \log x}$$
$$= \frac{\log y_2 - \log y_1}{\log x_2 - \log x_1} = \frac{\log y_2/y_1}{\log x_2/x_1} \qquad \textbf{(D.9)}$$

and the logs of the endpoints of the slope interval or their ratio must be found explicitly. (The ordinate and abscissa values on the log-log plot are y and x, *not* log y and log x.)

As in the case of the semi-log plot, the value of a in $y = ax^n$ can be read directly from the y-intercept of the graph. However, in this case, the intercept is not at $x = 0$ *but* at $x = 1$, since the intercept $\log y = \log a$ requires that $\log x = 0$ and $\log 1 = 0$.